MECHANICAL PROPERTIES OF MATTER

MECHANICAL PROPERTIES

OF

MATTER

BY

S. G. STARLING, B.Sc., A.R.C.Sc., F.Inst.P.

MACMILLAN AND CO., LIMITED
ST. MARTIN'S STREET, LONDON
1951

PRINTED IN GREAT BRITAIN

PREFACE

UNDER the title of General Physics, or Properties of Matter, it is usual to include the fundamental laws and principles of matter and motion, or what are known as Mechanics and Hydrostatics. Though these mechanical properties of solids, liquids and gases form a necessary part of the instruction in the most elementary course of physics, their full significance cannot be understood without a fair equipment of the mathematical principles involved. In this book, which is chiefly intended for students preparing for Higher School Certificate, or Intermediate Examinations in Physics, it is assumed, therefore, that they are acquainted with the operations of the differential and integral calculus.

It was formerly customary for work in these subjects to be deferred to a later stage. This, however, is no longer the case, for nearly all candidates for the Higher School Certificate receive instruction in the calculus as part of their mathematics course for this examination. But though the needs of these students have been borne particularly in mind, the book is not written for the syllabus of any one university, and subjects are included for the sake of continuity which may not appear in any syllabus.

Both classes and individuals vary much in their attainment, so that the choice of reading for the student must be left to the teacher. It should be remembered that the same examination serves not only to discriminate between passing and failing candidates, but also for the awarding of scholarships. It is, therefore, usual to set some questions of a more advanced character than the others, and it is hoped that this book will help the candidate in the more advanced as well as in the elementary parts.

Many points have been elaborated by means of examples, most of which are taken from examination papers.

Acknowledgments are due to those examining bodies which have kindly allowed questions to be taken from their Higher School Certificate examination papers, namely, the University of London

(L.H.S.C., Int. and B.Sc.); Oxford and Cambridge (O. and C.H.S.C.); Cambridge (C.H.S.C.); Oxford (O.H.S.C.); Joint Matriculation Board (J.M.B.H.S.C.); and Central Welsh Board (C.W.B.H.S.C.).

I must express my very great indebtedness to Sir Richard Gregory for help in all stages of the work, and to Mr. A. J. V. Gale for a number of suggestions made upon the proofs; also to Mr. H. J. Gray, B.Sc., for reading the manuscript and working out the examples.

S. G. STARLING.

1935.

CONTENTS

CHAPTER   PAGE

    I. VELOCITY AND ACCELERATION - - - - - - - 1

   II. FORCE, MOMENTUM, WORK - - - - - - 25

  III. MOMENTS, ROTATION AND EQUILIBRIUM - - - - 47

  IV. SIMPLE HARMONIC MOTION - - - - - - 86

   V. GRAVITATION - - - - - - - - - 109

  VI. ELASTICITY - - - - - - - - - 126

 VII. HYDROSTATICS - - - - - - - - - 153

VIII. FRICTION AND VISCOSITY - - - - - - - 183

  IX. FLOW OF LIQUIDS AND GASES - - - - - - 204

   X. KINETIC THEORY OF GASES - - - - - - 215

  XI. DIFFUSION AND OSMOSIS - - - - - - - 229

 XII. SURFACE TENSION - - - - - - - - 249

XIII. WAVES - - - - - - - - - - 291

ANSWERS - - - - - - - - - - - 329

INDEX - - - - - - - - - - - 333

CHAPTER I

VELOCITY AND ACCELERATION

General considerations.—The study of Nature begins with an examination of those phenomena that appeal directly to the senses. From sight and touch we obtain the idea of distance or length. From the muscular exertion required to set a body in motion we realise the quantity which we call " force," and the sequence of events gives us an instinctive feeling which we call " time." Hearing, colour sensation and taste are other primary sensations but with these we are not concerned here.

In choosing units for the measurement of physical quantities it is necessary to bear in mind that each unit must be constant and convenient. The unit of length chosen is the **metre**, the distance between two marks on a platinum-iridium bar preserved at the International Bureau of Metric Weights and Measures at Sèvres near Paris, when the temperature of the bar is 0° C. One hundredth of this, or one centimetre, is commonly used as the unit of length for scientific purposes. The unit of time is the mean solar second, or 1/86400 of the average time taken by the earth to make one complete rotation with respect to the sun.

One more unit must be defined before it is possible to measure the majority of physical quantities. There is a choice between force and mass. If either of these is given, the other can readily be defined, and the question will be discussed more fully when Newton's laws of motion are given (p. 25).

The quantity **mass** is chosen in preference to force, for its standard is easy to preserve and convenient to compare with other masses. Mass is a property of matter which is easy to realise, but difficult to define. Everyone knows that it is easier to set in motion a floating cork than a ship. This is chiefly because the ship has the greater mass. The standard of mass used in scientific work is a piece of platinum-iridium preserved at Sèvres and called the **kilogram**. One thousandth part of this is taken as unit and called the **gram**. Thus we measure our physical quantities in centimetres, grams and seconds ; hence this is called the c.g.s. system.

On the British system the foot, pound and second are used, and defined, in a similar manner to the c.g.s. units, with reference to standards preserved at the Standards Office of the Board of Trade, and 1 pound = 453·59 grams, 1 foot = 30·48 cm.

Uniform velocity.—A body moving in a straight line and travelling over the same distance in equal times is said to have uniform velocity. To specify velocity completely, the **direction** of the motion must be given, as well as the **distance** moved in **unit time**. The latter is the magnitude of the velocity, or the **speed**. When the time is not unity, the velocity is the ratio of the total distance moved to the time taken, or,

$$\text{velocity} = \frac{\text{distance}}{\text{time}},$$

$$\mathbf{v} = \frac{\mathbf{l}}{t},$$

$$\mathbf{l} = \mathbf{v}t.$$

If the motion is along a curve the direction is always changing, and, strictly speaking, the velocity is changing but the speed may be constant. In this case the distance measured along the curve bears a constant ratio to the time taken,

$$\text{speed} = \frac{\text{distance}}{\text{time}},$$

$$v = \frac{s}{t},$$

$$s = vt.$$

Vectors and scalars.—Some quantities have magnitude only, and there is no idea of direction in relation to them. Such are mass, volume, time, etc. They are called **scalar quantities,** or **invariants.** On the other hand, displacement, or distance measured in one definite direction, velocity and other quantities that will appear later, have direction as well as magnitude. These are called **vector quantities.** The typical vector is a displacement, and may be represented geometrically by a straight line. Thus a displacement from O to A (Fig. 1) is represented by the line OA, which is a vector and is designated **a**. Similarly a

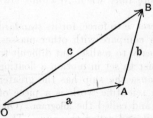

FIG. 1.—ADDITION OF TWO VECTORS.

displacement from A to B is represented by the vector AB or **b**. The point B has been reached by two displacements OA, followed by AB; but it might equally well have been reached by one displacement OB, represented by the vector **c**. This leads us to the law of addition of vectors, which is really only an extension of the law of addition of scalars or numbers. In fact a general law of addition may be stated as follows : **if the second quantity begins where the first quantity finishes, the quantity extending from the beginning of the first to the end of the second is the sum of the two.** In numbers and scalars this follows by the ordinary process of counting and is the basis of all arithmetic; but in the case of vector quantities, which from their geometrical nature involve direction, it can be seen from Fig. 1 that if **b** begins where **a** finishes, a vector **c** drawn from the beginning of **a** to the end of **b** is equivalent to the sum of the effects of **a** and **b**. Vectorially we write

$$c = a + b.$$

It should be noted that vector quantities are designated by heavy clarendon type, while scalar quantities are given in italics.

The result may be extended to the addition of any number of vectors; thus in Fig. 2

$$e = a + b + c + d.$$

If the end of **d** coincides with the starting point O, then **e** = 0 and

$$a + b + c + d = 0.$$

Again from Fig. 1 we see that the order in which the displacements are made is immaterial, for ordinary geo-

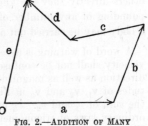

FIG. 2.—ADDITION OF MANY VECTORS.

metry shows that if the displacement **b** is made first, followed by displacement **a**, the point B is reached as before,

$$\therefore \ a + b = b + a.$$

Composition of velocities.—A velocity being a displacement divided by a time, it follows that velocity, like displacement, is a vector quantity. Referring again to Fig. 1, if OA is the displacement of a body which takes place in one second, it is also the velocity of the body. If at the same time the body has a displacement AB, this is a velocity simultaneous with the first. The velocity equi-

valent to these two is the velocity OB. This may be realised in a
simple case. Suppose a person at O (Fig. 3) to be standing on a

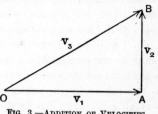

FIG. 3.—ADDITION OF VELOCITIES.

moving floor, say a railway carriage,
which has the velocity OA $= \mathbf{v}_1$. This
velocity would cause him to reach
A at the end of 1 second. If, however, he walks across the carriage
with velocity AB $= \mathbf{v}_2$, he will reach
B in 1 second instead of A. By
dividing the time into small intervals and considering his position at
the end of each, it will be seen that his actual path is along OB and
his velocity is represented by OB $= \mathbf{v}_3$.

Thus $$\mathbf{v}_3 = \mathbf{v}_1 + \mathbf{v}_2.$$

The velocity $\mathbf{v}_3$ is said to be the **resultant** of $\mathbf{v}_1$ and $\mathbf{v}_2$, and $\mathbf{v}_1$ and
$\mathbf{v}_2$ are the **components** of $\mathbf{v}_3$. Velocity being then a vector quantity,
velocities are compounded or added like all other vector quantities,
and the process of addition or compounding will be treated for all
others directly they are known to be vector quantities. The compounding of any number of velocities possessed simultaneously by
a body may be carried out as in Fig. 2.

A word of warning is necessary here, so that the magnitude of the
velocity shall not be confused with the complete velocity, which has
direction as well as magnitude. Thus, if v_1, v_2 and v_3 are the magni-
tudes of $\mathbf{v}_1$, $\mathbf{v}_2$ and $\mathbf{v}_3$ in Fig. 3, it is, of course, not true that v_3 is
the sum of v_1 and v_2. v_3 may be calculated from v_1 and v_2 by the
ordinary laws of trigonometry, or found by graphical construction.

The calculation may be
carried out to any desired
degree of accuracy, but
may be tedious or diffi-
cult. On the other hand,
if the velocities are drawn
to scale the resultant
may be found from the
drawing. This graphical
method is of great con-
venience and is simple,

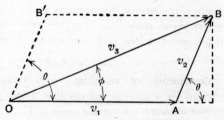

FIG. 4.—COMPOSITION OF VELOCITIES.

but the accuracy attainable is limited by the difficulty of measuring
with an ordinary rule.

In Fig. 4, if v_1 and v_2 are the magnitudes of the component velocities and v_3 the magnitude of the resultant, θ being the angle between the components, v_3 may be calculated from

$$v_3{}^2 = v_1{}^2 + v_2{}^2 + 2v_1v_2 \cos \theta,$$

and the angle ϕ it makes with v_1 is given by

$$\tan \phi = \frac{v_2 \sin \theta}{v_1 + v_2 \cos \theta}.$$

The graphical solution would consist in drawing OA to scale, say v_1 centimetres, and AB of length v_2 centimetres, the angle between their directions being θ°. Then OB is drawn and measured, and the value v_3 is its length in centimetres. Similarly ϕ may be measured with a protractor.

If OB' is drawn instead of AB and the parallelogram OB'BA completed, the diagonal OB is the required resultant. OB'BA is sometimes called the **parallelogram of velocities**.

EXAMPLE.—A vessel steams in such a direction that if there were no ocean current it would travel in a north-easterly direction at a speed of 23 knots. There is, however, a current of 3 knots in an easterly direction. What is the resultant speed and direction of the vessel ?

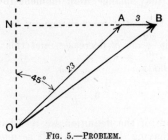

FIG. 5.—PROBLEM.

In Fig. 5, OA represents 23 knots and AB 3 knots. Then

$$OB^2 = 23^2 + 3^2 + (2 \times 3 \times 23 \cos 45^\circ)$$
$$= 529 + 9 + 97 \cdot 6,$$
$$= 635 \cdot 6.$$

$$\underline{OB = 25 \cdot 22 \text{ knots.}}$$

$$\tan BON = \frac{3 + 23 \cos 45^\circ}{23 \sin 45^\circ} = \frac{19 \cdot 27}{16 \cdot 27}.$$
$$= 1 \cdot 185.$$

Angle BON $= 49 \cdot 83^\circ$;

$\therefore$ <u>path OB is 49·83° east of north.</u>

Acceleration.—When the velocity of a body is changing, the simple definition of it on p. 2 no longer holds. If the distance travelled in a considerable time is divided by the time, the result is the **average** velocity, and not the velocity at any instant. If, however, the interval of time is made small, δt, and the distance travelled in a straight line is δl, the quantity $\dfrac{\delta l}{\delta t}$ approaches a limiting value as δt is made smaller and smaller. In the limit when δt is vanishingly small the ratio $\underset{\delta t=0}{\text{Lt}} \dfrac{\delta l}{\delta t}$ becomes $\dfrac{dl}{dt}$, and this is called the velocity at the instant considered.

Thus
$$\mathbf{v} = \frac{d\mathbf{l}}{dt}.$$

If the speed only is being considered,
$$v = \frac{ds}{dt}.$$

The velocity **v** may change from moment to moment; over a small interval of time δt it may change by $\delta \mathbf{v}$. The ratio $\dfrac{\delta \mathbf{v}}{\delta t}$ approaches the limit $\dfrac{d\mathbf{v}}{dt}$ as δt decreases, and this ratio is called the **acceleration** of the body.

Thus
$$\mathbf{a} = \frac{d\mathbf{v}}{dt}.$$

From the nature of the definition we see that acceleration is a vector quantity, having direction as well as magnitude, but for a moment we shall consider motion in one straight line only, so that the magnitudes only of length, velocity and acceleration will concern us.

Thus
$$v = \frac{ds}{dt}, \quad \text{and} \quad a = \frac{dv}{dt}.$$

If the velocity is increasing, dv and dt are both positive and the acceleration is positive. If the velocity is decreasing, dv is negative, and the acceleration is also negative. It is sometimes called a **retardation.** In any event, acceleration may be defined as the **rate of change of velocity** of the body.

The equations given above may be written $ds = v\,dt$ and $dv = a\,dt$.

Integrating these equations,

$$s = \int v\,dt \quad \text{and} \quad v = \int a\,dt.$$

If v is constant, the first of these gives

$$s = vt + c,$$

and if a is constant, the second equation gives

$$v = at + c',$$

where c and c' may be any constants. In the first case c may be the distance from a fixed point at the start, and $s = vt$ is the distance moved with constant speed in time t.

In the second case c' is the speed of the body at the beginning, and at the gain in speed in time t. Writing $c' = u$, it follows that

$$v = at + u.$$

Again, substituting $v = at + u$ in equation $ds = v\,dt$

$$ds = (at + u)\,dt,$$

$$s = \int at\,dt + \int u\,dt$$

$$= \tfrac{1}{2}at^2 + ut + c''.$$

Or,
$$a = \frac{dv}{dt} \quad \text{and} \quad v = \frac{ds}{dt},$$

$$\therefore \quad a = \frac{d^2s}{dt^2}.$$

Integrating once with respect to t,

$$c' + at = \frac{ds}{dt} = u + at;$$

and again,
$$s = \tfrac{1}{2}at^2 + ut + c''.$$

If the distance is calculated from the origin, $s = 0$ when $t = 0$, and it follows that $c'' = 0$.

And
$$s = ut + \tfrac{1}{2}at^2.$$

Another useful equation may be obtained by writing

$$v^2 = (at + u)^2$$

$$= a^2t^2 + 2uat + u^2$$

$$= a(at^2 + 2ut) + u^2$$

$$= a(2s) + u^2,$$

or
$$v^2 = u^2 + 2as.$$

The three most useful equations collected together are

$$s = vt, \quad \dots\dots\dots\dots\dots\dots\dots\dots\dots\dots\dots\dots(1)$$

$$s = ut + \tfrac{1}{2}at^2, \quad \dots\dots\dots\dots\dots\dots\dots(2)$$

$$v^2 = u^2 + 2as. \quad \dots\dots\dots\dots\dots\dots\dots(3)$$

Graphical illustrations.—If the velocity of a body at a sufficient number of points in time is known, a curve may be plotted, connect-

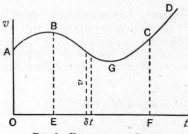

FIG. 6.—VELOCITY-TIME GRAPH.

ing velocity and time. Taking a curve ABCD (Fig. 6) of a general type, and dividing the diagram into vertical strips, it will be seen that if the width of one strip is δt, the area of the strip is $v\,\delta t$, where δt is taken to be so small that v does not vary appreciably during this interval. But $v\,\delta t$ is the distance travelled in the time δt, and is therefore represented by the area of the strip. Thus the distance travelled by the body in the time EF is, to scale, represented by the area BGCFEB, the sum of all the strips between BE and CF.

The acceleration $\dfrac{dv}{dt}$ is the slope of the curve at any point, which is zero at B and again at some point G.

When the acceleration is constant, the curve becomes a straight line, as in Fig. 7. The distance travelled in the time OC is then given by the area ABCO. It will be seen that OA is the velocity at the start, u, and BD is the gain in velocity, at, in time OC $= t$.

Then
$$\begin{aligned}
\text{area} &= \tfrac{1}{2}(OA + CB) \times OC \\
&= \tfrac{1}{2}(u + u + at) \times t \\
&= ut + \tfrac{1}{2}at^2,
\end{aligned}$$

which is equation (2). Also the rectangle ADCO represents the distance travelled if the acceleration is zero, and the triangle ABD is the distance travelled if the original velocity is zero. The actual distance travelled is the sum of these two.

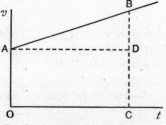

FIG. 7.—GRAPH INDICATING CONSTANT ACCELERATION.

EXAMPLE.—If you are given the velocity-time curve of a moving body, how can you determine the distance traversed by the body between two assigned instants ?

The speedometer of a motor-car showed the following speeds in M.P.H. at the ends of successive intervals of 3 sec. : 38·9, 52·8, 64·4, 73·6, 80·9, 86·1, 90·0, 92·5. Plot the velocity-time curve in the most convenient units, and find the distance in feet covered while the speed increases from 80 to 90 M.P.H. Find also the acceleration in foot-second units when the speed is 70 M.P.H.   C.H.S.C.

Plotting 5 mm. for a second and 1 mm. for 1 M.P.H., the curve of Fig. 8 is obtained, but is reduced to a convenient size for reproduction. As *near*

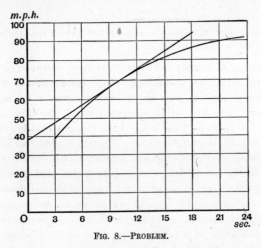

FIG. 8.—PROBLEM.

as can be read, the speed of 80 M.P.H. occurs at time 14·6 sec. and 90 M.P.H. occurs at time 21 sec. To calculate the distance travelled, the area between the ordinates at 14·6 and 21 sec. and the curve is found. The mean ordinate is greater than 85 and less than 86, so that as nearly as can be read it is 85·5.

Then average speed $= 85·5$ M.P.H.

$$= \frac{85·5 \times 1760 \times 3}{60 \times 60} \text{ ft. per sec.}$$

Distance travelled $= \frac{85·5 \times 88}{60} \times 6·4$ ft.

$$= 802·5 \text{ ft.}$$

In order to obtain the acceleration when the speed is 70 M.P.H. it is necessary to evaluate $\dfrac{dv}{dt}$ at this point, which is done by drawing a tangent to the curve. This tangent cuts the speed axis at 38 and the time 18 sec. ordinate at 94. Thus

$$\frac{dv}{dt} = \frac{94 - 38}{18} = \frac{56}{18} \text{ miles per hr. per sec.}$$

$$= \frac{56}{18} \times 1760 \times 3 \text{ ft. per hr. per sec.}$$

$$= \frac{56 \times 1760 \times 3}{18 \times 60 \times 60} \text{ ft. sec.}^{-2}.$$

$$= 4\cdot56 \text{ ft./sec.}^{2}.$$

Note that accelerations may be expressed as feet (or cm.) per second per second, ft./sec.^{2} or as ft. sec.$^{-2}$.

Acceleration of gravity.—The most obvious instance of acceleration occurs in the case of a falling body. **The acceleration of all bodies falling freely at any one place on the earth's surface is the same and is also constant.** The first of these statements is the great discovery of Galileo, as up to his time it had been thought that heavier bodies fall more rapidly than lighter ones. The effect of the air in resisting the fall, on account of friction and buoyancy, will certainly diminish appreciably the rate of fall of very light bodies, although for heavy bodies this effect is very small. In a vacuum the acceleration of all bodies is the same. The second statement is true so long as the distances fallen are small compared with radius of the earth.

The acceleration of a falling body, however, varies slightly from place to place. At the equator it is least and at the poles greatest, but the reasons for this variation and the methods of determination will be deferred to Chapter V. At the pole the value is 983·216 cm. per sec. per sec., and at the equator 978·030 cm. per sec. per sec. At London the value is 981·19 cm. per sec. per sec., and in this country the value 981 cm. sec.$^{-2}$ may be taken as sufficiently near for ordinary purposes. In British measure this is 32·2 ft. sec.$^{-2}$. The number 32 is often taken for purposes of rough calculation.

Equations (2) and (3) on p. 8 are now written with g replacing a, and are

$$s = ut + \tfrac{1}{2}gt^2, \dots\dots\dots\dots\dots\dots\dots(4)$$
$$v^2 = u^2 + 2gs. \dots\dots\dots\dots\dots\dots\dots(5)$$

EXAMPLE 1.—A body falls from rest. What is the time taken to fall 40 metres, and what velocity is acquired in the fall ? ($g = 981$ cm. sec.$^{-2}$.)

Since the body falls from rest, $u = 0$.

Then from (4),

$$4000 = \tfrac{1}{2} \times 981 t^2,$$
$$t^2 = 8 \cdot 15,$$
$$t = 2 \cdot 86 \text{ sec.}$$

From (5),

$$v^2 = 2 \times 981 \times 4000$$
$$= 7848000,$$
$$v = 2802 \text{ cm. sec.}^{-1}.$$

EXAMPLE 2.—A body is projected vertically upwards with a velocity of 80 ft. sec.$^{-1}$. How far will it rise and after what time will it be 40 ft. above the starting point ? ($g = 32 \cdot 2$ ft. sec.$^{-2}$.)

At its greatest height its velocity will, for an instant, be zero, since it ceases to rise. Therefore in (5) $v = 0$;

$$\therefore \ 0 = u^2 + 2gs.$$
$$s = - \frac{80^2}{2 \times 32 \cdot 2}$$
$$= - 99 \cdot 38 \text{ ft.}$$

Here g is considered to be positive and the downward direction positive. Directions measured upwards are therefore negative. The negative sign thus indicates that s is to be measured in the opposite direction to g.

From (4),

$$s = ut + \tfrac{1}{2}gt^2,$$
$$-40 = -80t + 16 \cdot 1t^2,$$
$$t^2 - \frac{80}{16 \cdot 1}\,t + \frac{40}{16 \cdot 1} = 0,$$
$$t = 2 \cdot 485 \pm 1 \cdot 921$$
$$= 4 \cdot 406 \text{ or } 0 \cdot 564 \text{ sec.}$$

The time 0·564 sec. is the time of passing the given point as the body is rising, and 4·406 sec. is the time taken to rise and then fall to the given point.

Projectiles.—If the velocity of a falling body is not vertical at any point, it may be resolved into two components, one horizontal and the other vertical. The term " vertical " means the direction in which gravity acts, and it is therefore the vertical component of the velocity that is subject to acceleration. The horizontal is at right angles to the vertical, and there is no acceleration of the body horizontally due to gravity. If the body is projected upwards at O (Fig. 9) with velocity $OC = u$, at angle θ to the horizontal, the vertical component of velocity is $OB = u \sin \theta$, and the horizontal component $OA = u \cos \theta$. Since the latter is not accelerated, the equation

$$x = u \cos \theta \cdot t$$

gives the x-ordinate, OD, after t sec. The y-coordinate after t sec. is DE and is the ordinate DF, or $u \sin \theta$, that would have been attained

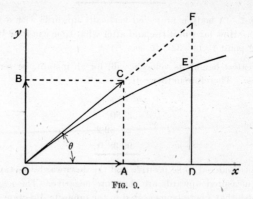

FIG. 9.

if there were no acceleration due to gravity, diminished by the amount $FE = \frac{1}{2}gt^2$, by which the body has fallen in the same time, or by equation (4) (p. 10),

$$y = u \sin \theta \cdot t - \tfrac{1}{2}gt^2,$$

remembering that the magnitudes only of the quantities are indicated by u and g. If the body is moving upwards, u will naturally be taken as positive in the positive direction of y. Gravity acts downwards, and, so long as the body is moving upwards, is really a retardation and is to be taken as negative; hence the negative sign in the above equation.

The horizontal component of velocity of the body at E is still $u \cos \theta$, or

$$\frac{dx}{dt} = u \cos \theta.$$

The quantity $\dfrac{dx}{dt}$ is frequently written $\dot{x}$, in the original notation of Sir Isaac Newton, thus

$$\dot{x} = u \cos \theta,$$

and $$\frac{dy}{dt} = \dot{y} = u \sin \theta - gt.$$

It will be seen that, so long as $u \sin \theta > gt$, $\dot{y}$ is positive and is directed upwards, but when $gt > u \sin \theta$, $\dot{y}$ is negative and is therefore directed downwards.

To find the magnitude of the resultant velocity v at any moment, note that

$$v^2 = (\dot{x})^2 + (\dot{y})^2.$$

Also, the angle ϕ which the resultant velocity makes with the horizontal is given by

$$\tan \phi = \frac{\dot{y}}{\dot{x}}.$$

EXAMPLE.—Prove that the path of a projectile moving under gravity in a non-resisting medium is a parabola.

Show that a particle starting with a velocity of 100 ft./sec. at an angle $\tan^{-1} \frac{3}{4}$ to the horizontal will just clear a wall 36 ft. high at a horizontal distance 80 yds. from the point of projection. Find also the direction of motion of the particle when it is passing over the wall. L.H.S.C.

For first part, see p. 15.

If $\tan \theta = \frac{3}{4}$, $\sin \theta = \frac{3}{5}$ and $\cos \theta = \frac{4}{5}$.

Horizontal velocity $\dot{x}$ at the start $= 100 \cos \theta$

$$= 100 \times \tfrac{4}{5} = 80 \text{ ft. sec.}^{-1}.$$

∴ Time to travel to the wall $= \frac{240}{80} = 3$ sec.

Vertical velocity $= 100 \sin \theta = 100 \times \frac{3}{5} = 60$ ft sec.$^{-1}$.

Now
$$y = 60 \times t - \tfrac{1}{2} \times 32 t^2$$
$$= (60 \times 3) - (16 \times 9)$$
$$= 180 - 144$$
$$= 36 \text{ ft.}$$

That is, the height of the particle above the ground is the height of the wall.

Now, $$\dot{x} = 80 \text{ ft. sec.}^{-1}.$$

Also, after three seconds from the start,

$$\dot{y} = 60 - 32 \times 3$$
$$= -36 \text{ ft. sec.}^{-1}.$$

Since $\dot{y}$ is negative the particle is falling, and the angle ϕ between its path and the horizontal is given by

$$\tan \phi = \frac{\dot{y}}{\dot{x}} = \frac{36}{80} = \frac{9}{20} = 0.45.$$

i.e. $\phi = 24\frac{1}{2}°$ approx.

Greatest height and horizontal range.—The height and range may be found by calculating the time taken for the body to rise to its highest point, starting with vertical velocity $u \sin \theta$. The time of rise is thus $\frac{u \sin \theta}{g}$, and twice this, or $\frac{2u \sin \theta}{g}$, is therefore the whole time of flight. Since the horizontal component of velocity is $u \cos \theta$, the horizontal distance travelled in time $\frac{2u \sin \theta}{g}$ is

$$u \cos \theta \times \frac{2u \sin \theta}{g} = \frac{2u^2 \sin \theta \cos \theta}{g}$$

$$= \frac{u^2 \sin 2\theta}{g}.$$

This is known as the **horizontal range** of the projectile.

The greatest height to which the body rises may be obtained from (5), p. 10, since the vertical velocity is then zero,

$$0 = u^2 \sin^2\theta - 2gs,$$

or
$$s = \frac{u^2 \sin^2\theta}{2g}.$$

For a given initial velocity u the range depends upon the angle of elevation θ, and in order to find the value of θ for greatest range, it is necessary to find the maximum of $\dfrac{u^2 \sin 2\theta}{g} = x.$

The usual method is to find $\dfrac{dx}{d\theta}$ and equate its value to zero.

Thus
$$\frac{dx}{d\theta} = \frac{2u^2}{g} \cos 2\theta = 0 ;$$

$$\therefore \quad \cos 2\theta = 0,$$

$$2\theta = 90°,$$

$$\theta = 45°.$$

That this is a maximum and not a minimum is fairly obvious, but it may be checked rigorously by obtaining $\dfrac{d^2x}{d\theta^2}$.

Thus

$$\frac{d^2x}{d\theta^2} = -\frac{4u^2}{g}\sin 2\theta,$$

when, for $\theta = 45°$,

$$\frac{d^2x}{d\theta^2} = -\frac{4u^2}{g}.$$

This is essentially negative since u^2 is positive whatever the sign of u, and g is the numerical value of the acceleration of gravity. Thus $\theta = 45°$ corresponds to maximum horizontal range.

Equation of path of projectile.—The path of a projectile is called its trajectory, and in order to obtain its equation it is necessary to eliminate t from the equations on p. 12 :

$$x = u \cos \theta \,.\, t,$$
$$y = u \sin \theta \,.\, t - \tfrac{1}{2}gt^2.$$

On substituting $t = -\dfrac{x}{u \cos \theta}$ in the second equation,

$$y = x\,\frac{\sin \theta}{\cos \theta} - \tfrac{1}{2}g \,.\, \frac{x^2}{u^2 \cos^2\theta}\,.$$

This, being an equation of the second degree in x and the first degree in y, is a parabola with its axis vertical. In order to obtain it

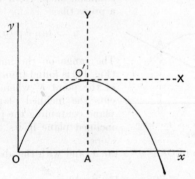

FIG. 10.—TRAJECTORY OF A PROJECTILE.

in a simpler form, the origin may be transferred to the apex O′ (Fig. 10) of the parabola. This is equivalent to deducting OA, half the horizontal range, from every abscissa, and AO', the greatest height, from every ordinate. That is,

$$x = \mathsf{X} + \frac{u^2 \sin \theta \cdot \cos \theta}{g}, \qquad \dots\dots\dots\dots\text{(p. 14)}$$

$$y = \mathsf{Y} + \frac{u^2 \sin^2\theta}{2g}. \qquad \dots\dots\dots\dots\dots\text{(p. 14)}$$

Then,

$$\mathsf{Y} + \frac{u^2 \sin^2\theta}{2g} = \left(\mathsf{X} + \frac{u^2 \sin\theta\cos\theta}{g}\right)\frac{\sin\theta}{\cos\theta} - \frac{g}{2u^2\cos^2\theta}\left(\mathsf{X} + \frac{u^2\sin\theta\cos\theta}{g}\right)^2,$$

$$\mathsf{Y} + \frac{u^2\sin^2\theta}{2g} = \mathsf{X}\frac{\sin\theta}{\cos\theta} + \frac{u^2\sin^2\theta}{g} - \frac{g\mathsf{X}^2}{2u^2\cos^2\theta} - \mathsf{X}\frac{\sin\theta}{\cos\theta} - \frac{u^2\sin^2\theta}{2g} ;$$

$$\therefore \ \mathsf{Y} = -\frac{g\mathsf{X}^2}{2u^2\cos^2\theta}.$$

This is the equation of a parabola with vertex at O' and axis O'A (Fig. 10).

It may be noticed that if a body is projected horizontally with velocity u, then $\theta = 0$ and $\cos\theta = 1$.

$$\therefore \ \mathsf{Y} = -\frac{g\mathsf{X}^2}{2u^2},$$

and in time $t = \dfrac{\mathsf{X}}{u}$, the body falls distance $\frac{1}{2}gt^2$.

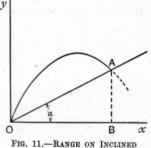

FIG. 11.—RANGE ON INCLINED PLANE.

Range on inclined plane.—From the equation on p. 15, it is seen that for a projectile

$$y = x \tan\theta - \frac{1}{2}g\frac{x^2}{u^2\cos^2\theta}.$$

The range on the inclined plane OA (Fig. 11) is found from the coordinates of the point A, where the trajectory cuts the inclined plane, the vertical plane containing the path cutting the inclined plane in its line of greatest slope.

The equation of OA is $y = x\tan\alpha$, and with the above equation,

$$x\tan\alpha = x\tan\theta - \frac{1}{2}g\frac{x^2}{u^2\cos^2\theta},$$

or

$$x = \frac{2(\tan\theta - \tan\alpha)u^2\cos^2\theta}{g}.$$

From this it is seen that there is no positive value of x unless $\tan \theta > \tan \alpha$ or $\theta > \alpha$, that is, unless the angle of elevation of the initial velocity is greater than that of the plane.

Again, $y = x \tan \alpha$
$$= \frac{2(\tan \theta - \tan \alpha) u^2 \cos^2\theta}{g} \tan \alpha.$$

But $OA^2 = x^2 + y^2 = \left\{ \dfrac{2(\tan \theta - \tan \alpha) u^2 \cos^2\theta}{g} \right\}^2 (1 + \tan^2\alpha)$;

but $1 + \tan^2\alpha = \sec^2\alpha = \dfrac{1}{\cos^2\alpha}$;

$$\therefore \ OA = \frac{2(\tan \theta - \tan \alpha) u^2 \cos^2\theta}{g \cos \alpha}.$$

EXAMPLE.—A particle is projected with velocity u from the foot of a plane of inclination β, the direction of projection lying in the vertical plane through the line of greatest slope and making an angle α with the horizontal. Show that the range on the inclined plane is

$$\frac{2u^2 \cos \alpha \sin (\alpha - \beta)}{g \cos^2\beta}.$$

If the particle strikes the plane at right angles, prove that
$$1 + 2 \tan^2\beta = \tan \alpha \tan \beta. \qquad \text{O. \& C.H.S.C.}$$

Using the letters in the question, the expression for the range on the plane becomes

$$\frac{2(\tan \alpha - \tan \beta) u^2 \cos^2\alpha}{g \cos \beta}.$$

That is,

$$\frac{2\left(\dfrac{\sin \alpha}{\cos \alpha} - \dfrac{\sin \beta}{\cos \beta} \right) u^2 \cos^2\alpha}{g \cos \beta}$$

$$= \frac{2u^2 (\sin \alpha \cos \beta - \cos \alpha \sin \beta) \cos^2\alpha}{g \cos \alpha \cos^2\beta}$$

$$= \frac{2u^2 \sin(\alpha - \beta) \cos \alpha}{g \cos^2\beta}.$$

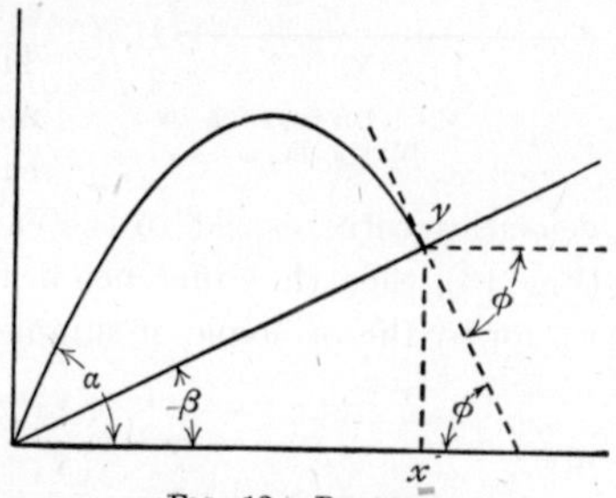

FIG. 12.—PROBLEM.

In Fig. 12, $\tan \beta = \dfrac{y}{x} = \dfrac{u \sin \alpha . t - \frac{1}{2}gt^2}{u \cos \alpha . t}$,

$$\tan \beta = \tan \alpha - \frac{gt}{2u \cos \alpha},$$

or, $\dfrac{gt}{u \cos \alpha} = 2 \tan \alpha - 2 \tan \beta.$

Again,
$$-\tan\phi = \frac{\dot{y}}{\dot{x}} = \frac{u\sin\alpha - gt}{u\cos\alpha}$$

$$= \tan\alpha - \frac{gt}{u\cos\alpha},$$

or,
$$\frac{gt}{u\cos\alpha} = \tan\alpha + \tan\phi;$$

$$\therefore\ 2\tan\alpha - 2\tan\beta = \tan\alpha + \tan\phi.$$

But for the velocity to be at right angles to the plane,

$$\phi = \frac{\pi}{2} - \beta,\ \text{or}\ \tan\phi = \cot\beta.$$

$$\therefore\ \tan\alpha - 2\tan\beta = \cot\beta = \frac{1}{\tan\beta};$$

$$\therefore\ \tan\alpha\tan\beta - 2\tan^2\beta = 1;$$

$$\underline{1 + 2\tan^2\beta = \tan\alpha\tan\beta.}$$

Relative velocity.—In a strict sense all velocity is relative, that is, in order to define a velocity it is necessary to specify the position of

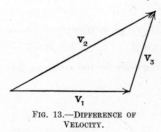

FIG. 13.—DIFFERENCE OF VELOCITY.

a body at different times with respect to some reference body which is considered to be at rest. For ordinary mechanical problems the earth is considered to be at rest, and all velocities are measured with respect to it. Thus velocity, as ordinarily given, means velocity with respect to the earth. If, then, two bodies have velocities with respect to the earth, given by the vectors v_1 and v_2 (Fig. 13), then the difference in their velocities is given by the vector v_3, for by the principle of summation of vectors (p. 3)

$$v_2 = v_1 + v_3,$$
or
$$v_3 = v_2 - v_1.$$

v_3 is then the **relative velocity** of the one body with respect to the other. The matter may be put in a different way as follows : if equal velocities be added to the two bodies, this will not change their relative velocity. On then adding a velocity $-v_1$ to both bodies, the first is reduced to rest since $v_1 - v_1 = 0$, but the second body will now have velocity compounded of v_2 and $-v_1$ which, in Fig. 14, will be seen to be the same as the $\mathbf{v}_3$ in Fig. 13. The relative velocity of the first body with respect to the second is by a similar process seen to be $-\mathbf{v}_3$. Thus the relative velocity of one body with respect to another

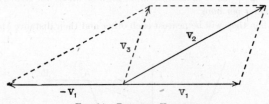

FIG. 14.—RELATIVE VELOCITY.

is represented by a vector which is the difference of the vectors representing the velocities of the two bodies, and may be found by superimposing on the two bodies velocities equal and opposite to the velocity of one of them, thus reducing this one to rest.

EXAMPLE 1.—What do you understand by relative velocity ?

To a man running at 7 M.P.H. due West the wind appears to blow from the North-west, but when he walks at 3 M.P.H. due West the wind appears to blow from the North. What is its actual direction and its velocity ?

O.H.S.C.

Let the vector OA (Fig. 15) represent the man's velocity when running due West at 7 M.P.H., and let OB be the actual velocity of the wind.

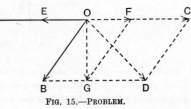

FIG. 15.—PROBLEM.

Superimpose on both the velocity $OC = -OA$. The man is now at rest, and the velocity of the wind relatively to him is OD.

Now repeat with $OE = 3$ M.P.H. The resultant of $OF = -OE$ and OB is OG.

Now in the problem $D\hat{O}G = 45°$ and $DG = FC = 4$.

$$\therefore\ OG = 4 \text{ and } BG = 3,$$
$$OB^2 = OG^2 + BG^2 ;$$
$$\therefore\ \underline{OB = 5 \text{ M.P.H.}}$$

Its direction makes angle GOB with the North, where
$$\tan GOB = \tfrac{3}{4} = 0·75,$$
$$\underline{GOB = 37° \text{ approx.}}$$

EXAMPLE 2.—Define the velocity of one moving body relative to another.

Two ships A and B are 30 nautical miles apart with A due N.N.E. of B. A is steaming due E. at 12 nautical miles per hour and B due N. at $12(1+\sqrt{2})$ nautical miles per hour.

Find when they will be nearest each other and their distance apart then.

L.H.S.C.

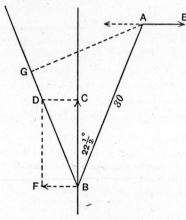

FIG. 16.—PROBLEM.

Superimpose on both ships a velocity −AE (Fig. 16) or 12 nautical M.P.H. due W. A is brought to rest and B has now a velocity BD, the resultant of BC and BF. BD is the velocity of B relative to A. Also

$$\tan DBC = \frac{DC}{BC} = \frac{12}{12(1+\sqrt{2})} = \frac{1}{1+\sqrt{2}}.$$

Thus $DBC = 22\frac{1}{2}°$, since $\tan 22\frac{1}{2}° = \dfrac{1}{1+\sqrt{2}}$. Therefore angle $ABD = 45°$.

The ships are nearest to each other when B is at the foot of the perpendicular dropped from A on to BD, that is, at G.

$$AG = AB \sin ABG = AB \sin 45°$$

$$= \frac{30}{\sqrt{2}}.$$

$$= \underline{21\cdot2 \text{ miles.}}$$

Also the velocity $BD = \sqrt{BF^2 + BC^2}$

$$= \sqrt{12^2 + 12^2(1+\sqrt{2})^2}$$

$$= 12\sqrt{1+1+2\sqrt{2}+2}$$

$$= 12\sqrt{4+2\sqrt{2}},$$

and

$$BG = AB \cos 45°$$

$$= \frac{30}{\sqrt{2}};$$

$\therefore$ time taken for nearest distance $= \dfrac{30}{\sqrt{2}} \cdot \dfrac{1}{12\sqrt{4+2\sqrt{2}}}$

$$= \frac{30}{12} \frac{1}{\sqrt{2}\sqrt{4+2\sqrt{2}}}$$

$$= \frac{30}{12\sqrt{13\cdot656}}$$

$$= 0\cdot676 \text{ hr.}$$

EXERCISES ON CHAPTER I

ACCELERATED MOTION

1. Prove that for uniformly accelerated motion in a straight line

$$s = ut + \tfrac{1}{2}ft^2.$$

A train 90 yards long starts from rest at a station with an acceleration of 6 ft. per sec. per sec. There is a signal post 100 yards from the point at which the front of the train started. Find the velocities with which the front and the back of the train respectively pass this post and the time taken by the train in passing it.   J.M.B.H.S.C.

2. What is a " velocity-time curve " ? Explain its use.

A train runs from rest at one station to rest at another 5 miles distant in 10 minutes. If it gets up full speed uniformly in the first $\frac{1}{4}$ mile and slows down uniformly to rest in the last $\frac{1}{8}$ mile, what is the maximum speed in miles per hour ?   O. & C.H.S.C.

3. Show how to find the distance travelled by a body when its velocity-time graph is given.

A man alights from a train when it is going at 5 ft./sec. and drawing up at the platform under uniform retardation. He walks forward in the direction of the train's motion at a uniform velocity of 5 ft./sec. He has walked 10 ft. when the train stops, 65 ft. when it starts again (with uniform acceleration), and 70 ft. when it begins to overtake him. Find how far he will have walked when the carriage he left passes him, assuming that the train is still being accelerated uniformly.   L.H.S.C.

4. Explain the use of a velocity-time graph in measuring (*a*) acceleration, (*b*) distance covered.

A load is being drawn with uniform velocity up a vertical shaft 112 feet long ; the rope snaps, and the load just reaches the level of the surface. If the total time taken from the bottom to the top of the shaft is 4 seconds, find the original velocity of ascent.   C.H.S.C.

5. Prove the formula for uniformly accelerated motion,

$$v^2 = u^2 + 2fs.$$

Two stations A and B are 5 miles apart on a straight track, and a train starts from A and comes to rest at B. For three-quarters of the distance the train is uniformly accelerated, and for the remainder uniformly retarded. If it takes 10 min. over the whole journey, find its acceleration, its retardation, and the maximum speed it attains.   J.M.B.H.S.C.

6. A point P moves in a straight line AB with a uniform acceleration of 5 feet per sec.^{2} in the direction AB, and its velocity at A is 10 feet per sec. in the same direction. Three seconds after P has left A, another point Q starts from A with a velocity of 38 feet per sec. in the direction AB and with an acceleration of 4 feet per sec.^{2} in the same direction.

At what distance from A will Q overtake P ? Show that, after passing P, Q will never be ahead of P by more than 32 feet.   L.H.S.C.

7. Prove the formula $v^2 = u^2 + 2fs$ for uniformly accelerated motion in a straight line.

Particles P and Q are moving in the same direction along neighbouring parallel lines with constant accelerations of 3 and 2 ft./sec.^{2} respectively. P starts from rest at the instant when Q is 39 ft. behind and moving with a velocity of 9·5 feet per second. Prove that P and Q will twice be abreast, and find their speeds when this happens.   C.W.B.H.S.C.

8. The velocity, *v* ft./sec., of a car decreases with the time, *t* secs., according to the formula

$$v = 40 - t^2.$$

Draw a velocity-time graph from $t=0$ to $t=7$. Find by graphical methods the distance travelled from $t=3$ to $t=6$ and the mean retardation in the same interval of time.   C.W.B.H.S.C.

9. During each third of the interval of time taken by a car to travel a journey from rest to rest, the car's acceleration is constant. By means of a speed-time graph, prove that the average speed for the journey is two-thirds of the car's speed at the middle of the interval. Prove also that, if one-*n*th of the journey is travelled in the first half of the interval, the accelerations during the 1st, 2nd, and 3rd thirds of the interval are in the ratios

$$(8 - n) : 8(n - 2) : (8 - 7n).$$ O.H.S.C.

Projectiles

10. Show that the path of a ball thrown in a horizontal direction is a parabola.

A man standing at the edge of a vertical cliff 108 feet high projects a ball with a velocity of 96 feet per second at an elevation of 30° so that it travels in a plane at right angles to that of the cliff. How far from the foot of the cliff does the ball strike the water ?   O.H.S.C.

11. If the only force acting on a particle is constant in magnitude and direction, prove that the path of the particle is a parabola.

A particle is projected upwards at an angle of 60° to the horizontal with a velocity of 400 ft./sec. What time will elapse before it is moving upwards at an angle of 45° to the horizontal ? Find also, to the nearest foot, the horizontal and vertical distances from the starting point.   C.H.S.C.

12. Particles are simultaneously projected in all directions with speed u feet per second from a stationary balloon. Prove that t seconds later all the particles, whose motion has not been interrupted, will be situated on a sphere. Find the centre and radius of the sphere.   O.H.S.C.

13. A particle is projected at an angle of elevation α with a velocity u. Find its vertical and horizontal velocities after a time t. Find also the greatest height attained and the horizontal range.

If the horizontal range is equal in length to the latus rectum of the parabolic path, find the angle of projection with the horizontal.

J.M.B.H.S.C.

14. A shell is projected with velocity V at an angle of elevation α. Write down equations giving its horizontal and vertical displacements from the point of projection at time t, and from them obtain and interpret an equation by eliminating α.

A particle is projected with given velocity so as to pass through a point at a distance r from the point of projection. Prove that, if t_1 and t_2 are the times taken to reach this point in the two possible ways in which the particle can be projected with a given velocity, then

$$t_1 t_2 = 2r/g.$$ C.W.B.H.S.C.

15. A stone is projected with velocity V at an angle of elevation α. Obtain the equations giving its horizontal and vertical displacements from the point of projection at time t.

Prove that a boy, who can throw a stone to a maximum distance of 64 yards on the level, can also throw it so as to clear a wall 24 yards high at a distance of 32 yards.   C.W.B.H.S.C.

16. If u and α are the speed and angle of projection respectively of a projectile, find the greatest height attained and the range on a horizontal plane.

A rifle bullet is fired at and hits a target 100 yards distant. If the bullet rises to a maximum height of $\frac{3}{4}$ in. above the horizontal line between the muzzle of the rifle and the point of impact on the target, find the muzzle velocity.   L.H.S.C.

17. A particle projected from a point O with a speed u ft. per sec., an elevation θ_1 to the horizontal, passes through a point P, the straight line OP being inclined at an angle α to the horizontal. Prove that it will also pass through P if projected from O with the same speed at an elevation θ_2, where
$$\theta_1 + \theta_2 - \alpha = 90°.$$

Prove also that if t_1 and t_2 are the corresponding times for the flight from O to P,
$$t_1 t_2 = \frac{2OP}{g}.$$

                                                    O.H.S.C.

Relative Velocity

18. A steamboat is travelling with a constant speed of 15 miles per hour. When the boat is moving eastwards, the wind appears to an observer on the boat to be coming from the North. When the boat is moving southwards, the wind appears to be coming from the North-west. Find either graphically or by calculation the magnitude and direction of the wind velocity.   C.H.S.C.

19. The directions of the smoke-trail of a ferry-boat whose speed is 7 knots differ by 90° on its outward and return journeys. Assuming no change in the wind's velocity, what is its speed ? [You may assume that the direction of the smoke-trail is that of the wind's velocity relative to the boat.]   O.H.S.C.

20. Show how to obtain the relative velocity of two points whose motion is given.

A ship A is moving with uniform velocity. To a passenger on another ship B going due East at 14 knots she appears to move due North, but when the speed of B is reduced to 8 knots she appears to be moving 30° East of North. Show that the speed of A is $4\sqrt{19}$ knots.   C.W.B.H.S.C.

21. Explain the term *relative velocity*.

An aeroplane flies at the rate of u miles per hour in still air, or at the same speed relative to the air in a wind. If there is a wind of v miles per hour, show that the time in hours required by the aeroplane to fly a distance d miles and back in a direction inclined at θ to that of the wind is
$$\frac{2d(u^2 - v^2 \sin^2\theta)^{\frac{1}{2}}}{u^2 - v^2}.$$

                                                    C.W.B.H.S.C.

CHAPTER II

FORCE, MOMENTUM, WORK

Newton's laws of motion.—Sir Isaac Newton expressed his ideas of motion in three laws, which are still looked upon as the foundation of mechanics. They are :

I. Every body perseveres in its state of rest, or of uniform motion in a straight line, except in so far as it is compelled to change that state by forces impressed on it.

Since there is always friction, however small, in the case of any motion of which we have direct experience, it can only be inferred, from the fact that when there is less friction the motion persists longer, that if there were no friction, the state of motion of a body would continue without change. The nearest approach to such a state is that of the motion of the earth and planets in space which we believe to be nearly devoid of matter. In most cases in which we can observe the motion of a body, friction supplies the force which is impressed on the body to change its state of motion and bring it to rest.

II. Change of motion is proportional to the moving force impressed, and takes place in the straight line in which that force is impressed.

By change of motion is meant change of momentum, where momentum is defined as mass × velocity ; but as mass is not yet defined, the second law has no meaning, unless taken in conjunction with the third law, which is :

III. An action is always opposed by an equal reaction ; or, the mutual actions of two bodies are always equal and act in opposite directions.

This means that whenever two bodies act on each other mechanically, both experience the action, and that the actions on the two are equal and opposite. This can be put to the test of experiment. But there are not many direct experiments by which to test the fact. The experiments which assume this law are numerous, and their

25

cumulative effect is to strengthen our belief in the law. For example, when two bodies collide, the actions on the two bodies are equal and opposite (see ballistic pendulum, p. 31), or when two bodies are pushed apart, as in the case of a bullet fired from a gun, the action on one body, resulting from their mutual reaction, is equal and opposite to the action on the other body.

If a body A reacts with another body B, it is the result of experience that the acceleration of A bears a constant ratio to the acceleration of B, whatever the actual accelerations may be. Let us express this as follows :

$$\frac{\text{acceleration of A}}{\text{acceleration of B}} = \text{constant} = \mathsf{K}_B^A.$$

Now consider a third body C. In a similar manner when B and C act upon each other,

$$\frac{\text{acceleration of B}}{\text{acceleration of C}} = \mathsf{K}_C^B.$$

Now let A and C react upon each other, then

$$\frac{\text{acceleration of A}}{\text{acceleration of C}} = \mathsf{K}_C^A.$$

Now it is the result of experience that

$$\mathsf{K}_C^A = \mathsf{K}_B^A \times \mathsf{K}_C^B. \qquad \dots\dots\dots\dots\dots\dots\dots(i)$$

There is thus some property of every body that remains with it whatever body it reacts with. This quantity is usually called its mass. Then, if

$$\mathsf{K}_B^A = \frac{\text{mass of B}}{\text{mass of A}},$$

and in the same way,

$$\mathsf{K}_C^B = \frac{\text{mass of C}}{\text{mass of B}},$$

and

$$\mathsf{K}_C^A = \frac{\text{mass of C}}{\text{mass of A}},$$

it follows that equation (i) becomes

$$\frac{\text{mass of C}}{\text{mass of A}} = \frac{\text{mass of B}}{\text{mass of A}} \times \frac{\text{mass of C}}{\text{mass of B}},$$

which is consistent if the mass is a permanent property of each body. For any particular reaction between A and B,

$$(\text{mass} \times \text{acceleration})_A = (\text{mass} \times \text{acceleration})_B.$$

The quantity, mass, of any body is something that belongs to it, and the greater the mass the less will be the acceleration when the body reacts with a second one. It is the property of a body which determines its inertia or reluctance to change its velocity. Mass is defined as above, but the method described does not lend itself to accurate comparisons. A more convenient method of comparing masses is described on p. 52.

The unit of mass is quite arbitrary. It is the mass of a piece of platinum preserved in the International Bureau of Weights and Measures at Sèvres, and is called the kilogram. One thousandth of this is used for scientific purposes and is called the gram. On the British system the unit is the mass of a piece of platinum kept in the Standards Office, and is called the pound.

$$1 \text{ pound} = 453 \cdot 59 \text{ grams.}$$

Force.—In the statement of Newton's third law of motion on p. 25, the "action" and "reaction" are the quantities (mass × acceleration) for the two bodies, and since the accelerations are in opposite directions for the two bodies we see that the action and reaction are equal and opposite. This quantity (mass × acceleration) is known as the force acting on any body, and thus the force on one body is equal and opposite to the force on the other when the bodies react on each other.

Newton's second law (p. 25) does not involve any new idea, because the fact that there is an "impressed force" implies that there is some second body, but its nature and position may be unknown. The fact that a body has acceleration is the only evidence we have that there is a force acting upon it, and this force we define as the mass of the body multiplied by its acceleration. Also the direction of the acceleration indicates the direction of the force.

Mass is a scalar quantity, since it does not involve direction ; force, however, is a vector quantity whose direction is that of the acceleration produced. Thus the equation for the force acting upon a body is

$$\mathbf{f} = m \times \mathbf{a}. \quad \dots\dots\dots\dots\dots\dots\dots\dots\dots\dots\text{(i)}$$

Units of force.—On any system, a unit force is said to be acting when a unit mass has unit acceleration. On the c.g.s. system the unit of force is called the dyne, and is the force which produces an acceleration of 1 cm./sec.² when acting on 1 gram. On the British system the unit of force is called the **poundal**, and is the force which when acting on a mass of 1 pound produces an acceleration of 1 foot/sec.².

It follows at once that the **weight** of a body is known in terms of its mass and the acceleration of gravity at the place where the body is situated, since the weight is the force pulling the body vertically downwards due to the proximity of the earth. The weight is therefore $m g$ dynes or poundals, according to the system of units employed.

Momentum.—Equation (i) (p. 27) may be written in a slightly different manner. Since $\mathbf{a} = \dfrac{\mathbf{v}}{t}$ (p. 6), then

$$\mathbf{f} = \frac{m\mathbf{v}}{t}. \qquad\qquad \text{.............................(ii)}$$

On p. 25 it was seen that $m\mathbf{v}$ is the **momentum** of the body, and equation (ii) then states that when a constant force $\mathbf{f}$ acts on a body, it is measured by the **rate of change of momentum** it produces. Even if the force is not constant we can still use equation (ii) in the form,

$$\mathbf{f} = \frac{d(m\mathbf{v})}{dt},$$

or,
$$\mathbf{f}\,dt = d(m\mathbf{v}),$$

and integrating, it becomes

$$\int_{t_1}^{t_2} \mathbf{f}\,dt = m\mathbf{v},$$

where $m\mathbf{v}$ is the change in momentum that has occurred in the interval of time $t_2 - t_1$. This change in momentum is always equal to the quantity $\int_{t_1}^{t_2} \mathbf{f}\,dt$, however the force may vary with the time, and whatever the time taken for the operation.

Impulse.—There is a class of operation in which the time is extremely short and the force correspondingly large, so that $\int_{t_1}^{t_2} \mathbf{f}\,dt$ is finite. In this case the name **impulse** is used, and although neither t nor $\mathbf{f}$ is known, the effect of the impulse is measured by the change in momentum produced.

EXAMPLE.—A smooth iron ball of mass 3 kg. is struck a blow horizontally by a smooth hammer. If the ball has a horizontal velocity of
40 cm./sec.[1] immediately after the blow, what is the value of the impulse ?
If the actual contact is supposed to last for 10^{-3} sec., what is the average
force between hammer and ball ?

Change of momentum of ball $= 3000 \times 40 = \underline{120000}$ C.G.S. units, which is
therefore the value of the impulse.

If force is assumed to be constant, change of momentum $= \mathbf{f} \times t$;

$$\therefore \quad \mathbf{f} = 120000/10^{-3} = \underline{1 \cdot 2 \times 10^8 \text{ dynes.}}$$

Collision.—One of the commonest examples of the reaction between
two bodies is that in which two bodies meet or collide. Since the
force on one body is equal and opposite to the force on the other,
at every instant, and the time of contact must be the same for the
two bodies, it follows that $\int_{t_1}^{t_2} \mathbf{f} \, dt$ must be the same for both, but
opposite in directions, therefore

$$m_1 \mathbf{v}_1 = - m_2 \mathbf{v}_2$$

where $\mathbf{v}_1$ and $\mathbf{v}_2$ are the changes in velocity of the two bodies respectively. That is, one body gains in momentum exactly the amount
that the other body loses. Hence the total momentum of the two
bodies remains constant. This may be stated as a general principle,
that, when two bodies act on each other there is no change in their total
momentum. This is known as the principle of the conservation of
momentum. On fixing one direction as positive, this principle may
be expressed by the equation,

$$m_1 \mathbf{u}_1 + m_2 \mathbf{u}_2 = m_1 \mathbf{u}_1' + m_2 \mathbf{u}_2', \quad \dots\dots\dots\dots\dots(1)$$

where $\mathbf{u}_1$ and $\mathbf{u}_2$ are the velocities of m_1 and m_2 before collision and
$\mathbf{u}_1'$ and $\mathbf{u}_2'$ their velocities afterwards.

EXAMPLE 1.—Two bodies of masses 200 and 300 gm. respectively are
moving in opposite directions with velocities 80 cm. sec.$^{-1}$ and 40 cm. sec.$^{-1}$.
If they stick together on collision, what is their velocity ?
Here, $\mathbf{u}_1' = \mathbf{u}_2'$;

$$\therefore \quad (200 \times 80) - (300 \times 40) = (200 + 300) \, \mathbf{u}',$$
$$16000 - 12000 = 500 \mathbf{u}' ;$$
$$\therefore \quad \mathbf{u}' = \tfrac{4000}{500} = 8 \text{ cm. sec.}^{-1}.$$

That is, the bodies have a velocity of 8 cm. sec.$^{-1}$ in the direction of
motion of the first body.

EXAMPLE 2.—A gun has mass 7 kg. and the bullet mass 150 gm. After firing, the velocity of the bullet is 350 m. sec.$^{-1}$. What is the velocity of recoil of the gun ?

In this case, $u_1 = u_2 = 0$;

$$\therefore \quad 0 = m_1 u_1' + m_2 u_2',$$
$$0 = 7000 u_1' + 150 \times 35000.$$
$$\underline{u_1' = -750 \text{ cm. sec.}^{-1}.}$$

Coefficient of restitution.—In the two examples just given, the bodies have a common velocity before or after their action upon each other. If, however, this is not the case, equation (1) on p. 29 is not sufficient to find their velocities after collision. The further information necessary is supplied by the fact that their velocity of separation bears a definite ratio to their velocity of approach. This ratio is called the **coefficient of restitution** for the two bodies.

Thus their relative velocity of separation is $u_2' - u_1'$, and their relative velocity of approach is $u_1 - u_2$, and

$$\frac{u_2' - u_1'}{u_1 - u_2} = \text{coefficient of restitution}$$
$$= e. \quad \dots\dots\dots\dots\dots\dots\dots\dots\dots\dots\dots\dots\dots\dots\dots(2)$$

The coefficient of restitution is approximately constant for bodies consisting of two definite materials, and varies from zero, for two soft bodies which stick together on impact, to nearly unity for very hard bodies.

The coefficient of restitution of certain common bodies :

Lead—lead -	-	-	0·20	Ivory—ivory -	-	-	0·81
Lead—soft brass -	-	-	0·16	Lead—glass -	-	-	0·25
Glass—glass -	-	-	0·94	Lead—ivory -	-	-	0·44
Cork—cork -	-	-	0·65	Cast iron—glass -	-	-	0·91
Cast iron—cast iron	-	-	0·66	Brass—ivory -	-	-	0·78

EXAMPLE 1.—A body of mass 600 gm. which has velocity of 450 cm./sec. overtakes a body of mass 200 gm. moving in the same direction with velocity 300 cm./sec. If the coefficient of restitution is 0·8, what are the velocities of the bodies after collision ?

Using equation (1) on p. 29,

$$(600 \times 450) + (200 \times 300) = 600 u_1' + 200 u_2',$$

and from equation (2), $\dfrac{u_2' - u_1'}{450 - 300} = 0·8,$

$$3u_1' + u_2' = 1650,$$
$$u_1' - u_2' = -120,$$
$$4u_1' = 1530,$$
$$\underline{u_1' = 382\cdot5 \text{ cm./sec.}}$$
$$3u_1' - 3u_2' = -360,$$
$$4u_2' = 2010,$$
$$\underline{u_2' = 502\cdot5 \text{ cm./sec.}}$$

EXAMPLE 2.—A ball is dropped on to a horizontal plane from a height h ft. above it. Find the time that elapses before the ball comes to rest in terms of h and e, the coefficient of restitution.   O.H.S.C.

The first fall takes time $\sqrt{\dfrac{2h}{g}}$ and the ball strikes the ground with velocity $\sqrt{2gh}$.

$$\text{Velocity of rebound} \qquad = e\sqrt{2gh}.$$

$$\text{Height of rebound} \qquad = \frac{e^2 \cdot 2gh}{2g} = e^2h.$$

$$\text{Time for up and down travel} = 2\sqrt{\frac{2e^2h}{g}} = 2e\sqrt{\frac{2h}{g}}.$$

$$\text{Time for 2nd} \quad ,, \quad ,, \quad = 2e^2\sqrt{\frac{2h}{g}}.$$

$$\text{Time for 3rd} \quad ,, \quad ,, \quad = 2e^3\sqrt{\frac{2h}{g}}.$$

$$\therefore \text{ total time} = \sqrt{\frac{2h}{g}}\{1 + 2e + 2e^2 + 2e^3 + \ldots\}.$$

Since e is less than unity the series $2e + 2e^2 + 2e^3 + \ldots$ is convergent and the sum of an infinite number of terms is $\dfrac{2e}{1-e}$. As the time of flight after a rebound becomes less and less, it will eventually be vanishingly small, and the ball is at rest.

$$\therefore \text{ total time} = \sqrt{\frac{2h}{g}}\left(1 + \frac{2e}{1-e}\right)$$
$$= \underline{\sqrt{\frac{2h}{g}} \cdot \frac{1+e}{1-e}}.$$

Ballistic pendulum.—The simplest method of investigating the result of collision is due to Newton, and employs the apparatus known as the ballistic pendulum.

Two blocks A and B are suspended by four strings each, as shown

in Fig. 17. Only two strings for each block are shown, ab and cd for
the block A. As either block is drawn aside it moves without rota-

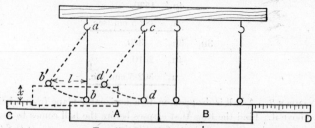

FIG. 17.—BALLISTIC PENDULUM.

tion, remaining always horizontal, since the rectangle $abdc$ becomes
the parallelogram $ab'd'c$. If, then, the block A is raised to a height x
above its lowest position and allowed to fall, it acquires a velocity
of magnitude $v_1 = \sqrt{2gx}$ in falling through the height x (p. 8). This
velocity is, of course, horizontal, and the velocities of A and B after
impact will be determined by equations (1) (p. 29) and (2) (p. 30).
The velocities after collision determine the heights to which each body
will rise. Thus if A has velocity v_1' it will rise to a height x' where
$v_1' = \sqrt{2gx'}$, and if B has velocity v_2' it will rise to height y' where
$v_2' = \sqrt{2gy'}$.

On varying the masses and materials of A and B the truth of
equation (1) (p. 29) may be established, and from equation (2) (p. 30)
the coefficient of restitution for the two materials may be found.

The chief experimental difficulty is that of observing the height
to which each body rises, since the heights are small and the
bodies are only situated in their highest positions for an instant
of time. This difficulty is lessened by observing the horizontal
travel of each body by means of the scale CD placed parallel to the
plane of motion. If l is the horizontal distance of travel as measured
on CD for the maximum distance from their rest position before or
after impact, then from the property of the circle,

$$l^2 = x(2r - x),$$

where r is the length of the string ab, or, if the motion is small,

$$l^2 = 2rx,$$

so that $$v = \sqrt{2gx}$$

becomes $$v = \sqrt{\frac{g}{r}}\, l.$$

EXAMPLE 1.—The block A (Fig. 17) is drawn aside through a horizontal distance 10 cm. and released, and it is found that, after collision, B moves to the right through distance 4 cm. and A to the left through distance 3 cm. If A has mass m_1 and B mass m_2, find the ratio m_2/m_1 and the coefficient of restitution of the bodies.

Taking the positive direction from left to right.

Velocity, before collision :

$$\text{A,} \quad \mathbf{v}_1 = \sqrt{\frac{g}{r}} 10 ; \quad \text{B,} \quad \mathbf{v}_2 = 0. ;$$

after collision :

$$\text{A,} \quad \mathbf{v}_1' = -\sqrt{\frac{g}{r}} 3 ; \quad \text{B,} \quad \mathbf{v}_2' = \sqrt{\frac{g}{r}} 4.$$

Now
$$m_1 \mathbf{v}_1 + m_2 \mathbf{v}_2 = m_1 \mathbf{v}_1' + m_2 \mathbf{v}_2',$$

$$m_1 \sqrt{\frac{g}{r}} 10 + (m_2 \times 0) = -m_1 \sqrt{\frac{g}{r}} 3 + m_2 \sqrt{\frac{g}{r}} 4,$$

$$10 m_1 = -3 m_1 + 4 m_2,$$

$$\underline{\frac{m_2}{m_1} = \frac{13}{4} = 3{\cdot}25.}$$

Again,
$$e = \frac{\mathbf{v}_2' - \mathbf{v}_1'}{\mathbf{v}_1 - \mathbf{v}_2}$$

$$= \frac{\sqrt{\frac{g}{r}} 4 + \sqrt{\frac{g}{r}} 3}{\sqrt{\frac{g}{r}} 10 - 0}$$

$$= \underline{0{\cdot}7.}$$

EXAMPLE 2.—Explain the principle of the conservation of momentum. How far is this principle capable of experimental verification ?

A block of wood weighing 5 lb. is suspended from fixed pegs by vertical strings 10 ft. long. A bullet weighing $\frac{1}{2}$ oz. and moving horizontally with a velocity of 1500 ft. per sec., enters and remains in the block. Find the angle through which the block swings.   C.H.S.C.

Let the block be A (Fig. 17), then

$$m_1 = 5 \text{ lb.,} \quad m_2 = 1/32 \text{ lb.,}$$
$$\mathbf{v}_1 = 0, \quad \mathbf{v}_2 = 1500 \text{ ft./sec.}$$

Also
$$\mathbf{v}_1' = \mathbf{v}_2',$$
$$m_1 \mathbf{v}_1 + m_2 \mathbf{v}_2 = (m_1 + m_2) \mathbf{v}_1',$$
$$(5 \times 0) + (\tfrac{1}{32} \times 1500) = 5 \tfrac{1}{32} \times \mathbf{v}_1',$$
$$\mathbf{v}_1' = \tfrac{1500}{161} \text{ ft./sec.}$$

In Fig. 17, $$\cos bab' = \frac{r-x}{r},$$

where x is the height through which the block rises ; and

$$2gx = \left(\frac{1500}{161}\right)^2 \quad \text{or} \quad x = \left(\frac{1500}{161}\right)^2 \frac{1}{2g} = 1{\cdot}356.$$

$$\therefore \cos bab' = \frac{r-x}{r} = \frac{10-x}{10} = \frac{10-1{\cdot}356}{10} = \frac{8{\cdot}644}{10} ;$$

$$\therefore \underline{bab' = 30° \; 11'}.$$

Work and energy.—Those quantities used in Physics which are given definite names have been evolved by experience. Their usefulness has led to their adoption. When two bodies react, as in collision, the quantity that remains constant is the momentum, but in many other changes it is some other quantity that remains constant. This is best understood by developing our ideas regarding force. It has already been seen that, force × time = change of momentum. Now consider the quantity force × distance. That is, the product of the force and the distance the body moves while the force acts upon it, the distance being measured in the direction of the force. Then the product **force × distance** is defined as the **work** done upon the body by the force.

$$\text{Work} = \mathbf{f} \times \mathbf{s}.$$

The unit of work on the c.g.s. system is the work done when a body, upon which a force of one dyne acts, moves through a distance of one centimetre ; it is called the **erg**. On the British system the unit is the **foot-poundal**, although engineers use the weight of one pound as the unit of force, which gives the **foot-pound** as the corresponding unit of work.

In the case of a body rising or falling, the force of gravity acts upon it and the work done is thus $m\mathbf{g} \times \mathbf{h}$ ergs, where $m\mathbf{g}$ dynes is its weight and $\mathbf{h}$ cm. the vertical distance through which it rises or falls.

If only one force acts upon the body, it has acceleration $\mathbf{a}$ given by

$$\mathbf{f} = m \times \mathbf{a},$$

and if the force, and therefore acceleration, are constant and both sides of the equation are multiplied by $\mathbf{s}$, the distance travelled from rest,

$$\mathbf{fs} = m\mathbf{as} ;$$

but the velocity acquired in moving from rest through distance $\mathbf{s}$ is given by

$$\mathbf{v}^2 = 2\mathbf{as} ;$$

$$\therefore \mathbf{fs} = \tfrac{1}{2}m\mathbf{v}^2.$$

The work done upon the body is thus $\frac{1}{2}m\mathbf{v}^2$ ergs, and is called the **kinetic energy** of the body. It is energy or power of doing work possessed by the body on account of its motion. If the force $\mathbf{f}$ were then reversed in direction, the body would be brought to rest in distance $\mathbf{s}$.

Even when the force and acceleration are not constant, the same consideration holds, for, at any instant,

$$\mathbf{f} = m\mathbf{a},$$

and for an infinitesimal displacement $d\mathbf{s}$,

$$\text{work done} = \mathbf{f}\,d\mathbf{s} = m\,\frac{d\mathbf{v}}{dt}\,d\mathbf{s}$$

$$= m\,d\mathbf{v}\,\frac{d\mathbf{s}}{dt}$$

$$= m\mathbf{v}\,d\mathbf{v}.$$

∴ Work done in moving from a distance $\mathbf{s}_1$ from the origin to a distance $\mathbf{s}_2$ is

$$\int_{s_1}^{s_2} \mathbf{f}\,d\mathbf{s} = \int_{v_1}^{v_2} m\mathbf{v}\,d\mathbf{v}$$

$$= \left[\tfrac{1}{2}m\mathbf{v}^2 \right]_{v_1}^{v_2}$$

$$= \tfrac{1}{2}m\mathbf{v}_2^2 - \tfrac{1}{2}m\mathbf{v}_1^2,$$

where $\mathbf{v}_1$ is the velocity of the body at position $\mathbf{s}_1$ and $\mathbf{v}_2$ that at $\mathbf{s}_2$. The equation expresses the fact that the change in kinetic energy of a body is the work done upon it.

EXAMPLE.—Two elastic spheres of masses m_1 and m_2, moving with velocities u_1 and u_2 respectively, come into direct collision. Assuming that the coefficient of restitution is e, find an expression for the whole change of kinetic energy on impact.

A mass of 10 lb. drops vertically on a fixed plane with a velocity of 20 ft. per sec. If the coefficient of restitution is 0·6, and the duration of impact is 0·1 sec., find the average force exerted on the plane.

C.W.B.H.S.C.

The total kinetic energy before impact is $\frac{1}{2}m_1u_1^2 + \frac{1}{2}m_2u_2^2$. If v_1 and v_2 are the velocities after collision, the two equations for determining them are

$$m_1u_1 + m_2u_2 = m_1v_1 + m_2v_2, \quad \dots\dots\dots\dots\dots(\text{p. 29})$$

and

$$e(u_2 - u_1) = v_1 - v_2. \quad \dots\dots\dots\dots\dots(\text{p. 30})$$

Multiply the second equation by m_2 and add to the first

$$m_1u_1 + m_2u_2 + m_2e(u_2 - u_1) = (m_1 + m_2)v_1 \; ;$$

$$\therefore \; v_1 = \frac{m_1u_1 + m_2u_2}{m_1 + m_2} + \frac{m_2e}{m_1 + m_2}(u_2 - u_1).$$

Similarly by multiplying the second equation by m_1 and subtracting it from the first,

$$v_2 = \frac{m_1u_1 + m_2u_2}{m_1 + m_2} - \frac{m_1e}{m_1 + m_2}(u_2 - u_1).$$

These may be written, $v_1 = \alpha + \beta m_2$, and $v_2 = \alpha - \beta m_1$;

$$\therefore \; \tfrac{1}{2}m_1v_1^2 + \tfrac{1}{2}m_2v_2^2 = \tfrac{1}{2}(m_1 + m_2)\alpha^2 + \tfrac{1}{2}m_1m_2(m_1 + m_2)\beta^2$$

$$= \frac{1}{2(m_1 + m_2)}\{(m_1u_1 + m_2u_2)^2 + e^2m_1m_2(u_2 - u_1)^2)\}.$$

Squaring out $(m_1u_1 + m_2u_2)^2$ and adding and subtracting

$$m_1m_2(u_2 - u_1)^2,$$

$$\tfrac{1}{2}m_1v_1^2 + \tfrac{1}{2}m_2v_2^2 = \frac{1}{2(m_1 + m_2)}\{m_1{}^2u_1{}^2 + m_2{}^2u_2{}^2 + 2m_1m_2u_1u_2$$
$$+ m_1m_2u_2{}^2 - 2m_1m_2u_1u_2 + m_1m_2u_1{}^2$$
$$- m_1m_2(u_2 - u_1)^2 + e^2m_1m_2(u_2 - u_1)^2\}$$
$$= \frac{1}{2(m_1 + m_2)}\{m_1(m_1 + m_2)u_1{}^2 + m_2(m_1 + m_2)u_2{}^2$$
$$- (1 - e^2)m_1m_2(u_2 - u_1)^2\} \; ;$$

that is,

$$\tfrac{1}{2}m_1v_1^2 + \tfrac{1}{2}m_2v_2^2 = \tfrac{1}{2}m_1u_1^2 + \tfrac{1}{2}m_2u_2^2 - \tfrac{1}{2}(1 - e^2)\frac{m_1m_2}{m_1 + m_2}(u_2 - u_1)^2.$$

Thus the kinetic energy is diminished on collision by the amount $\tfrac{1}{2}(1 - e^2)\dfrac{m_1m_2}{m_1 + m_2}(u_2 - u_1)^2.$ This expression is always positive because e is always less than unity and $(u_2 - u_1)^2$ must be positive, whatever the signs of u_1 and u_2.

In the problem, velocity of approach of mass and plane is 20 ft./sec. and

$$\frac{\text{velocity of separation}}{\text{velocity of approach}} = 0.6 \; ;$$

$$\therefore \; \text{velocity of rebound} \quad = 20 \times 0.6$$

$$= 12 \text{ ft./sec.}$$

$\therefore$ total change of momentum of 10 lb. mass $= 10\{20 - (-12)\} = 320,$

and $f \times t = $ change of momentum,

$$f \times 0.1 = 320,$$

$$\underline{f = 3200 \text{ poundals.}}$$

Composition and resolution of forces.—The fact that a force is a directed or vector quantity implies that forces may be added or compounded in the same manner as other vector quantities. This may be realised more particularly by referring to the vector diagram (Fig. 18). It was seen on p. 4 that if a body has two simultaneous velocities represented by the vectors OA and AB its actual or resultant velocity is represented by the vector OB. If now OA and OB represent velocities gained in unit time they are accelera-

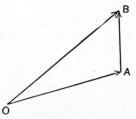

FIG. 18.—VECTOR ADDITION OF FORCES.

tions, and the resultant acceleration is OB. Again, let the body have mass m, then $m \times$ OA is a force acting upon it and $m \times$ AB a second force acting upon it. The resultant force acting is then $m \times$ OB. By using an appropriate scale, OA, AB and OB may represent the forces themselves.

The above construction is sometimes represented in another manner. Thus in Fig. 19, if OA and OB are two forces acting at the

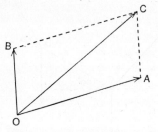

FIG. 19.—PARALLELOGRAM OF FORCES.

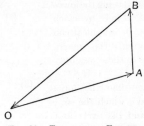

FIG. 20.—TRIANGLE OF FORCES.

point O, their resultant is represented by the diagonal OC of the parallelogram of which OA and OB are two sides. This is known as the **parallelogram of forces**.

There is still another way of stating the same fact, which is, that if three forces acting at a point can be represented in magnitude and direction by the three sides of a triangle taken in order, then the resultant of the three forces at the point is zero. In Fig. 20, OA, AB and BO represent the three forces, and since they form an exact triangle their resultant is zero. It follows that any one of the forces, say BO, is equal and opposite to the resultant of the other two, which is really the same statement as that corresponding to Figs. 18 and 19. The triangle in diagram (Fig. 20) is

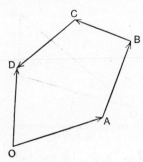

known as the **triangle of forces**. It may be extended to apply to any number of forces acting at a point, in which case it is known as the **polygon of forces**. Thus if the vectors OA, AB, BC and CD act at a point, their resultant is OD (Fig. 21). OD reversed would then be equal and opposite to the resultant of the other forces, and added to them would give resultant zero, so that if OA, AB, BC, CD and DO form a closed figure their resultant is zero.

FIG. 21.—POLYGON OF FORCES.

EXAMPLE.—Explain how three or more vector quantities can be compounded.

The ends of a string ABCDE are attached to fixed points A and E, and a weight of 10 lb. is hung from C. Weights are hung from B and D of such amounts that AB, BC, CD, and DE are inclined respectively at 60°, 45°, 30°, and 60° to the horizontal, C being the lowest point. Find, by calculation or graphical construction, the magnitudes of these weights.

C.H.S.C.

First find the forces p and q which the cords BC and CD exert at C (Fig 22 (a)). Since C is at rest, the forces p, q and 10 lb. weight have resultant zero.

Draw the triangle FGH (b) with sides FG vertical, GH parallel to CD and FH parallel to BC. Then FGH is the triangle of forces for the point C, and if FG corre-

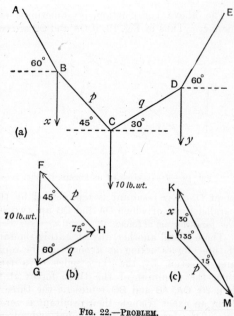

FIG. 22.—PROBLEM.

sponds to a force 10 lb. wt.,

$$\frac{p}{10}=\frac{\sin 60°}{\sin 75°}, \quad \text{and} \quad \frac{q}{10}=\frac{\sin 45°}{\sin 75°},$$

$$p=10\frac{\sin 60°}{\sin 75°} \text{ lb. wt.}, \quad q=10\frac{\sin 45°}{\sin 75°} \text{ lb. wt.}$$

Another triangle KLM (Fig. 22 (c)) for the forces at B may be drawn, for the force p is the **tension** in the string BC, and since the string is at rest the force it exerts at B is equal to the force it exerts at C.

In triangle KLM,

$$\frac{x}{p}=\frac{\sin 15°}{\sin 30°};$$

$$\therefore \quad x=p\frac{\sin 15°}{\sin 30°}=10 \cdot \frac{\sin 60°}{\sin 75°}\times\frac{\sin 15°}{\sin 30°}$$

$$=4\cdot640 \text{ lb. wt.}$$

In a similar manner, by drawing the triangle of forces for the point D,

$$y=q\frac{\sin 30°}{\sin 30°}=10\frac{\sin 45°}{\sin 75°}$$

$$=7\cdot321 \text{ lb. wt.}$$

Work for any path.—When the motion of the body is not in the direction of the force acting upon it, the work done during the motion, on account of this force, is found by resolving the force into two components, one along the path and the other perpendicular to it. The quantity (force component along path × element of path) for the whole travel is then integrated. If **f** is the force (Fig. 23) whose value is f and $d\mathbf{s}$ an element of path whose length is $d\mathbf{s}$, $f \cos \theta$ is the value of the component of the force acting along the path and $f \cos \theta . d\mathbf{s}$ is the work done for this element of path. The whole work done by the force as the body

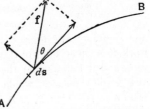

FIG. 23.—WORK DONE IN CURVED PATH.

moves from A to B is then $\int_A^B f \cos \theta . d\mathbf{s}$. The component $f \sin \theta$ at any point of the path is at right angles to the motion, and therefore does not involve any work done. It may be noticed that $\cos \theta . d\mathbf{s}$ is the element of path resolved in the direction of the force, and the product $f \cos \theta . d\mathbf{s}$ is again the work done for the element of path. It is therefore immaterial whether the force is resolved in the direction of the path or the path resolved in the direction of the force. Both **f** and $d\mathbf{s}$ are vector quantities, but work is a scalar quantity. For this reason the **scalar product** of the two vectors is defined as the quantity $f \cos \theta \cdot ds$. When the two vectors are at right angles their scalar product is zero. There is another possible product of two vectors. This, however, does not concern us here.

Potential energy.—In all the cases considered here, the work done when a body moves from one point to another is independent of the

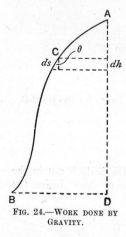

FIG. 24.—WORK DONE BY GRAVITY.

path taken. In the particular case of gravity, if the body moves along a smooth surface ACB (Fig. 24), the work done for an element of path ds at C is

$$mg \cos \theta \cdot ds = mg \, dh.$$
$$\therefore \int_A^B f \cos \theta \cdot ds = \int_A^B mg \, dh$$
$$= mg \int_A^B dh$$
$$= mg \cdot \text{AD}.$$

That is, the work done is the same as though the body had moved vertically through the distance AD. If the surface ACB is perfectly smooth it does not exert any force in its own direction on a body, and therefore any force it exerts is at right angles to itself. The work done on account of the force exerted by the surface is therefore zero, and it follows that the kinetic energy of the body on arriving at B is the same as it would have been if the body had fallen freely from A to D. That is, at B,

$$\tfrac{1}{2}mv^2 = mg \cdot \text{AD},$$
or
$$v^2 = 2g \cdot \text{AD}.$$

The velocity acquired is thus the same as would be acquired in falling freely through the same height, provided always that the surface is perfectly smooth, that is, it does not exert any force on the body in its direction of motion.

If the body is raised through the height AD the work done upon it **in** opposition to gravity is $mg \cdot \text{AD}$. On account of this work done upon it, it can again acquire kinetic energy mg . $AD = \frac{1}{2}mv^2$ if allowed to fall through the vertical distance AD. It thus possesses energy when at the position A, which is called **potential energy** or **energy of position**. Potential energy and kinetic energy are mutually convertible. If a body is projected vertically upwards it possesses kinetic energy $\frac{1}{2}mv^2$, but as it rises this kinetic energy decreases, and the potential energy increases. When the kinetic energy is reduced to zero, the potential energy is exactly sufficient to give the body its original velocity and kinetic energy on regaining its starting point.

Conservation of energy.—The mutual convertibility of potential energy and kinetic energy, suggests a more general principle. It is not possible here to study other forms of energy, such as heat, electrical energy, light, etc. But there are ample grounds for believing that whenever energy in one form is converted into energy of another form, there is an exact equivalence between the amounts of energy in the two forms. That is, if the energy of the first form can be converted entirely into energy of the second form and then converted entirely back again, the original amount of energy in the first form will be obtained. It is not often that such a complete conversion can be performed. For example, if a body falls, some of its potential energy is converted into heat by friction with the air. It is true, however, that the heat energy together with the kinetic energy will be together equal to the original potential energy. Thus if we could obtain a closed system, cut off entirely from outside, then energy changes in this closed system may occur, but they will not alter the total amount of energy in the system. Energy is merely converted from one form to another. This is known as the principle of the **conservation of energy.**

EXAMPLE.—A smooth sphere is moving with a velocity u in a direction making an angle α with the normal to a fixed smooth plane. Find the velocity and direction of motion of the sphere after impact with the plane assuming the coefficient of restitution is e.

A glass marble of mass 10 gm. falls from a height of 3 m. on to a horizontal glass plate. If the coefficient of restitution is 0·9, find (a) the height to which the marble will rise after impact, and (b) the loss of kinetic energy.

J.M.B.H.S.C.

Component of velocity normal to plane $= u \cos \alpha$.

Normal velocity of rebound $= eu \cos \alpha$.

Component of velocity parallel to plane $= u \sin \alpha$.

This component is unchanged on impact.

$$\therefore \text{ Resultant velocity} = \sqrt{u^2 \sin^2\alpha + e^2 u^2 \cos^2\alpha}$$
$$= u\sqrt{\sin^2\alpha + e^2 \cos^2\alpha}.$$

If θ is the angle between velocity and normal

$$\tan \theta = \frac{u \sin \alpha}{eu \cos \alpha} = \frac{\tan \alpha}{e}.$$

(a) Velocity of marble on striking glass plate $= \sqrt{2gh}$
$$= \sqrt{2 \times 981 \times 300}.$$

Velocity of rebound $= e\sqrt{2gh}$
$$= 0.9\sqrt{2 \times 981 \times 300}.$$

Height of rise $\quad = \dfrac{v^2}{2g} = \dfrac{(0.9)^2 \times (2 \times 981 \times 300)}{2 \times 981}$

$$= 300 \times 0.81$$
$$= \underline{243 \text{ cm.}}$$

(b) Kinetic energy before impact $= \frac{1}{2}mv^2$
$$= mgh = 10 \times 981 \times 300.$$

Kinetic energy after impact $= \frac{1}{2}me^2(2gh)$
$$= me^2gh$$
$$= 10 \times 981 \times 300 \times .81.$$

Loss of kinetic energy $\quad = 10 \times 981 \times 300(1 - 0.81)$
$$= \underline{5.59 \times 10^5 \text{ ergs.}}$$

Rate of working.—When work is being performed, the rate at which energy is converted from one form to another may be as important as, or more important than, the total amount of work done. In the case of a steam engine or electric motor it is the rate at which mechanical energy can be produced that fixes the usefulness of the machine. Rate of working is also called power, and the natural unit of power is one erg per second on the C.G.S. system or one foot-pound per second on the engineers' British system. These units are small for practical use, so multiples of them are taken. On the British system 33,000 foot-pounds per minute is taken as unit, and is called the horse-power. On the scientific system the larger units have been developed from electrical usage, but they are nevertheless mechanical units. For example, 10^7 ergs are taken as a unit of energy and called the joule.

A rate of working of one joule per second is called one watt. The watt is thus a rate of working of 10^7 ergs per second. Even this unit is small when measuring the power produced by large machinery, so that 1000 watts are taken as one **kilowatt** (kw.). To correspond to the power of the kilowatt, the **kilowatt-hour** is employed in measuring energy for commercial purposes; it is the amount of work done in one hour when the rate of working is one kilowatt.

It is useful to convert horse-power into watts or kilowatts. If pounds' weight are converted into dynes, feet to centimetres, etc., it is found that 1 horse-power = 746 watts = 0·746 kw.

Dimensions.—There is a very convenient method of expressing physical quantities which illustrates their nature as apart from their magnitude. It is possible to derive all quantities from three suitably chosen, and the three selected have already been seen to be **mass, length** and **time**. A length must be expressed as a number of units of length. But if the magnitude of the quantity be excluded, its nature may still be indicated by writing it in some special form. For example $[L]$ represents the quality of length, and an area is $[L \times L]$ or $[L^2]$, and a volume $[L \times L \times L]$ or $[L^3]$. Thus an area is of two dimensions in length and a volume of three dimensions.

Following the same principle, a velocity is always a length divided by a time, or $\left[\dfrac{L}{T}\right]$ or $[LT^{-1}]$. Continuing in the same manner, an acceleration is a velocity divided by a time, that is, $\left[\dfrac{LT^{-1}}{T}\right]$ or $[LT^{-2}]$. The following table gives the dimensions of the quantities so far considered.

Length	-	-	-	-	$[L]$	
Area	-	-	-	-	$[L^2]$	
Volume	-	-	-	-	$[L^3]$	
Velocity	-	-	-	-	$[LT^{-1}]$	
Acceleration	-	-	-	-	$[LT^{-2}]$	
Force	-	-	-	-	$[MLT^{-2}]$	(p. 27)
Momentum or impulse	-	-	-	$[MLT^{-1}]$	(p. 25)
Energy or work	-	-	-	$[ML^2T^{-2}]$	(p. 40)
Power	-	-	-	-	$[ML^2T^{-3}]$	(p. 42)

It will be seen that kinetic energy, which is $\frac{1}{2}$ mass × (velocity)^2, has the dimensions $[ML^2T^{-2}]$ and potential energy mg . AD (p. 40) is $[M . LT^{-2} . L]$ or $[ML^2T^{-2}]$, since the acceleration g has the dimensions $[LT^{-2}]$ and AD is a height or length. Thus energy, whether kinetic or potential, has the same dimensions. This would be expected from the fact that the two are mutually convertible.

The method of dimensions serves the useful purpose of expressing a physical quantity in a recognisable form, but it also serves as a check on the accuracy of certain calculations. For all the terms of any equation must be of the same dimensions, as quantities of different kinds cannot be added together. As an example, consider the equation

$$v_1 = \frac{m_1 u_1 + m_2 u_2}{m_1 + m_2} + \frac{m_2 e}{m_1 + m_2}(u_2 - u_1), \qquad \dots\dots\dots(p.\ 36)$$

which may be written

$$v_1 = \frac{m_1}{m_1 + m_2} u_1 + \frac{m_2}{m_1 + m_2} u_2 + \frac{m_2 e}{m_1 + m_2}(u_2 - u_1).$$

Notice that $m_1 + m_2$ is a mass and has dimension [M], and $(u_2 - u_1)$ is a velocity $[\text{LT}^{-1}]$, while e is a ratio of one velocity to another and has therefore zero dimensions. The equation written dimensionally is thus

$$[\text{LT}^{-1}] = \left[\frac{\text{M}}{\text{M}} \text{LT}^{-1}\right] + \left[\frac{\text{M}}{\text{M}} \text{LT}^{-1}\right] + \left[\frac{\text{M}}{\text{M}} \text{LT}^{-1}\right],$$

or $\qquad [\text{LT}^{-1}] = [\text{LT}^{-1}] + [\text{LT}^{-1}] + [\text{LT}^{-1}].$

Every term has the same dimensions.

If on putting in the dimensions of the various terms of an equation it is found that they are of different dimensions, some error has crept in, which must be sought.

EXERCISES ON CHAPTER II

1. State Newton's three laws of motion.

A particle hangs by a string from the roof of a railway carriage. Find the inclination of the string to the vertical when it is at relative rest in the carriage and the train is accelerating at the rate of 3 feet per second per second. J.M.B.H.S.C.

2. State Newton's laws of motion, and give an example of the application of each.

Two masses of 5 lb. and 3 lb. at rest at a distance of 16 ft. apart are connected by a string in which a constant tension equal to the weight of 4 oz. is maintained.

When will the masses meet, and how far will each have moved ?
C.W.B.H.S.C.

3. Rain is falling at the rate of V ft./sec. in a direction inclined at an angle α to the vertical; it is falling at such a rate that 1 inch of rain falls in 3 hours. If it hits a vertical wall without rebounding, find in poundals the average force exerted on the wall per sq. ft. C.H.S.C.

4. Explain what is meant by the conservation of momentum and the conservation of energy.

A rifle bullet is fired horizontally into a massive block of wood forming the bob of a pendulum. Describe the measurements which you would make in order to find the velocity of the bullet, and explain how the result is deduced from them.   C.W.B.H.S.C.

5. State and explain the principle of conservation of momentum.

A wind whose velocity is 60 miles per hour blows normally against a wall. Assuming the air moves parallel to the wall after striking it, find the pressure on the wall. (1 cubic foot of air weighs $1\frac{1}{4}$ oz.)
                                                        O. & C.H.S.C.

6. State the laws which determine the change of motion of two particles produced by their direct collision.

Two spheres of masses 6 oz. and 8 oz. are moving towards each other in the same line with velocities 10 ft./sec. and 6 ft./sec. respectively and they collide directly. Find their velocities after impact if the coefficient of restitution is 0·75, and determine the loss of energy resulting from the impact.   J.M.B.H.S.C.

7. Two spheres of masses m, m' moving with relative velocity V collide directly ; prove that the loss of kinetic energy is

$$\frac{1}{2}\frac{mm'}{m+m'}(1-e^2)V^2,$$

where e is the coefficient of restitution.

Two spheres of equal mass moving in the same straight line with velocities u, u' collide and rebound, the coefficient of restitution being $\frac{1}{2}$. Prove that exactly half the energy is lost in collision if

$$(1-\sqrt{2})u=(1+\sqrt{2})u'.\qquad\text{C.W.B.H.S.C.}$$

8. A 3 oz. ball moving with velocity of 7 ft./sec. overtakes and collides directly with a 7 oz. ball moving with a velocity of 1 ft./sec. in the same straight line. Find the value of the coefficient of restitution if the smaller ball is reduced to rest by the collision and prove that, in this case, the loss of kinetic energy is $\frac{21}{16}$ ft.-pdls.   C.W.B.H.S.C.

9. A small body of mass M hangs in equilibrium at one end of a light string of length l, the upper end of which is fixed. A small body of mass m moving horizontally with velocity $2\sqrt{gl}$ strikes the former body and adheres to it.

Find the velocity with which the combined bodies begin to move, and the angle through which the string turns before coming to rest for an instant.

How much kinetic energy is lost in the impact ?   L.H.S.C.

10. Prove that the work done by an impulse I acting on a particle is $\frac{1}{2}I(v_1+v_2)$, where v_1 and v_2 are the component velocities of the particle in the direction of I, just before and just after the impact respectively.

A sphere of mass m, moving with velocity u, impinges on an equal sphere at rest, and the impulse between them is R. Show that the kinetic energy lost by the first sphere is

$$\tfrac{1}{4}Ru(3-e)$$

where e is the coefficient of restitution between the spheres.

C.W.B.H.S.C.

11. Define momentum and kinetic energy.

A mass of 10 lb. forming the bob of a simple pendulum of length 13 ft. is drawn aside to a distance of 5 ft. from the vertical line through the point of suspension and then released. Find the momentum and the kinetic energy of this mass when it reaches its lowest point.

If at this point it strikes and adheres to a mass of 15 lb. at rest which forms the bob of another pendulum, find the velocity with which the two move away together. C.W.B.H.S.C.

12. A smooth sphere of mass 1 lb. moving with a speed of 3 feet per second impinges directly on another smooth sphere of mass 2 lb. moving in the opposite direction with a speed of 2 feet per second. As a result of the impact the total kinetic energy of the spheres is reduced by one-half. Find the velocity of each sphere after impact, and the coefficient of restitution. C.H.S.C.

13. State Newton's third law of motion.

Prove that when two small masses directly approach each other and collide, the sum of their momenta is unchanged by the impact.

A long wooden beam of mass 50 lb. is suspended from the ceiling by two vertical cords, each 2 ft. long, one at each end of the beam. A pistol is fired at the beam, and the bullet, of mass 0·8 oz., travels in line with the long axis and remains embedded in the beam, producing a longitudinal deflection of 2 in. from the equilibrium position. Find an approximate value for the initial velocity of the bullet. C.W.B.H.S.C.

14. Find the dimensions of Velocity and Acceleration.

Assuming that when a body falls from rest under gravity the velocity v is given by $v = kg^p h^q$, where h is the distance fallen through, g the acceleration of gravity, and k, p and q are constants, show, by a consideration of the dimensions involved, that $v = k\sqrt{gh}$. L.H.S.C.

CHAPTER III

MOMENTS, ROTATION AND EQUILIBRIUM

Rigid body.—In the first two chapters, the size of the bodies concerned has been left out of the question, and for each body considered it was assumed that the mass was concentrated at the point at which the force acts. When dealing with actual bodies it becomes evident at once that the mass is not concentrated at one point, for each body has size. It is possible that the body may move without rotation, in which case the results already obtained are valid, but now the question of rotation must be taken into account. Those bodies only will be considered which retain constant shape. They are called **rigid bodies,** and may be more exactly defined by saying that any pair of points in the body chosen at random remain at constant distance apart.

Angular velocity.—The simplest case of rotation is that of a body rotating about a fixed axis with constant angular velocity. If the body rotates about the axis O (Fig. 25) and a line OA in the body is drawn perpendicularly to the axis, then OA turns through equal angles in equal times. If the angle AOA′ = θ is described in time t, then the angular velocity is

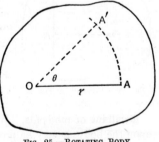

FIG. 25.—ROTATING BODY.

$$\frac{\theta}{t} = \omega.$$

If the angular velocity is not constant, it may be expressed at any instant in the form

$$\frac{d\theta}{dt} = \omega.$$

Every point in the body describes a circle about the axis,

and in the case of a point such as A whose distance from the axis is r,

$$\text{arc } AA' = r \cdot \theta, \quad \text{and} \quad \frac{AA'}{t} = r \cdot \frac{\theta}{t},$$

or

$$v = r \cdot \omega.$$

The linear velocity v of the point A remains constant in magnitude, but is continually changing its direction. The vector **v** which represents the velocity is therefore continually changing, but the speed of A is constant.

Angular acceleration.—Following the analogy of linear velocity and acceleration (p. 6), it will be seen that the rate of change of angular velocity is the angular acceleration, or

$$\text{angular acceleration} = \frac{d\omega}{dt} = \frac{d^2\theta}{dt^2} = \dot{\omega},$$

and since $v = r\omega$,

$$\text{linear acceleration perpendicular to } r = r\frac{d\omega}{dt}$$

$$= r\dot{\omega}.$$

There is, in addition, a linear acceleration along r (see p. 76).

Moment of force about a point.—Rotation, like linear motion, may be attributed to one or more forces acting upon the body. If the

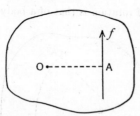

FIG. 26.—MOMENT OF FORCE.

body can rotate about a fixed axis O (Fig. 26), a force such as f will cause it to rotate about O. The turning effect of f depends, in the first place, on its own magnitude, and, in the second place, upon the length of the perpendicular let fall from O upon the line in which the force acts. The quantity $f \times (OA)$ is called the moment of the force about the point O.

Resultant of moments.—When several forces act simultaneously upon the body, it may be proved, as follows, that the moment about O of the resultant of the forces is equal to the algebraic sum of the moments of the forces.

In the first place it will be seen that the moment of a force about a point is numerically equal to twice the area of the triangle made by joining the axis of rotation to the ends of the vector representing the force. In Fig. 27 the moment of the force represented by the vector AB is AB × OP, and is numerically equal to twice the area of the triangle OAB. Also the moment of the force is independent of the position of its point of application, provided that this point remains in the line BP. This follows from the fact that the area of a triangle is

$$\tfrac{1}{2}(\text{base} \times \text{perpendicular height}).$$

Now consider two forces whose lines of action are AB and AC (Fig. 28) intersecting at A, O being the axis of rotation. Through O

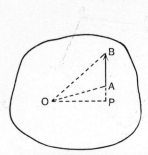

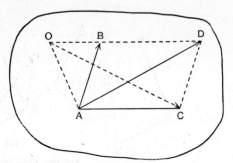

FIG. 27.—REPRESENTATION OF
THE MOMENT OF A FORCE.

FIG. 28.—SUM OF MOMENTS.

draw the straight line OBD parallel to AC. Taking AB to represent to scale the first force, make AC, on the same scale, to represent the second force. On completing the parallelogram ACDB, AD represents, on the same scale, the resultant of AB and AC.

Now $\triangle OAC = \triangle ADC = \triangle ABD,$

and $\triangle ABD + \triangle OAB = \triangle OAD \; ;$

$$\therefore \; 2\triangle OAC + 2\triangle OAB = 2\triangle OAD,$$

and it follows that the moment of force AD about O is the sum of the moments of AB and AC. If the point O lies within the angle BAC, the moments of AB and AC are in opposite directions, that is, the forces tend to rotate the body in opposite directions, and a proof similar to the above shows that the moment of their resultant is the difference of their separate moments.

Also, if there is a third force, its moment may be compounded in a similar manner with the resultant moment of the first two. Thus the resultant moment of any number of forces about a point is the algebraic sum of the moments of the separate forces.

EXAMPLE.—Show that for a system of forces represented by the sides taken in order of a closed polygon lying in one plane, the algebraical sum of their moments about any point in the plane is constant.

Assuming that quantities which have magnitude and direction are termed vectors, state (giving your reasons in each case) which of the following are vectors :—force, momentum, kinetic energy, work, heat.

C.W.B.H.S.C.

Let AB, BC, CD, DE and EA (Fig. 29 (a)) form a closed polygon. First consider the point P to be inside the polygon. The numerical values of the

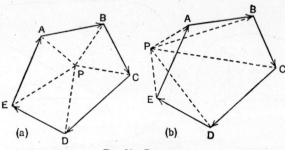

FIG. 29.—PROBLEM.

moments of the forces about P are $2\triangle PAB$, $2\triangle PBC$, etc., and since the forces are represented by the sides taken in order the moments are all in the same direction.

∴ Total moment has numerical value $2\triangle PAB + 2\triangle PBC + \ldots$, etc., which sum is twice the area of the polygon and is therefore constant.

If P is outside the polygon as in Fig. 29 (b), the moments of AB, BC, CD and DE are in one direction and of AE in the opposite direction.

∴ Numerical value of moment $= 2\triangle PAB + 2\triangle PBC + 2\triangle PCD$

$$+ 2\triangle PDE - 2\triangle PAE$$

$$= 2(\text{area of polygon}),$$

which is independent of the position of P.

The student may extend the reasoning of the last part to the case of a polygon with re-entrant angles.

Force is a vector (see p. 27).

Momentum is a vector (see p. 28).

Kinetic energy (p. 40) is not a vector, because it is the product of a mass (scalar) and the square of a velocity. It is therefore independent of the sign or direction of the velocity.

Work (p. 34) is not a vector, as it is equivalent to kinetic energy, the two being mutually convertible.

Heat is kinetic energy of molecules (Chap. X), and again is not a vector.

Parallel forces.—The proof on p. 49 is quite general and may be applied to several limiting cases. For example, if two forces are equal and opposite and in the same straight line, their resultant is zero and the resulting moment about any axis is zero. Or if two forces are acting in parallel lines, the triangles of Fig. 28 become infinite. But if the angle between AB and AC is gradually diminished the proof still holds, and there is no reason to suppose that it would cease to hold if the angle is diminished to zero so that the two forces are parallel.

The resultant of two parallel forces is equal to their algebraic sum. The line in which this acts must be found. If f_1 and f_2 are the forces (Fig. 30), take any axis O and use the fact that the moment of the

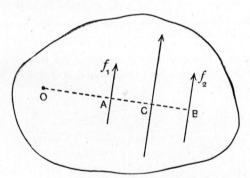

FIG. 30.—RESULTANT OF PARALLEL FORCES.

resultant force $(f_1 + f_2)$ about O is the sum of the moments of the separate forces f_1 and f_2. Drop a perpendicular OAB from O upon the direction of f_1 and f_2. Then

$$(f_1 + f_2) \times OC = (f_1 \times OA) + (f_2 \times OB) ;$$
$$\therefore OC = \frac{(f_1 \times OA) + (f_2 \times OB)}{f_1 + f_2}.$$

This determines the line in which the resultant acts.

If then the axis be transferred from O to C, the resultant moment is zero, $\therefore f_1 \times AC = f_2 \times BC.$

This result may be verified experimentally in a simple manner. By suspending a metre scale from its mid-point (Fig. 31), and then

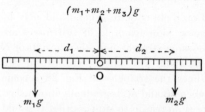

FIG. 31.—EXPERIMENT ON MOMENTS.

suspending weights from points such that the scale remains horizontally in equilibrium, it will be found that

$$m_1 g \times d_1 = m_2 g \, d_2,$$

or $$m_1 d_1 = m_2 d_2.$$

Since the scale is at rest, the force required to support it is equal and opposite to the downward forces acting upon it, which are its own weight $m_3 g$ and that of m_1 and m_2. If the scale is suspended at its mid-point, the force $m_3 g$ does not tend to rotate it. The resultant of $m_1 g$ and $m_2 g$ therefore passes through the point O, such that

$$m_1 g \, d_1 = m_2 g \, d_2., \quad \text{or} \quad m_1 d_1 = m_2 d_2,$$ as found by experiment.

If the scale is supported by a spring balance, the resultant force $(m_1 + m_2 + m_3) g$ can be found.

The balance.—This principle is employed for the comparison of masses, for it will be seen from the above that if $d_1 = d_2$, for equili-

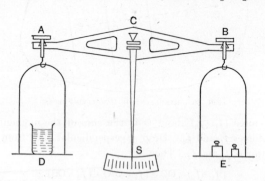

FIG. 32.—THE BALANCE.

brium, then $m_1 = m_2$. The suspended scale is a very rough instrument, and by means of it an accurate comparison of m_1 and m_2 is impossible. A diagrammatic representation of a delicate balance is shown in Fig. 32. The beam AB is supported on a steel or agate knife-edge resting on an agate plane at C carried by a pillar which is not shown. A pan D is suspended by means of an agate plane resting on a knife-edge attached to the beam at A. Similarly the pan E is suspended at B. If then the pans and their attachments are of equal mass and the length of beam AC is equal to the length CB, the balance will be in equilibrium when there are no weights in the pans. Also when equal masses are placed in D and E the balance remains in equilibrium, as is indicated by the pointer CS remaining at the middle of the scale S.

Since g may be considered to be constant over the small space occupied by the balance, the force m_1g due to a body placed in the pan D is equal to the force m_2g due to standard masses placed in the pan E when equilibrium is attained, so that whatever the value of g, $m_1 = m_2$.

Errors and sensitiveness of balance.—The most likely source of error in a balance arises from the fact that the arms AC and CB may not be of equal length. By interchanging the body to be weighed and the standard weights and reweighing, the ratio of the length of the arms and also the correct weight may be found. For if d_1 and d_2 are the lengths of the arms AC and CB, then for equilibrium with body of mass m_1 in pan D and standard weights m_2 in E, taking moments about C

$$m_1d_1 = m_2d_2.$$

On interchanging and finding the mass m_3 that is required in pan A to balance m_1 in pan B,

$$m_3d_1 = m_1d_2,$$

$$\frac{d_1}{d_2} = \frac{m_2}{m_1} = \frac{m_1}{m_3};$$

$$\therefore \frac{d_1}{d_2} = \sqrt{\frac{m_2}{m_3}},$$

and $$m_1{}^2 = m_2m_3,$$

$$m_1 = \sqrt{m_2m_3}.$$

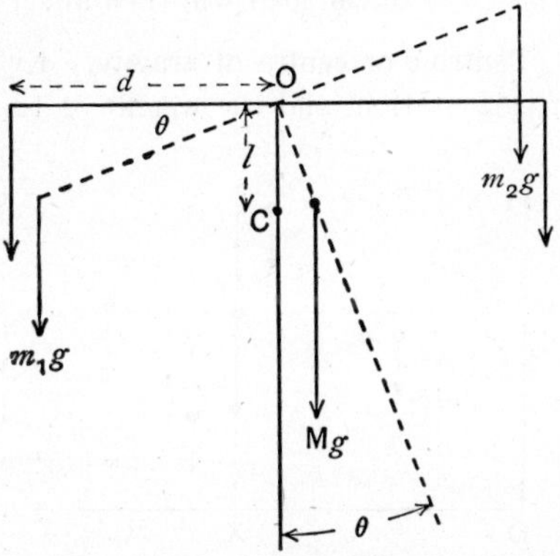

FIG. 33.—DIAGRAM OF THE FORCES ACTING ON A BALANCE.

If the centre of gravity (p. 55) of the beam and its attachments is situated at C (Fig. 33), a distance l below the point of suspension O, a difference in the weights m_1 and m_2 will produce a displacement of the beam from the horizontal. The beam will come to rest when the moment of its weight, M, about the point of support O is equal and opposite to the resultant moment of m_1g and m_2g about O, that is,

$$Mgl \sin \theta = (m_1 - m_2)gd \cos \theta,$$

$$\tan \theta = \frac{m_1 - m_2}{M} \cdot \frac{d}{l}.$$

For great sensitiveness θ must be large for a very small value of $m_1 - m_2$. It will be seen that a large value of d and small values of M and l tend to this result. M is determined by the necessity for rigidity of the beam. If d is too large and l too small, the beam swings very slowly and is tedious to use. Taking h as the length of the pointer CS (Fig. 32) the actual deflection s on the scale S is $h\theta$, and when the deflection is small enough to take $\theta = \tan \theta$,

$$s = h \frac{m_1 - m_2}{M} \cdot \frac{d}{l}$$

For a sensitive balance s is of the order of one scale division for a value of $m_1 - m_2$ of 1 milligram.

If the pan knife-edges are on the same level as the central knife edge, one pan rises as much as the other falls and the sensitiveness is not affected by the load. But if this is not so, a displacement causes a rise or fall of the centre of gravity of the pans and load, and the value of the load will then affect the sensitiveness.

Centroid or centre of gravity.—Every particle of a body is subject to gravitation, and the weight of the body is therefore a system of

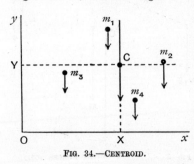

FIG. 34.—CENTROID.

parallel forces. Materials are of such fine structure that they may be looked upon as continuous, but in the first place, a system of point masses will be considered. Take four points in a vertical plane (Fig. 34) whose masses are m_1, m_2, m_3, m_4, and take the axis Oy vertical and Ox horizontal. Let the four points maintain their configuration, so that collectively they may be looked upon as a rigid body. The weights of the masses will be m_1g, m_2g, m_3g and m_4g, and the resultant is Mg where $M = m_1 + m_2 + m_3 + m_4$.

Taking moments about O,

$$Mg\mathsf{X} = m_1 gx_1 + m_2 gx_2 + m_3 gx_3 + m_4 gx_4,$$

or
$$\mathsf{X} = \frac{m_1 x_1 + m_2 x_2 + m_3 x_3 + m_4 x_4}{M};$$

X is the abscissa of the point C through which the resultant weight acts.

If the system and the axes be rotated through a right angle so that Ox is vertical and Oy horizontal, it is found as before, by taking moments about O, that

$$\mathsf{Y} = \frac{m_1 y_1 + m_2 y_2 + m_3 y_3 + m_4 y_4}{M}.$$

The point C whose coordinates are X and Y is called the **centre of gravity** of the system. It is
the point through which the
resultant weight of the system
always acts. This point has
many important properties,
apart from gravity, and it is
therefore also called the **centroid or centre of mass.**

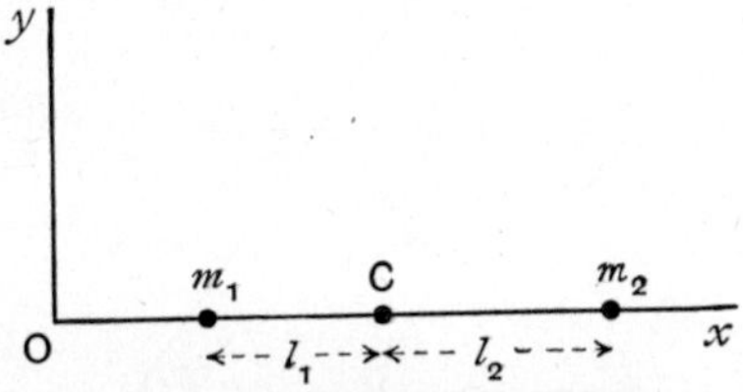

FIG. 35.—CENTROID OF TWO BODIES.

The case of two masses
m_1 and m_2 is important. On
taking the x-axis through them (Fig. 35) the centroid C is on this
axis and has ordinate X, where $\mathsf{X} = \dfrac{m_1 x_1 + m_2 x_2}{m_1 + m_2}$.

Now
$$x_1 = \mathsf{X} - l_1,$$
and
$$x_2 = \mathsf{X} + l_2;$$
$$\therefore\ m_1\mathsf{X} + m_2\mathsf{X} = m_1\mathsf{X} - m_1 l_1 + m_2\mathsf{X} + m_2 l_2;$$
$$\therefore\ m_1 l_1 = m_2 l_2,$$
or
$$\frac{l_1}{l_2} = \frac{m_2}{m_1}.$$

That is, the centroid is situated at a point between the masses whose distance from each mass is inversely proportional to that mass.

Centroid of uniform rod.—The last result may be used to find the centroid of many regular bodies. For example, a uniform rod may be looked upon as a collection of pairs of equal small masses, the two of each pair being at equal distances from the middle of the rod. The centroid of every pair is therefore at the middle of the rod. Therefore the centroid of the rod is its middle point.

Centroid of uniform triangular plate.—Imagine the plate divided into a great number of very small strips parallel to the side BC (Fig. 36). The centroid of every strip is at its middle point, so that the centroid of the whole triangle must be in the median AD, since it passes through the centroids of all the strips. A similar reasoning shows that the centroid also lies in the median BE and in the median CF. It must therefore be at O, the intersection of the medians. A well-known theorem in geometry proves that $OD = \frac{1}{3}AD$.

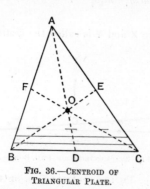

FIG. 36.—CENTROID OF
TRIANGULAR PLATE.

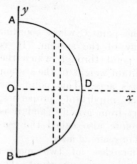

FIG. 37.—CENTROID OF SEMI-
CIRCULAR PLATE.

General method.—It is obvious that bodies which are symmetrical about a point have their centroid at the point of symmetry. Thus the centroid of a circular ring or plate or of a sphere will be at the centre. For a body of irregular form, the method of p. 54 may be employed, by dividing the body into infinitesimal strips or layers and performing the integration $\int mx\,dx$ for the body, where mdx is the mass of a strip or layer of infinitesimal width or thickness dx.

Then
$$X = \frac{\int mx\,dx}{\int mdx} = \frac{\int mx\,dx}{M}.$$

The process may then be repeated for the y-axis if necessary, and in the case of a solid body, for the z-axis also.

Centroid of semicircular plate.—If ADB (Fig. 37) is a semicircular segment of a uniform plate whose radius is r and mass per square centimetre is ρ, take the x-axis through the centre of the circle and at right angles to AB. Then, from symmetry, the centroid must lie in the axis of x. Divide the figure into strips of width dx. The length of each strip is $2y$ and its area $2y\,dx$, so that its mass is $2\rho y\,dx$.

$$\therefore\; \mathsf{X} = \frac{\int_0^r 2x\rho y\,dx}{\int_0^r 2\rho y\,dx} = \frac{\int_0^r 2xy\,dx}{\int_0^r 2y\,dx}.$$

$\int_0^r 2y\,dx$ is the area of the semicircle, that is $\frac{1}{2}\pi r^2$;

$$\therefore\; \mathsf{X} = 2\int_0^r 2xy\,dx \Big/ \pi r^2.$$

Now the equation of a circle is $x^2 + y^2 = r^2$;

$$\therefore\; \int_0^r 2xy\,dx = \int_0^r 2x\sqrt{r^2 - x^2}\,dx.$$

Let $x^2 = n$, then $2x\,dx = dn$;

$$\therefore\; \int 2x\sqrt{r^2 - x^2}\,dx = \int \sqrt{r^2 - n}\,dn = -\tfrac{2}{3}(r^2 - n)^{\frac{3}{2}};$$

$$\therefore\; \int_0^r 2xy\,dx = \left[-\frac{2}{3}(r^2 - x^2)^{\frac{3}{2}} \right]_0^r = \tfrac{2}{3}r^3,$$

and

$$\mathsf{X} = \frac{\frac{4}{3}r^3}{\pi r^2} = \frac{4r}{3\pi}.$$

Centroid of cone.—If the density ρ of the solid cone (Fig. 38) is uniform, take the axis of the cone as the x-axis, the apex being at O. A circular section perpendicular to the axis Ox has volume $\pi y^2\,dx$ and mass $\rho\pi y^2\,dx$. The volume of the whole cone is $\int_0^h \pi y^2\,dx$ and its mass $\rho\int_0^h \pi y^2\,dx$ where h is the axial height.

$$\therefore\; \mathsf{X} = \frac{\int_0^h x\rho\pi y^2\,dx}{\rho\int_0^h \pi y^2\,dx}.$$

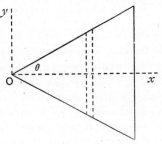

FIG. 38.—CENTROID OF CONE.

c

Also, $$y = x \tan \theta \;;$$

$$\therefore \; \mathsf{X} = \frac{\displaystyle\int_0^h x^3 \tan^2\theta \, dx}{\displaystyle\int_0^h x^2 \tan^2\theta \, dx},$$

and since θ is constant, $$\mathsf{X} = \frac{\displaystyle\int_0^h x^3 \, dx}{\displaystyle\int_0^h x^2 \, dx} = \frac{\dfrac{h^4}{4}}{\dfrac{h^3}{3}} = \frac{3h}{4} \,.$$

It follows that the centroid is in the axis at a quarter of the height of the cone from the base.

Equilibrium.—A body suspended by a support situated in a vertical line passing through the centre of gravity is in equilibrium, since the resultant weight has no moment about the point of support. There are however, three possibilities. If as in Fig. 39 (a) the

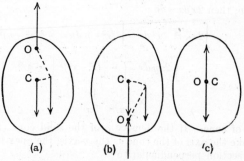

(a)   (b)   (c)

FIG. 39.—THE THREE CASES OF EQUILIBRIUM.

point of support O is above the centre of gravity C, then any rotation of the body about O produces a moment tending to restore the body to its original position. The equilibrium is then said to be stable. In Fig. 39 (b) the point of support is below the centre of gravity. Any displacement then gives rise to a moment which tends to increase the displacement. The equilibrium is then unstable. If the point of support coincides with the centre of gravity a displacement of the body does not give rise to any moment, and the body will remain in any position. The equilibrium is then neutral. If, then, the displacement raises the centre of gravity, the equilibrium is stable, if it lowers the centre of gravity the equilibrium is unstable, and if the displacement neither raises nor lowers the centre of gravity, the equilibrium is neutral.

As an example consider a circular cone resting on a horizontal plane. If it stands on its base the equilibrium is stable; if balanced on its apex the equilibrium is unstable. But if the cone rolls on its side it is in neutral equilibrium.

EXAMPLE.—Prove that the position of the centre of gravity of a uniform lamina in the shape of a semicircle of radius a is at a distance $4a/3\pi$ from the base.

A rectangular strip of tin-plate ABCD measures 4 cm. by 8 cm. A semicircular portion is stamped out of it by a circular punch, of radius 1 cm., the centre of the circle being at the middle point of the long side AB. Show that the distance of the centre of gravity of the remainder from CD is 1·92 cm. approximately.   C.H.S.C.

See p. 57.

Take area as proportional to mass.

Area of semicircle $=\dfrac{\pi}{2}$.   Area of whole rectangle $=8 \times 4 = 32$.

$\therefore$ Area of remainder $=32 - \dfrac{\pi}{2}$.

Let its centre of gravity be at G (Fig. 40).

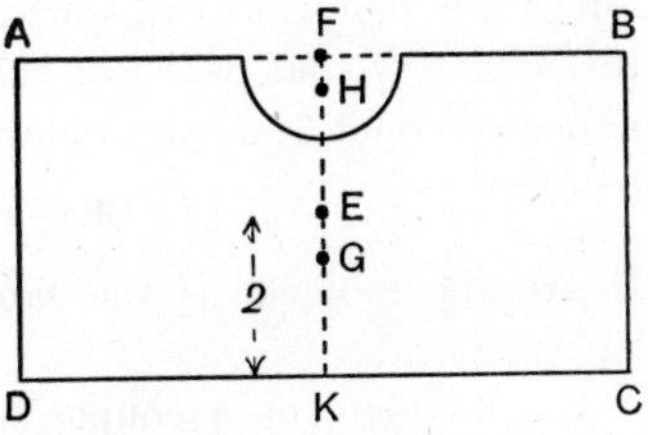

FIG. 40.—PROBLEM.

The complete rectangle has centre of gravity at its mid-point E, and that of the semicircle is at H, where

$$FH = \frac{4}{3\pi}, \quad \text{or} \quad KH = 4 - \frac{4}{3\pi} = 4\left(\frac{3\pi - 1}{3\pi}\right).$$

Taking moments about DC,

$$32 \times EK = \left(32 - \frac{\pi}{2}\right) GK + \left(\frac{\pi}{2} \times HK\right),$$

$$32 \times 2 = \left(32 - \frac{\pi}{2}\right) GK + \frac{\pi}{2} \cdot 4\left(\frac{3\pi - 1}{3\pi}\right),$$

$$64 = \frac{64 - \pi}{2} \cdot GK + \frac{2(3\pi - 1)}{3},$$

$$128 = (64 - \pi)GK + 11 \cdot 233,$$

$$GK = \frac{128 - 11 \cdot 23}{60 \cdot 86} = \underline{\underline{1 \cdot 92 \text{ approx.}}}$$

Couples.—When a force produces rotation of a body, without motion of translation, there must be a second force acting upon the

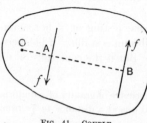

FIG. 41.—COUPLE.

body, equal and opposite to the first, so that the resultant force is zero. This second force may be due to the axle or whatever constraint causes the body to rotate on its axis. When two equal and opposite forces act on a body they are said to constitute a couple, and the turning moment of the couple is the product of either force into the perpendicular distance between them.

The moment of the couple is independent of the position of the actual axis of rotation of the body.

If ff (Fig. 41) is the couple and A is a point in the line of one of the forces, the moment of this force about A is zero, and the moment of the other is $f \times AB$, which is the moment of the couple. Or, taking moments about O, a point not on the line of either force, the resultant is

$$(f \times OB) - (f \times OA) = f \times AB.$$

Hence the moment is the same wherever the axis of rotation is situated.

The moment of a couple is sometimes called the **torque** acting upon the body.

If any number of couples in one plane act upon a body simultaneously, their resultant is a couple whose moment is the **algebraic** sum of the moments of the separate couples.

This follows from the fact that the moment of any couple is the same for all axes of rotation. For if $f_1 f_1'$ and $f_2 f_2'$ are two couples (Fig. 42) the intersection, A, of the directions of f_1 and f_2 may be chosen as axis of rotation. Then the resultant moment of f_1' and f_2' about A is the algebraic sum of their

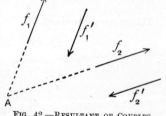

FIG. 42.—RESULTANT OF COUPLES.

separate moments (p. 49), while the moments of f_1 and f_2 about A are both zero. That is, the resultant moment is the algebraic sum of the moments of the separate couples. Having found the resultant of any two couples, this resultant may be combined with further couples in the same plane.

Resultant of a number of forces in one plane.—If two forces such as f_1 and f_2 (Fig. 43) act on a body, f_1 acting at A and f_2 at C, they are equivalent to a single force acting at an arbitrary point O in the body together with a single couple. At O introduce two forces equal to f_1 and in opposite directions such as OB and OD. Since the resultant of these two is zero, their introduction will not alter the condition of the body. Now AE and OD form a couple of moment f_1p_1, and there remains the single force OB. Now perform the same operation for f_2, and obtain the single

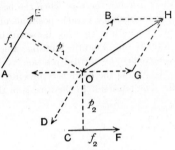

FIG. 43.—RESULTANT OF SEVERAL FORCES.

force OG and the couple f_2p_2. OB and OG may now be compounded into the single force OH, and there remain the couples f_1p_1 and f_2p_2, which may be added algebraically to form a single couple. If there are more forces in the same plane they may be treated in a similar manner, giving a single force applied at O, and single couple whose moment is the algebraic sum of the moments about O of the separate forces.

Thus when any number of forces in a plane act upon a body, they may be reduced to a single force acting at an arbitrary point and a single couple. From Fig. 43 it will be seen that the single force does not depend upon the position of the point chosen, but the couple will depend upon it.

Conditions of equilibrium of a body.—When a body is at rest, the resultant couple acting on it must be zero, otherwise there would be rotation. Likewise the resultant force must be zero, otherwise there would be motion of translation. If the forces are reduced to a single force and couple, the former must be zero and the latter zero for any choice of point. It is a useful fact to remember that when a body is in equilibrium under three coplanar forces, these three must act through one point. For if not, the resultant of two would not act in the same line as the third force and there would be a couple, due to this resultant and the third force, causing rotation.

EXAMPLE.—A uniform beam 10 ft. long and weighing 33 lb. is pivoted at one end by a frictionless hinge so that it can move in a vertical plane. A rope is attached to the other end of the beam, and is led over a small smooth pulley 11 ft. vertically above the hinge. Find by a force diagram the tension in the rope when the beam is 35° above the horizontal.

Show that for various positions of the beam the tension is proportional to the length of the rope between the pulley and the point of attachment to the beam. Find the limiting value of the tension of the rope as the beam approaches the vertical position.   C.H.S.C.

In Fig. 44 the beam is represented by OD, and its centre of gravity is at E. The tension T in the rope is in the line DG which intersects a vertical

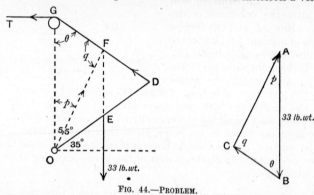

FIG. 44.—PROBLEM.

through E in the point F. As there are only three forces acting on the beam and two of them pass through F, the third force OF, which is the reaction of the hinge, must also pass through F. Then if AB is drawn vertically and to scale equal to 33, BC parallel to DG, AC parallel to FO will complete the triangle of forces ABC for the point F. BC is then to scale equal to the tension T.

Now OD is bisected at E, and since EF is parallel to OG, GD is bisected at F,

$$\therefore \; GF = \tfrac{1}{2}GD = l/2, \text{ where } GD = l.$$

Again,

$$\frac{T}{33} = \frac{BC}{AB} = \frac{\sin p}{\sin q}.$$

But in triangle OGF,

$$\frac{\sin p}{\sin q} = \frac{GF}{OG} = \frac{l}{2 \cdot OG} = \frac{l}{22};$$

$$\therefore \; \frac{T}{33} = \frac{l}{22},$$

$$T = \tfrac{3}{2}l, \text{ numerically.}$$

In triangle OGD,

$$l^2 = 11^2 + 10^2 - 2 \cdot 11 \cdot 10 \cdot \cos 55°$$
$$= 221 - 220 \cos 55° ;$$
$$\therefore \ \mathsf{T} = \tfrac{3}{2}\sqrt{221 - 220 \cos 55°} = \underline{14 \cdot 6 \ \text{lb. wt.}}$$

The second part of the question is answered by the relation $\mathsf{T} = \tfrac{3}{2}l$, which shows that as the beam approaches the vertical position the tension in the rope approaches $1 \cdot 5$ lb. wt. At the vertical position the tension is indeterminate since $\sin p = 0$ and $\sin q = 0$.

Work performed by couple.—When a couple causes rotation, work is performed. In order to calculate this work let one of the forces of the couple act through the axis of rotation O (Fig. 45).

If OP is the perpendicular from O to the other force f, then as the body rotates through angle $d\theta$ the point P moves through distance OP. $d\theta$, and the work done by the force f is OP. f. $d\theta$. The point O does not move, so that no work is done on account of the force through it. Hence work done by couple = OP. f. $d\theta$.

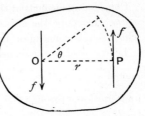

FIG. 45.—COUPLE AND WORK.

And for rotation θ,

$$\text{work} = \int_0^\theta \text{OP}.f.\,d\theta$$
$$= \text{OP}.f.\theta$$
$$= \text{couple} \times \theta = c\theta.$$

For a complete rotation, $\theta = 2\pi$, and for n complete rotations,

$$\text{work} = 2\pi n c.$$

EXAMPLE.—In a motor the couple applied to the armature is equivalent to a force of 100 kg. wt. at a distance of 20 cm. from the axis of rotation. If the armature makes 1500 revolutions per minute, what is the rate of working in kilowatts and in horse-power ?

$$\text{Work per second} = 2\pi \cdot \tfrac{1500}{60} \cdot 100000 \cdot 981 \times 20 \text{ ergs}$$
$$= 2\pi \cdot 25 \cdot 981 \cdot 2 \cdot 10^6$$
$$= \pi \cdot 981 \cdot 10^8 \text{ ergs per sec.}$$
$$= \pi \cdot 9810 \text{ watts}$$

$$= 9 \cdot 81\pi \text{ kilowatts}$$
$$= 30 \cdot 8 \text{ kilowatts.}$$

$$1 \text{ H.P.} = 746 \text{ watts}$$
$$\therefore \text{ rate of working} = \frac{30800}{746}$$
$$= 41 \cdot 3 \text{ H.P.}$$

Moment of inertia.—When the resultant couple acting on a body is not zero, angular acceleration occurs. It is now our object to find the relation between the couple and the angular acceleration it produces.

Consider an element of the body situated at P (Fig. 45) whose mass is dm. Let O be the axis of rotation and the distance OP $= r$. The whole couple c acting on the body may be resolved into elements.

Let the element dc cause rotation of dm about O. This may be looked upon as a force $\dfrac{dc}{r}$ acting through P together with an equal and opposite force through O. Then the acceleration of dm will be $\dfrac{dc}{r \cdot dm}$ (p. 27).

But the linear acceleration at right angles to r is $\dot{\omega}r$ (p. 48);

$$\therefore \quad \frac{dc}{r \cdot dm} = \dot{\omega}r,$$
$$dc = \dot{\omega} \cdot dm \cdot r^2,$$
$$c = \int \dot{\omega} \cdot dm \cdot r^2$$
$$= \dot{\omega} \int r^2 \cdot dm,$$

because $\dot{\omega}$ is the same for all parts of a rigid body; also the integration extends over the whole body.

The quantity $\int r^2 \, dm$ is called the **moment of inertia** of the body about the axis O, and if we take $\int r^2 \, dm = I$,

then $$c = I\dot{\omega}.$$

This is an equation concerning rotation which is analogous to $f = ma$ for linear motion. The moment of inertia I is the counterpart of the mass.

When the body consists of a number of small separate masses, the quantity mr^2 is obtained for each separate mass and the sum is found. But where the body is of continuous structure, the integral $\int r^2 \, dm$ must be found.

EXAMPLE.—Three masses each of 5 kg. are placed on a horizontal plate whose weight can be neglected. The plate can rotate about a vertical axis and the masses are all at distance 15 cm. from the axis. What is the moment of inertia of the system ?

$$\text{Moment of inertia of each mass} = 5000 \times 15^2$$
$$= 1125000.$$
$$\text{,,} \qquad \text{,,} \qquad \text{all together} = 3 \times 1125000$$
$$= 3{\cdot}375 \times 10^6 \text{ c.g.s. units.}$$

Radius of gyration.—The moment of inertia of a body involves its mass and the distribution of the mass. These two ideas may be separated by finding the moment of inertia first, and then expressing it as the product of the mass and the square of a length. Thus $I = mk^2$, where m is the mass of the body and I its moment of inertia about a particular axis. The quantity k is called the **radius of gyration** of the body about that axis.

Moment of inertia of rod.—Consider a uniform rod of length l and mass ρ per unit length. Let the rod rotate about its centre of gravity O (Fig. 46).

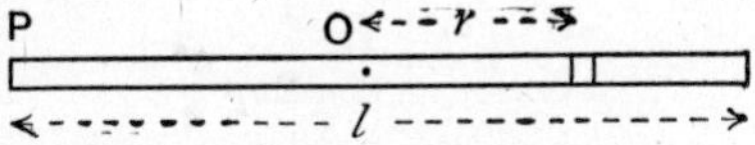

FIG. 46.—MOMENT OF INERTIA OF ROD.

An element of length dr has mass $\rho \, . \, dr$ and its distance from O is r.

$\therefore$ Moment of inertia of element $= r^2 \, \rho \, . \, dr$.

$$\text{,,} \qquad \text{,,} \qquad \text{,,} \qquad \text{rod} \qquad = \rho \int_{-\frac{l}{2}}^{+\frac{l}{2}} r^2 \, dr$$

$$= \rho \left[\frac{r^3}{3} \right]_{-\frac{l}{2}}^{+\frac{l}{2}}$$

$$= 2\rho \, . \, \frac{l^3}{24}.$$

If the mass of the rod is m, $\quad m = \rho l$.

$\therefore$ Moment of inertia about O $= \dfrac{ml^2}{12}$.

In a similar manner, the moment of inertia about P is found on transferring the origin to P. It is $\displaystyle\int_0^l \rho \,.\, r^2 .\, dr = \rho \,\dfrac{l^3}{3}$

$$= \dfrac{ml^2}{3}.$$

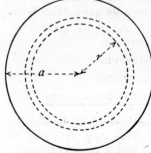

FIG. 47.—CIRCULAR PLATE.

Moment of inertia of circular plate.—First notice that the moment of a circle of thin wire about an axis passing through its centre and at right angles to its plane is mr^2 because every point of the circle is at the same distance, r, from the axis.

Now proceed to the disc, of radius a and mass ρ per unit area. For ring of radius r (Fig. 47) and radial thickness dr :

$$\text{Mass of ring} = \rho \,.\, 2\pi r \,.\, dr.$$

$$\text{Moment of inertia of ring} = \rho \,.\, 2\pi r^3 .\, dr.$$

$$\text{Moment of inertia of disc} = \int_0^a \rho \,.\, 2\pi r^3 .\, dr$$

$$= 2\pi\rho \,\dfrac{a^4}{4}.$$

But mass of disc $= \pi a^2 \rho$;

$$\therefore I = \dfrac{ma^2}{2}.$$

Angular momentum.—The momentum of any element dm of a rotating body is $v \,.\, dm$, where v is the value of the linear velocity of the element. On multiplying this by r, the distance of dm from the axis of rotation, the quantity $rv \,.\, dm$ obtained is called the **moment of momentum** about O of the mass dm.

Now $\qquad\qquad v = r \,.\, \omega \quad$ (p. 48) ;

$\qquad \therefore$ moment of momentum $= r^2 \,.\, \omega \,.\, dm$.

The sum of all the moments of momentum of the elements of the body is called its **angular momentum**;

$$\therefore \text{ angular momentum} = \int r^2 \omega \,.\, dm$$

$$= \omega \int r^2 \, dm$$

$$= I\omega,$$

since
$$I = \int r^2 \, dm.$$

Further, from equation $I\dot{\omega} = c$ (p. 64),

$$I d\omega = c \, dt,$$

and
$$I\omega = \int_0^t c \, dt.$$

Thus the angular momentum acquired by a body is the quantity $\int_0^t c \, dt$. This is true however c may vary with time. If the couple c is constant, $\int_0^t c \, dt$ becomes ct which is then the angular momentum acquired in time t. But if the time is extremely short and the couple great, $\int_0^t c \, dt$ is an **angular impulse**. It is thus seen, on comparing with linear impulse on p. 28, that when considering rotation, moment of inertia takes the place of mass, and couple takes the place of force.

Kinetic energy of rotating body.—When the element dm (Fig. 45) has velocity v, its kinetic energy is $\frac{1}{2}v^2 . dm$ (p. 35). Now $v = r\omega$;

$$\therefore \text{ kinetic energy of } dm \qquad = \frac{1}{2}r^2\omega^2 \, dm,$$

$$\text{kinetic energy of whole body} = \frac{1}{2}\omega^2 \int r^2 \, dm$$

$$= \frac{1}{2}I\omega^2.$$

Again the analogy with linear motion may be noted, for in that case the kinetic energy is $\frac{1}{2}mv^2$.

EXAMPLE.—Find an expression for the moment of inertia of a *thin* uniform rod about an axis perpendicular to it and intersecting it at one quarter of its length from one end.

If the diameter of a penny is 3 cm. and its mass is 9 gm., calculate its total energy when it rolls along a table with a velocity of 6 cm. per second.

J.M.B.H.S.C.

As on p. 65,
$$I = \rho \int_0^{\frac{l}{4}} r^2 \, dr + \rho \int_0^{\frac{3l}{4}} r^2 \, dr = \frac{\rho}{3}\left\{ \left[r^3 \right]_0^{\frac{l}{4}} + \left[r^3 \right]_0^{\frac{3l}{4}} \right\}$$
$$= \frac{\rho}{3}\left(\frac{l^3}{64} + \frac{27l^3}{64} \right) = \frac{28\rho l^3}{3 \times 64} = \frac{7ml^2}{48}.$$

For the penny,
$$I = \frac{9 \times 1\cdot5^2}{2},$$
$$\omega = \frac{6}{1\cdot5} = 4.$$

K.E. due to rotation $= \frac{1}{2}I\omega^2 = \frac{1}{2} \cdot \frac{9 \times 1\cdot5^2}{2} \times 4^2$
$$= 81 \text{ ergs.}$$
K.E. due to translation $= \frac{1}{2}mv^2 = \frac{1}{2} \cdot 9 \cdot 6^2$
$$= 162 \text{ ergs;}$$
∴ total kinetic energy $= 243$ ergs.

Moments of inertia about parallel axes.—Consider a body rotating about O, when the centre of mass of the body is at C (Fig. 48). The mass dm at P contributes an amount $OP^2 . dm$ to the moment of inertia about O. Calling the total moment of inertia about O, I_0,

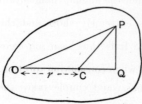

FIG. 48.—PARALLEL AXES.

$$I_0 = \int OP^2 dm.$$

Drop perpendicular PQ upon OC, then $OP^2 = OQ^2 + PQ^2$,

and
$$I_0 = \int (OQ^2 + PQ^2) \, dm$$
$$= \int \{ (OC + CQ)^2 + PQ^2 \} \, dm$$
$$= \int \{ OC^2 + 2OC \cdot CQ + CQ^2 + PQ^2 \} \, dm$$
$$= \int OC^2 dm + 2OC \int CQ \, dm + \int CP^2 . dm.$$

If it is remembered that OC is constant, then calling it r,

$$I_0 = r^2 m + 2\text{OC} \int \text{CQ} \,.\, dm + I_c,$$

where I_c is the moment of inertia about C as axis, that is $\int \text{CP}^2 \,.\, dm$.

If C is the centre of mass of the body, $\int \text{CQ} \,.\, dm = 0$;

$$\therefore \ I_0 = I_c + mr^2.$$

In this way the moment of inertia about any axis parallel to that chosen may be found. It will be seen that the moment of inertia about any axis consists of two parts, the moment of inertia about a parallel axis through the centre of mass, together with the moment of inertia about the given axis of the mass of the whole body supposed concentrated at the centre of mass. Incidentally it appears that the moment of inertia of a body about an axis through the centre of mass is less than that about any other parallel axis.

Moment of inertia of rectangular plate.—Taking the axis of rotation through the centre O of the plate (Fig. 49) and perpendicular to

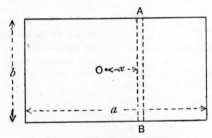

FIG. 49.—RECTANGULAR PLATE.

the plate, divide the plate into strips AB of width dx parallel to one pair of sides of the rectangle.

$$\text{Area of strip} = b \, dx.$$

$$\text{Mass of strip} = \rho b \,.\, dx.$$

$$\text{Moment of inertia about middle of strip} = \frac{\rho b^3 \, dx}{12} \text{ (p. 66).}$$

$\therefore$ Moment of inertia of strip about O

$$= \frac{\rho b^3 \, dx}{12} + x^2 \rho b \,.\, dx.$$

∴ Moment of inertia of plate

$$= \int_{-\frac{a}{2}}^{+\frac{a}{2}} \frac{\rho b^3 \, dx}{12} + \int_{-\frac{a}{2}}^{+\frac{a}{2}} x^2 \rho b \, . \, dx$$

$$= \frac{\rho b^3}{12} \left[x \right]_{-\frac{a}{2}}^{+\frac{a}{2}} + \rho b \left[\frac{x^3}{3} \right]_{-\frac{a}{2}}^{+\frac{a}{2}}$$

$$= \frac{\rho a b^3}{12} + \frac{\rho b a^3}{12}.$$

The mass m of the plate is ρab ;

$$\therefore I = m \frac{a^2 + b^2}{12}.$$

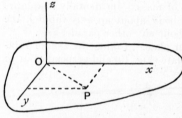

FIG. 50.—PERPENDICULAR AXES.

Lamina and perpendicular axes.—There is a useful relation for the moments of inertia about axes at right angles in the case of a lamina. If Ox and Oy (Fig. 50) are two axes at right angles to each other and in the plane of the lamina, while Oz is an axis through O at right angles to the plane of the lamina, then the moment of inertia of the element dm at P about Ox is $y^2 . dm$, and if I_x is the moment of inertia about Ox,

$$I_x = \int y^2 . \, dm.$$

Similarly

$$I_y = \int x^2 . \, dm \; ;$$

$$\therefore \; I_x + I_y = \int x^2 \, dm + \int y^2 \, dm$$

$$= \int (x^2 + y^2) \, dm$$

$$= \int \mathsf{OP}^2 . \, dm$$

$$= I_z.$$

Thus the moment of inertia about an axis perpendicular to the plane of the lamina is the sum of the moments of inertia about two perpendicular axes in the plane of the lamina and passing through the point where the perpendicular axis cuts the lamina.

Moment of inertia of disc about a diameter.—Choose the axes Ox and Oy (Fig. 50) as diameters of the disc. Then $I_x = I_y$. If the Oz-axis is perpendicular to the disc,

$$I_z = 2I_x.$$

But

$$I_z = \frac{mr^2}{2};$$

$$\therefore I_x = \frac{mr^2}{4}.$$

Moment of inertia of cylinder.—If the axis of rotation coincides with the axis of the cylinder, the moment of inertia is $\frac{mr^2}{2}$ as for a circular plate, for the thickness of the plate does not enter into the result, except in determining the mass. If the axis of rotation is perpendicular to the axis of the cylinder, divide the cylinder into thin

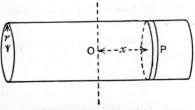

FIG. 51.—SOLID CYLINDER.

discs as at P (Fig. 51). Moment of inertia about a diameter of the disc is

$$\frac{mr^2}{4} = \frac{\rho \pi r^2 \, dx \cdot r^2}{4} = \frac{\pi \rho r^4 \, dx}{4},$$

the mass of the disc being $\rho \cdot \pi r^2 \cdot dx$.

$\therefore$ Moment of inertia of disc about axis O is

$$\frac{\pi \rho r^4 \, dx}{4} + \rho \cdot \pi r^2 \cdot dx \cdot x^2.$$

$$\therefore I_0 = \int_{-\frac{l}{2}}^{+\frac{l}{2}} \frac{\pi \rho r^4 \, dx}{4} + \int_{-\frac{l}{2}}^{+\frac{l}{2}} \rho \pi r^2 x^2 \, dx$$

$$= \frac{\pi \rho r^4}{4} \left[x \right]_{-\frac{l}{2}}^{+\frac{l}{2}} + \pi \rho r^2 \left[\frac{x^3}{3} \right]_{-\frac{l}{2}}^{+\frac{l}{2}}$$

$$= \frac{\pi \rho r^4 l}{4} + \frac{\pi \rho r^2 l^3}{12}.$$

The mass of the cylinder is $\pi r^2 l \cdot \rho = m$;

$$\therefore I_0 = m \left(\frac{r^2}{4} + \frac{l^2}{12} \right).$$

EXAMPLE.—Explain what is meant by "moment of inertia" and "angular momentum."

A thin hollow cylinder, open at both ends and weighing 96 lb., (a) slides with a speed of 10 ft. per sec., without rotating, (b) rolls with the same speed, without slipping. Compare the kinetic energies of the cylinder in the two cases.

J.M.B.H.S.C.

(a) When the cylinder slides without rotating its kinetic energy is $\frac{1}{2}mv^2 = \frac{1}{2} \times 96 \times 10^2$ foot-poundals.

(b) When the cylinder rolls without slipping, its angular velocity is $\frac{10}{r}$ where r is its radius.

Since the mass is all at the same distance r from the axis, the moment of inertia is $mr^2 = 96r^2$;

$$\therefore \text{ kinetic energy of rotation} = \frac{1}{2}I\omega^2$$

$$= \frac{1}{2} \times 96r^2 \times \frac{10^2}{r^2}$$

$$= \frac{1}{2} \times 96 \times 100 ;$$

$$\therefore \text{ total kinetic energy } (b) = \frac{1}{2}mv^2 + \frac{1}{2}I\omega^2$$

$$= \frac{1}{2} \times 96 \times 10^2 + \frac{1}{2} \times 96 \times 100$$

$$= mv^2 ;$$

$$\therefore \frac{\text{kinetic energy } (b)}{\text{kinetic energy } (a)} = \frac{\frac{1}{2} \times 96 \times 200}{\frac{1}{2} \times 96 \times 100} = \frac{mv^2}{\frac{1}{2}mv^2}$$

$$= \underline{2}.$$

Direct determination of moment of inertia.—By applying a known couple to a body and measuring the angular acceleration produced, the moment of inertia may be deduced. When the body is of the nature of a flywheel, a cord may be wound upon a cylinder A (Fig. 52) coaxial with and attached to the flywheel. If a mass m gr. is attached to the cord, the couple applied to the wheel is fr, where r is the radius of A and f is the tension in the cord. Then $I\dot{\omega} = fr$. But $r\dot{\omega} = a$, where a is the vertical acceleration of the weight. Now mg is the force due to the weight when it has no acceleration ; but when it has acceleration a the force f is given by

$$ma = mg - f,$$

or

$$f = m(g - a),$$

and

$$I\dot{\omega} = m(g-a)r,$$

$$I\frac{a}{r} = m(g-a)r,$$

$$I = mr^2\frac{(g-a)}{a}.$$

If the instant at which the weight begins to fall is noted on a stop-clock, and again when the weight has fallen a measured distance, s, the time t for falling distance s from the start is known.

Then

$$s = \tfrac{1}{2}at^2,$$

or

$$a = \frac{2s}{t^2},$$

and substituting this value for a in the above equation, I will be found to be equal to $\dfrac{m(gt^2-2s)r^2}{2s}$.

The equation for I may also be found by equating the work done by the weight in falling, to the kinetic energy produced in the wheel and weight.

$$\tfrac{1}{2}I\omega^2 + \tfrac{1}{2}mv^2 = mgs,$$

$$I\omega^2 = 2mgs - mv^2,$$

$$I = \frac{m(2gs-v^2)}{\omega^2}$$

$$= \frac{m(2gs-v^2)r^2}{v^2};$$

and since $v^2 = 2as$,

$$I = \frac{m(g-a)r^2}{a} = \frac{m(gt^2-2s)r^2}{2s}.$$

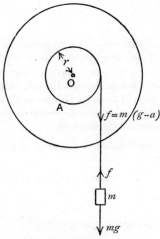

There should be a small correction made for the friction at the bearings. This may be made by finding the small mass m' that will just keep the wheel turning without acceleration, and using $(m-m')$ instead of m in the above equation. Another way is to detach the

FIG. 52.—WHEEL AND AXLE.

weight m when it has descended the distance s, and count the subsequent turns made by the wheel before coming to rest. If the friction at the bearings gives rise to a couple c, the work done by this couple in n turns of the wheel is $2\pi nc$. The wheel comes to rest when its kinetic energy $\frac{1}{2}I\omega^2$ is expended in overcoming this friction. Then $\frac{1}{2}I\omega^2 = 2\pi nc$ or $c = \dfrac{I\omega^2}{4\pi n}$. As the weight falls through distance s, the the wheel makes $\dfrac{s}{2\pi r}$ turns and the work done against friction is

$$\frac{2\pi sc}{2\pi r} = \frac{sc}{r} = \frac{I\omega^2 s}{4\pi nr}.$$

The energy equation then becomes

$$\tfrac{1}{2}I\omega^2 + \tfrac{1}{2}mv^2 + \frac{I\omega^2 s}{4\pi nr} = mgs,$$

$$\tfrac{1}{2}I\omega^2\left(1 + \frac{s}{2\pi nr}\right) + \tfrac{1}{2}mv^2 = mgs,$$

and

$$I = \frac{m(g-a)r^2}{a} \cdot \frac{1}{1 + \dfrac{s}{2\pi nr}}$$

$$= \frac{m(gt^2 - 2s)r^2}{2s} \cdot \frac{1}{\left(1 + \dfrac{s}{2\pi nr}\right)}.$$

EXAMPLE 1.—A cord is wound round the horizontal axle (whose radius is 1·2 cm.) of a flywheel, and a weight of 2 kilograms is attached to the free end of the cord. Starting from rest, the weight is released from the axle after falling through 100 cm. After the weight is released the flywheel is observed to make 14 turns in 5·8 sec. Neglecting friction calculate (a) the kinetic energy of the weight at the moment of release, (b) the moment of inertia of the flywheel. C.H.S.C.

(a) Velocity of weight at moment of release $= \dfrac{2\pi(1\cdot2)14}{5\cdot8}$ cm. sec.$^{-1}$.

$\therefore$ Kinetic energy of weight $= \tfrac{1}{2}2000 \cdot \left(\dfrac{2\pi(1\cdot2)14}{5\cdot8}\right)^2$

$= 3\cdot311 \times 10^5$ ergs.

(b) Work done in falling $= 2000 \times 981 \times 100$

$= 1\cdot962 \times 10^8$ ergs.

Now neglecting friction,

$$\tfrac{1}{2}I\omega^2 + \tfrac{1}{2}mv^2 = mgs ;$$

$$\therefore \tfrac{1}{2}I\omega^2 = 1\cdot962 \times 10^8 - 3\cdot311 \times 10^5$$

$$= 1\cdot959 \times 10^8 \text{ ergs.}$$

$$\omega = \frac{2\pi \cdot 14}{5 \cdot 8} \; ;$$

$$\therefore \; I = 2 \times 1 \cdot 959 \times 10^8 \times \left(\frac{5 \cdot 8}{2\pi \cdot 14}\right)^2$$

$$= \underline{1 \cdot 703 \times 10^6} \text{ gm. cm.}^2$$

EXAMPLE 2.—Explain what is meant by the moment of inertia of a body, and describe how you could compare experimentally the moments of inertia of two rods about an axis through the C.G. and perpendicular to the length.

A kilogram weight is attached to the end of a string which is wrapped round the axle of a flywheel of moment of inertia 10^5 C.G.S. units, and is allowed to fall. How many revolutions per sec. will the wheel be making when the weight has fallen through 1 metre ? The kinetic energy of the weight may be neglected.   C.H.S.C.

For experiment, see p. 100.

When the weight has fallen 1 m. work done $= mgs$

$$= 1000 \times 981 \times 100$$
$$= 9 \cdot 81 \times 10^7 \text{ ergs.}$$

Neglecting friction and the kinetic energy of the weight,

$$\tfrac{1}{2} I \omega^2 = 9 \cdot 81 \times 10^7 \text{ ergs.}$$
$$\tfrac{1}{2} \cdot 10^5 \omega^2 = 9 \cdot 81 \times 10^7.$$
$$\omega^2 = 19 \cdot 62 \times 10^2.$$
$$\omega = 44 \cdot 3 \text{ radians per sec.}$$

If n is the number of revolutions per second, $2\pi n = \omega$;

$$\therefore \; n = \frac{44 \cdot 3}{2\pi}$$
$$= \underline{7 \cdot 05} \text{ revolutions per sec.}$$

Motion of a point in a circle.—On p. 48 the angular velocity of a rigid body was considered, and it was seen that a point distant r from the axis has a linear velocity of magnitude v, when the angular velocity of r is ω. r is really a vector defining the position of the point with respect to the axes, and v is likewise a vector. Any change in the vector **r**, taking place in time dt, is the real velocity **v**, and the acceleration of the point is $\dfrac{d\mathbf{v}}{dt}$. This is itself a vector, and may therefore be resolved into two components, one along the radius and the other at right angles to it. When the point moves in a circle r is constant; the magnitude of the latter acceleration is $r\dfrac{d\omega}{dt}$ and has been dealt with on pp. 48 and 64. The magnitude of the former must now be found.

In Fig. 53, the velocity in the circle is supposed to have a constant

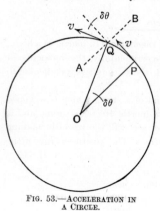

value v, and is shown at two near points P and Q. The line AB is drawn parallel to OP. Then at P the component of velocity parallel to OP is zero, and at Q it is $v \sin \delta\theta$. If the time for the point to travel from P to Q is δt, the acceleration parallel to OP is $\dfrac{v \sin \delta\theta}{\delta t}$. If δt and $\delta\theta$ are infinitesimal $\sin \delta\theta = \delta\theta$, and the acceleration parallel to OP is $v \cdot \dfrac{d\theta}{dt}$,

FIG. 53.—ACCELERATION IN A CIRCLE.

and since the angular velocity $\omega = \dfrac{d\theta}{dt}$,

$$\text{radial acceleration} = v\omega$$

$$= \frac{v^2}{r}$$

$$= \omega^2 r.$$

When the angular velocity is not constant there will be a tangential acceleration which will be calculated later, but for the present the relation between radial and tangential acceleration will be deferred.

Thus when v remains constant the only change in velocity is a change in direction, the acceleration being at right angles to **v** and directed along the radius of the circle.

The hodograph.—Another method of arriving at the same result is to draw an auxiliary diagram of velocities as in Fig. 54. If PQ, RS, etc., are vectors representing the velocity of the point at P and R, take a separate point A and draw vectors AB, AC, etc., equivalent to PQ, RS, etc. Then if many points are taken and the points B, C, etc., are joined, a continuous curve called a **hodograph** is obtained. In this case the hodograph is a circle of radius $v = $ PQ. In a small interval of time, P moves to P′ and B to B′, and the change in velocity is thus BB′, which from the figure is seen to be parallel to OP; that is, it is directed towards the centre, O, of the circle. The total change in velocity in one revolution is the circumference $2\pi \cdot$ AB $= 2\pi v$, and this takes place while the point P travels round the circle with velocity v, that is, in time $\dfrac{2\pi r}{v}$. The acceleration of P is therefore

$$\frac{2\pi v}{\dfrac{2\pi r}{v}} = \frac{v^2}{r}.$$

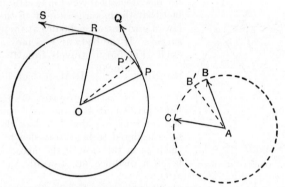

FIG. 54.—HODOGRAPH OF POINT MOVING IN A CIRCLE.

Centrifugal force.—The case of a body moving in a circle is frequently met with ; for example, a weight whirled round at the end of a string ; a railway train or motor-car rounding a curve ; the planets moving round the sun and the moon round the earth. It is true that these orbits are not exactly circles, but the radial acceleration is still v^2/r where v is the orbital velocity and r the radius of curvature of the path at the point considered. It was seen on p. 25 that a body continues to move in a straight line unless acted upon by some force. When therefore a body moves along a circular path it must be acted upon by a force, since its path is continually being deflected from a straight line, and this force is in the direction of the acceleration produced, that is, towards the centre of the circle. It is called a **centripetal force,** and may be the pull in the string, a push due to the rails on the wheels of the train, or in the case of the planets, the pull of gravitational attraction. The force which is equal and opposite to this is called the **centrifugal force.** Centrifugal force and centripetal force are, of course, action and reaction in the sense of Newton's third law of motion (p. 25). For either, the value is

$\dfrac{mv^2}{r}$ where m is the mass of the moving body, and v is the magnitude of its linear velocity. It is also $m\omega^2 r$, where ω is the angular velocity of the radius vector from the centre to the body, since $v = \omega r$.

Newton's method.—There is a third method of establishing the value of the acceleration in circular motion which is of historic interest,

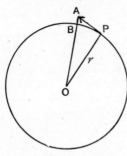

FIG. 55.—ORBITAL MOTION.

because it enabled Newton to establish the fact that the moon is subject to the same law of gravitation as bodies at the earth's surface. If the body at P is moving in a circle (Fig. 55), it travels from P to B in the time $\dfrac{\text{arc PB}}{v}$. If there had been no force on it acting towards O it would have arrived at A in the same time. In the interval considered it may therefore be considered to have travelled to A and then, as in the case of the moon, to have fallen a distance AB, towards the earth at O.

If the interval of time is small, AB approaches the limit given by

$$\text{AB} \cdot 2r = \text{AP}^2.$$

But in the limit, AP and the arc BP become equal in length,

$$\therefore \text{AB} = \frac{\text{BP}^2}{2r} ;$$

and since

$$s = \tfrac{1}{2}at^2, \quad \text{(p. 8)}$$

$$\text{AB} = \tfrac{1}{2}at^2,$$

that is,

$$\frac{\text{BP}^2}{2r} = \tfrac{1}{2}a\,\frac{\text{BP}^2}{v^2},$$

or

$$a = \frac{v^2}{r}.$$

This value of the acceleration is in agreement with those found on pp. 76 and 77.

If the period of rotation of the moon about the earth is taken as 27·3 days and the earth's radius as 4000 miles, the acceleration of the moon towards the earth is $\dfrac{v^2}{r}$, or

$$\left(\frac{2\pi \cdot 60 \cdot 4000 \cdot 1760 \cdot 3}{27 \cdot 3 \times 24 \times 3600} \right)^2 \frac{1}{60 \times 4000 \cdot 1760 \cdot 3}$$

in feet per sec. per sec., the moon's distance being 60 times the earth's radius. This is equal to 0·00899 ft./sec.².

If the acceleration of gravity at the surface of the earth is 32·2 ft./sec.², at the moon's distance it should be $\dfrac{32·2}{60^2} = 0·00894$ if the force on unit mass varies inversely as the square of the distance from the earth's centre (see p. 109). The fair agreement shows that the force on the moon due to the earth obeys the same law as the force on bodies at the earth's surface.

EXAMPLE 1.—Show that when a body is moving with uniform velocity in a circular path it has an acceleration, and find the value of this acceleration in terms of the radius of the path and the number of revolutions per minute.

A body of weight 300 gm. is tied to the end of a string 2 metres long and revolves with uniform speed in a horizontal circle at 90 revolutions per minute. Find the tension in the string.   O.H.S.C.

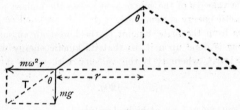

FIG. 56.—PROBLEM.

Two forces are acting on the body, $m\omega^2 r$ horizontally and mg vertically. The body will be in steady motion when the resultant of these two forces acts along the string.

From Fig. 56,

$$\tan \theta = \frac{m\omega^2 r}{mg} = \frac{\omega^2 r}{g} .$$

But

$$\omega = \frac{2\pi \cdot 90}{60} = 3\pi,$$

and

$$r = 200 \sin \theta ;$$

$$\therefore \ \tan \theta = \frac{9\pi^2 \cdot 200 \sin \theta}{g} ,$$

or,

$$\cos \theta = \frac{g}{1800\pi^2} .$$

Now from the diagram, $\cos \theta = \dfrac{mg}{T}$;

$$\therefore \ T = \frac{300 \cdot g}{\cos \theta}$$

$$= 300 \cdot 1800\pi^2$$

$$= \underline{5 \cdot 33 \times 10^6 \text{ dynes.}}$$

EXAMPLE 2.—A body of mass m gm. is attached to a fixed point A on a smooth horizontal table by a string of length l cm., and describes a circle round A as centre with uniform speed v cm. per sec. Find the tension in the string.

A small sphere is attached to a fixed point by a string of length 30 cm., and whirls round in a vertical circle under the action of gravity at such speed that the tension in the string when the sphere is at its lowest point is three times the tension when the sphere is at its highest point. Find the speed of the sphere at its highest point. C.H.S.C.

For the first part, see p. 78.

Let v be the velocity of the sphere as it passes the highest point of the circle. Its kinetic energy is then $\frac{1}{2}mv^2$.

As it passes from the highest point to the lowest an amount of work equal to 60 mg is done upon it, so that its kinetic energy will now be $\frac{1}{2}mv^2 + 60mg = \frac{1}{2}mv_1^2$, where v_1 is the velocity with which it passes the lowest point.

$$v_1^2 = v^2 + 120g.$$

Centrifugal force at highest point $= \dfrac{mv^2}{30}$,

,, ,, ,, lowest point $= \dfrac{mv_1^2}{30}$;

$\therefore$ tension in string for highest point $= \dfrac{mv^2}{30} - mg$,

,, ,, ,, lowest point $= \dfrac{mv_1^2}{30} + mg$.

$$\therefore \ \frac{mv_1^2}{30} + mg = 3\left(\frac{mv^2}{30} - mg\right),$$

$$v_1^2 = 3v^2 - 120g = v^2 + 120g \ ;$$

$$\therefore \ 2v^2 = 240g,$$

$$v^2 = 120 \times 981,$$

$$\underline{v = 343 \cdot 1 \text{ cm. sec.}^{-1}.}$$

EXERCISES ON CHAPTER III

MOMENTS AND COUPLES

1. Prove that the moment of a couple about any point in its plane is constant. Prove also that the resultant of a number of couples acting in a plane is equal to a couple of which the moment is the sum of the moments of the given couples.

A uniform rectangular gate ABCD of weight 300 lb. in which AB = 10 ft., BC = 4 ft., is hinged at A and D, where A is vertically above D. If the reaction at A is horizontal, find its magnitude. J.M.B.H.S.C.

2. Prove that the sum of the moments of two forces acting in intersecting lines in a plane about any point in that plane is equal to the moment of their resultant about that point.

A uniform rod AB, of length $2a$ and weight W, is suspended freely from the end A, and a couple of moment $G(<aW)$ in a vertical plane is applied to the rod. Find the angle the rod makes with the vertical and the action it exerts on the hinge. C.W.B.H.S.C.

3. Find the magnitude, direction, and line of action of the resultant of two given unlike parallel forces.

Like parallel forces P, 2P, 3P act at the vertices A, B, C of a triangle, their lines of action being always in the plane ABC. Prove that whatever the common direction of the forces in this plane their resultant passes through a fixed point, and find the point. J.M.B.H.S.C.

4. Define a couple, and prove that it has the same moment about all points in its plane.

A light equilateral triangle ABC is free to rotate in a vertical plane about an axis through its centre. At the corners A, B, C are attached masses of 3, 5, 2 lb. respectively, while along AB a force P is applied to maintain equilibrium. Find the magnitude of P when AB is inclined at an angle θ to the downward vertical through A, and verify that the triangle is in equilibrium without the force P when $\tan \theta = 2/\sqrt{3}$. L.H.S.C.

5. Three non-parallel coplanar forces act on a body and keep it in equilibrium. Prove that their lines of action are concurrent.

A uniform rod AB, of mass 10 lb., is freely hinged about the end A, which is fixed, and is supported in an inclined position by a light string joining the end B to a fixed point C vertically above A. If AB = AC = 2BC, find completely the action of the hinge on the rod and the tension in the string. L.H.S.C.

6. Define the moment of a force and prove that the algebraic sum of the moments of any two parallel forces about a point is equal to the moment of their resultant about that point.

The arms of a balance are unequal in length but, without the scale pans, the beam and scale-pan holders are correctly balanced. The scale pans A and B are of weight $2w_1$, $2w_2$ respectively. A body placed in pan A has an apparent weight W_1, and placed in pan B has an apparent weight W_2. Show that the true weight of the body is

$$\sqrt{\{W_1W_2 + 2(w_1W_: + w_2W_2) + (w_1+w_2)^2\}} - (w_1+w_2).$$

L.H.S.C.

7. What are the most important qualities of a good balance, and how are they secured in practice ?

Show that the sensitiveness of a balance is independent of the load carried by the scale pans when the terminal knife edges are in the same plane as the central knife edge. How does the behaviour of the balance depend upon the position of the centre of gravity of the beam ?

C.W.B.H.S.C.

8. State briefly on what factors the sensitivity of a balance depends.

The arms of a balance are similar and of equal length, a. The scale pans are similar and of equal weight, P. When the beam of the balance is horizontal, the central knife edge is a distance, x, vertically above the middle of the line joining the knife edges of the scale pans, and the c.g. of the balance is a distance, y, vertically below the same point. Assuming that the weight of the moving system of the balance is W, derive an expression for the angle of deflection of the beam when weights w_1 and w_2 are placed on the scale pans. [$w_1 > w_2$.]   J.M.B.H.S.C.

Centre of Mass

9. Find the centre of gravity of a solid right circular cone.

A hollow right circular cone, without base, of mass M, and made of a thin metallic sheet, is placed with its axis vertical and vertex downwards. Water is poured in to a depth of one-half of the vertical height. Prove that, if the centre of gravity of the cone and its contents is at the surface of the water, the mass of water is $\frac{4}{3}$M.   C.H.S.C.

10. Find the centre of gravity of a triangular lamina ; and show that it is the same as that of three equal particles at the mid-points of its sides.

A lamina in the shape of a trapezium has parallel sides AB, DC ; and EF is the straight line parallel to them which bisects AD and BC. Show that the centre of gravity of the trapezium coincides with that of masses proportional to AB, DC, 4EF at the mid-points of AB, DC, EF respectively.

J.M.B.H.S.C.

11. Find the position of the centre of mass of a uniform plane triangular lamina.

A triangle ABC is made of three uniform heavy rods. Show that its centre of mass is at the centre of the inscribed circle of the triangle formed by joining the mid-points of the sides of the triangle ABC.   J.M.B.H.S.C.

12. Prove that the centre of gravity of a uniform triangular lamina coincides with the centre of gravity of three equal weights at its vertices.

A regular pyramid whose base is a regular hexagon is made of uniform thin sheet metal. If a is the radius of the circumcircle of its base and $2a$

is the length of the slant edges, find the position of the centre of gravity of the total surface of the pyramid, and state its distance from the base.

L.H.S.C.

MOMENT OF INERTIA

13. Show that the moment of inertia of a uniform circular lamina about a tangent is $\frac{5}{4}Ma^2$, where M is the mass of the lamina and a its radius.

C.H.S.C.

14. A flywheel of mass 100 kg. and radius of gyration 20 cm. is mounted on a light horizontal axle of radius 2 cm. and is free to rotate in bearings whose friction may be neglected. A light string wound on the axle carries at its free end a mass of 5 kg. The system is released from rest with the 5 kg. mass hanging freely. Prove that the acceleration of this mass is

$$g/2001 \text{ cm./sec.}^2.$$

If the string slips off the axle after the weight has descended 2 metres, prove that the couple of moment 31·8 kg. wt.-cm. (approximately) must be applied in order to bring the flywheel to rest in 5 revolutions.

C.H.S.C.

15. Prove that the moment of inertia of a uniform circular disc about an axis through its centre and perpendicular to its plane is $\frac{1}{2}Ma^2$, where M and a are respectively the mass and radius of the disc.

Hence find the moment of inertia of

(i) a uniform solid sphere of radius r and mass M about a diameter ;

(ii) a uniform solid right circular cone of mass M about its axis, the radius of the base being a.　　　　　　　　　　　　　C.H.S.C.

16. Find by integration the moment of inertia of a uniform lamina (mass M) in the form of an equilateral triangle (side a), about one side.

A uniform plate is in the form of an equilateral triangle CAB and a semicircle ABD described on opposite sides of a straight line AB, 12 inches long. Find its radius of gyration about AB.　　　　　　　　C.H.S.C.

FLYWHEEL

17. A flywheel of weight 200 lb. which may be regarded as a uniform disc of radius 1 ft., is set rotating about its axis with an angular velocity of 5 revolutions per second. At the end of 40 sec. this velocity, owing to the action of a constant frictional couple, has dropped to 4 revolutions per second. What constant couple must now be applied so that in a further 20 sec. the angular velocity will be 8 revolutions per second ?

Find the total angle turned through during the minute.　　C.H.S.C.

18. A flywheel of mass 65·4 kg. is made in the form of a circular disc of radius 18 cm. ; it is driven by a belt whose tensions at the points where it runs on and off the rim of the flywheel are 2 kg. and 5 kg. weight respectively. If the wheel is rotating at a certain instant at 60 revolutions

per minute, find how long it will be before the speed has reached 210 revolutions per minute.

While the flywheel is rotating at this latter speed the belt is slipped off and a brake applied. Find the constant braking couple required to stop the wheel in 7 revolutions. [g may be taken as 981 cm. per sec. per sec.]
C.H.S.C.

19. (a) Explain what you understand by the term *moment of inertia* and show that the kinetic energy of a body revolving about a fixed axis is $\frac{1}{2}I\omega^2$, where I is its moment of inertia about that axis and ω is its angular velocity.

(b) A rope hanging over a pulley of radius 2 ft. has attached to it at one end a mass of 24 lb. and at the other end a mass of 20 lb. Initially motion is prevented by holding one of the masses. If the moment of inertia of the pulley about its axis of rotation is 336 lb. ft.², find the velocity of the masses when they have moved a distance of 4 ft. from rest. There is no slip between the rope and the pulley and the friction at the axle of the pulley may be neglected.
J.M.B.H.S.C.

MOTION IN CIRCLE

20. Prove that when a particle describes a circle of radius r with velocity v, it has an acceleration of v^2/r towards the centre.

A particle of mass m is attached to a fixed point A by means of a string of length l and hangs freely. It is then projected horizontally with velocity $\sqrt{6gl}$. Show that it completely describes a vertical circle.
L.H.S.C.

21. Prove that when a particle describes a circle of radius a with constant angular velocity ω, the acceleration is directed towards the centre and has a magnitude $a\omega^2$.

Four masses, each of 10 lb., are fastened together with four strings each 3 feet long so as to form a square. This square rotates in a horizontal plane on a smooth table at a speed of one revolution per second; find in pounds weight the tensions in the strings.
C.H.S.C.

22. Find the tangential and normal components of the acceleration of a particle describing a circle with speed v, not necessarily uniform.

A half-pound weight is being whirled in a horizontal circle at the end of a string 2 feet long, the other end of the string being fixed. If the breaking tension of the string is 112 lb. wt., find the greatest speed which can be given to the weight.
C.W.B.H.S.C.

23. A body moves in a circle with uniform speed. Find the magnitude and direction of the acceleration of the body at any instant.

A Schneider Cup seaplane flies in a horizontal circle of radius 2 miles at a speed of 330 miles per hour. What is the direction of the resultant force on the seaplane?
O. & C.H.S.C.

24. A seaplane of total mass 1000 lb. (including the pilot) rounds a pylon in a circular arc of radius half a mile at a speed of 300 M.P.H. Draw a diagram showing the forces acting on the seaplane, and calculate the

resultant force at right angles to its direction of motion exerted upon it by the air. Assuming that the pilot weighs 12 stone, calculate the force with which he is pressed against his seat during the " turn." C.H.S.C.

25. Show that a particle moving with constant speed in a circle is acted on by a force directed towards the centre of the circle, and deduce an expression for this force in terms of the radius of the circle and the velocity of the particle at any instant.

Assuming that the moon revolves uniformly in a circle round the earth's centre, calculate the acceleration of gravity at the earth's surface from the following data : radius of earth, $6\cdot4 \times 10^8$ cm., radius of moon's orbit, $3\cdot84 \times 10^{10}$ cm., period of rotation of moon, $27\cdot3$ days.

(The force of gravity on a particle is inversely proportional to the square of its distance from the earth's centre.) O. & C.H.S.C.

CHAPTER IV

SIMPLE HARMONIC MOTION

Definition of simple harmonic motion.—There are many examples of a body moving in a symmetrical manner about a point. If the body moves in a straight line and the force acting on the body is directed towards a point in the line, and further, if the force is proportional to the distance of the body from the point, the **motion of the body is simple harmonic.** Among the examples to be studied are the vertical motion of a mass suspended by a spring or elastic cord, a point on the prong of a tuning fork, a pendulum whose oscillations are small.

Equation of simple harmonic motion.—Suppose the body of mass m to be situated at P (Fig. 57), and the force acting upon the body

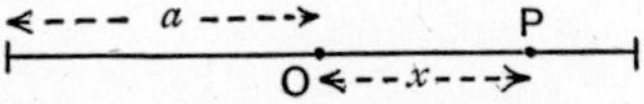

FIG. 57.—SIMPLE HARMONIC MOTION.

to be directed towards O and of value proportional to the distance, x, of P from O. Then the velocity of P is $\dfrac{dx}{dt}$ and its acceleration $\dfrac{d^2x}{dt^2}$, and the force acting on it is $m\dfrac{d^2x}{dt^2}$. But this is proportional to x. Let it be μx. Since this force is directed towards O it is always opposite in direction to x, and the negative sign is therefore taken for μx.

Then
$$m\frac{d^2x}{dt^2} = -\mu x,$$

or
$$m\frac{d^2x}{dt^2} + \mu x = 0,$$

$$\frac{d^2x}{dt^2} + \frac{\mu}{m}x = 0.$$

An equation of this type may always be solved by assuming that

$$x = A\epsilon^{\alpha t},$$

where ϵ is the base of Naperian logarithms and A is any constant we like to choose.

Then
$$\frac{dx}{dt} = A\alpha\epsilon^{\alpha t},$$

$$\frac{d^2x}{dt^2} = A\alpha^2\epsilon^{\alpha t},$$

and substituting in the equation we have,

$$A\alpha^2\epsilon^{\alpha t} + A\frac{\mu}{m}\epsilon^{\alpha t} = 0,$$

or
$$\alpha^2 = -\frac{\mu}{m},$$

$$\alpha = \pm\sqrt{-1}\sqrt{\frac{\mu}{m}}.$$

Thus $x = 2A\epsilon^{+\sqrt{-1}\sqrt{\mu/m}\,t}$ is one solution and $x = 2B\epsilon^{-\sqrt{-1}\sqrt{\mu/m}\,t}$ is another; remembering that A and B may be any constants whatever. Adding them together,

$$x = A\epsilon^{+\sqrt{-1}\sqrt{\mu/m}\,t} + B\epsilon^{-\sqrt{-1}\sqrt{\mu/m}\,t}.$$

Since A and B may have any values we like, let us assume that the body passes through O at time $t = 0$, so that $x = 0$ when $t = 0$.

Then
$$0 = A + B.$$

Again, suppose that the body is moving from left to right through O with velocity v when $t = 0$:

Then $v = \dfrac{dx}{dt} = A\sqrt{-1}\sqrt{\dfrac{\mu}{m}}\epsilon^{\sqrt{-1}\sqrt{\mu/m}\,t} - B\sqrt{-1}\sqrt{\dfrac{\mu}{m}}\epsilon^{-\sqrt{-1}\sqrt{\mu/m}\,t}$

and, when $t = 0$, $\qquad \epsilon^{\sqrt{-1}\sqrt{\mu/m}\,t} = 1$;

$$\therefore \quad v = A\sqrt{-1}\sqrt{\frac{\mu}{m}} - B\sqrt{-1}\sqrt{\frac{\mu}{m}}.$$

Remembering that $0 = A + B$,

we have $$= 2A\sqrt{-1}\sqrt{\frac{\mu}{m}},$$

or $$A = \frac{v\sqrt{\frac{m}{\mu}}}{2\sqrt{-1}},$$

and $$x = v\sqrt{\frac{m}{\mu}}\,\frac{\epsilon^{\sqrt{-1}\sqrt{\mu/m}\,t} - \epsilon^{-\sqrt{-1}\sqrt{\mu/m}\,t}}{2\sqrt{-1}}.$$

From de Moivre's theorem, the last part is seen to be $\sin\sqrt{\frac{\mu}{m}}t$;

$$\therefore\ x = v\sqrt{\frac{m}{\mu}}\sin\sqrt{\frac{\mu}{m}}t.$$

The body therefore moves backwards and forwards between two points, for which $\sin\sqrt{\frac{\mu}{m}}t$ has the values $+1$ and -1. For these points, $x = \pm v\sqrt{\frac{m}{\mu}}$, and this is called the **amplitude** of the simple harmonic motion, and writing $v\sqrt{\frac{m}{\mu}} = a$,

$$x = a\sin\sqrt{\frac{\mu}{m}}t.$$

Again, as t increases, the motion of the body is repeated, for if t increases by the amount $2\pi\sqrt{\frac{m}{\mu}}$,

$$x = a\sin\sqrt{\frac{\mu}{m}}\left(t + 2\pi\sqrt{\frac{m}{\mu}}\right)$$

$$= a\sin\left(\sqrt{\frac{\mu}{m}}t + 2\pi\right) = a\sin\sqrt{\frac{\mu}{m}}t.$$

The time $2\pi\sqrt{\frac{m}{\mu}}$ is called the **periodic time** T,

$$\therefore\ T = 2\pi\sqrt{\frac{m}{\mu}}.$$

The number of complete oscillations made in unit time is $\frac{1}{T}$, and this is called the **frequency**, n ;

$$\therefore\ n = \frac{1}{T} = \frac{1}{2\pi}\sqrt{\frac{\mu}{m}}.$$

EXAMPLE 1.—Find an expression for the periodic time of a body moving in a straight line with s.h.m.

A steel spiral spring has an unstretched length of 8 cm., and when a weight is hung on it, its length becomes 14 cm. Calculate the periodic time of oscillation of the weight if displaced vertically.   C.H.S.C.

The force required to stretch a spiral spring is proportional to the amount of stretch, unless the extension is excessive.

Let m be the mass hung on the string, then mg is the stretching force and the upward force due to the spring is mg dynes when the weight is $(14-8)$ or 6 cm. from its mean position ;

$$\therefore \text{ as above, } \mu = \frac{mg}{6} \text{ dynes for displacement of 1 cm. ;}$$

$$\therefore\ T = 2\pi\sqrt{\frac{m \cdot 6}{mg}}$$

$$= 2\pi\sqrt{\frac{6}{981}}$$

$$= \underline{0\cdot491} \text{ sec.}$$

EXAMPLE 2.—Define " simple harmonic motion," and find the period of a particle executing such motion.

A cylindrical air-tight piston, of mass M and cross-sectional area A, slides without friction in the vertical neck of a bottle of volume V filled with air originally at atmospheric pressure P. Show that if the piston is displaced from its position of equilibrium, under isothermal conditions, it will oscillate with simple harmonic motion, and find an expression for the period.

O. & C.H.S.C.

If x is the displacement of the piston, xA is the change in volume. If p is the corresponding change in pressure and the change is isothermal, then from Boyle's law (p. 174),

$$P \cdot V = (P + p)(V - x A),$$
or
$$= (P - p)(V + x A).$$
$$P \cdot V = P \cdot V - p x A + p V - P x A,$$
$$0 = - p x A + p V - P x A.$$

If p and x are small in comparison with the other quantities, pxA is negligible ;

$$\therefore\ p V = P x A,$$
$$\frac{p A}{x} = \frac{P A^2}{V}.$$

The ratio of restoring force pA to displacement x is therefore constant and equal to $\dfrac{P A^2}{V} = \mu.$

Therefore the motion of the piston is simple harmonic, and the period is

$$T = 2\pi \sqrt{\frac{m}{\mu}} \quad \text{(p. 86)}$$

$$= 2\pi \sqrt{\frac{MV}{PA^2}} = \frac{2\pi}{A} \sqrt{\frac{MV}{P}}.$$

Graphical treatment.—Insight into the phenomenon of simple harmonic motion may be obtained by considering it as the projection of a rotating vector upon a fixed straight line. If a point P (Fig. 58) is travelling in a circle whose centre is O and radius a with constant speed v, the radius vector OP rotates with angular velocity ω where

$$v = a\omega.$$

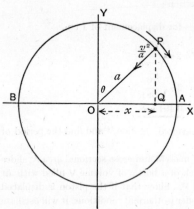

OQ is the projection of OP upon the axis of x, and as P travels round the circle, Q moves backwards and forwards between A and B.

The acceleration of P is $\frac{v^2}{a}$

FIG. 58.—PROJECTION OF ROTATING VECTOR.

in the direction PO. The component of this acceleration parallel to OX is $\frac{v^2}{a} \sin \theta$, which is therefore the acceleration of the point Q, and the force which would give a mass m the same motion as the point Q is $\frac{mv^2}{a} \sin \theta$, or $m\omega^2 a \sin \theta$. Since $a \sin \theta = x$, the force is $m\omega^2 x$. It is thus proportional to x and is directed towards O, so that the motion is simple harmonic (p. 86).

Writing μx for the force, $\mu = m\omega^2$, so that $\omega = \sqrt{\frac{\mu}{m}}$. The equation of the motion is

$$x = a \sin \theta$$

$$= a \sin \omega t$$

$$= a \sin \sqrt{\frac{\mu}{m}} t,$$

as found on p. 88.   Moreover, the periodic time T is $\dfrac{2\pi}{\omega} = 2\pi\sqrt{\dfrac{m}{\mu}}$ and the frequency n is $\dfrac{1}{2\pi}\sqrt{\dfrac{\mu}{m}}$.

Again, the greatest velocity of Q is its velocity on passing O, and is then equal to the velocity of P, because at that moment P is moving parallel to OX.   At any instant the velocity is $\dfrac{dx}{dt} = \omega a \cos \omega t$, which is ωa or v, when $t=0$ and $x=0$.

Energy of vibration.—On passing the point O (Fig. 58) the body has kinetic energy $\frac{1}{2}mv^2$.   At the end of its travel the velocity and kinetic energy are zero, the force directed towards O having brought the body to rest.   The force at any point being μx, the work done for an infinitesimal displacement dx is $\mu x\,dx$, and the total work done in moving from O, through the amplitude a, is

$$\int_0^a \mu x\,dx = \tfrac{1}{2}\mu a^2 \;;$$

$$\therefore\ \ \tfrac{1}{2}mv^2 = \tfrac{1}{2}\mu a^2,$$

or
$$a = v\sqrt{\frac{m}{\mu}},$$

which agrees with the result on p. 88.   The energy thus alternates between the kinetic and potential form, but the total amount is constant for every instant.

For at displacement x the velocity is

$$\frac{dx}{dt} = \sqrt{\frac{\mu}{m}}\,a \cos \sqrt{\frac{\mu}{m}}\,t = v \cos \sqrt{\frac{\mu}{m}}\,t,$$

and the kinetic energy is $\frac{1}{2}mv^2 \cos^2\sqrt{\dfrac{\mu}{m}}\,t$.

The potential energy is $\frac{1}{2}\mu x^2 = \frac{1}{2}\mu \cdot v^2\dfrac{m}{\mu}\sin^2\sqrt{\dfrac{\mu}{m}}\,t$

$$= \tfrac{1}{2}mv^2 \sin^2\sqrt{\frac{\mu}{m}}\,t \;;$$

$$\therefore\ \text{kinetic energy} + \text{potential energy} = \tfrac{1}{2}mv^2\left(\cos^2\sqrt{\frac{\mu}{m}}\,t + \sin^2\sqrt{\frac{\mu}{m}}\,t\right)$$

$$= \tfrac{1}{2}mv^2 = \tfrac{1}{2}\mu a^2.$$

The energy may also be expressed in terms of the frequency and amplitude, for $n = \dfrac{1}{2\pi}\sqrt{\dfrac{\mu}{m}}$ (p. 88), so that $\mu = 4\pi^2 n^2 m$.

$$\therefore \; \tfrac{1}{2}\mu a^2 = \tfrac{1}{2} \cdot 4\pi^2 n^2 m a^2$$
$$= 2\pi^2 m n^2 a^2.$$

From which it is seen that the energy of a vibrating body is proportional to the **square of the frequency** and to the **square of the amplitude**.

EXAMPLE 1.—A particle is moving with simple harmonic motion in a straight line. When the distance of the particle from the equilibrium position has the values x_1 and x_2, the corresponding values of the velocity are u_1 and u_2. Show that the period is

$$2\pi\{(x_2^2 - x_1^2)/(u_1^2 - u_2^2)\}^{\frac{1}{2}}.$$

Find also (i) the maximum velocity, (ii) the amplitude.　　C.H.S.C.

Let the simple harmonic motion be represented by $x = a \sin \omega t$, then

$$u = \frac{dx}{dt} = \omega a \cos \omega t.$$

$$\therefore \; \frac{u}{\omega a} = \cos \omega t \quad \text{and} \quad \frac{x}{a} = \sin \omega t.$$

$$\therefore \; \frac{u^2}{\omega^2 a^2} + \frac{x^2}{a^2} = 1,$$

$$\frac{u_1^2}{\omega^2} + x_1^2 = a^2,$$

$$\frac{u_2^2}{\omega^2} + x_2^2 = a^2.$$

Subtracting we get

$$\frac{u_1^2 - u_2^2}{\omega^2} = x_2^2 - x_1^2 \; ;$$

$$\therefore \; \omega = \sqrt{(u_1^2 - u_2^2)/(x_2^2 - x_1^2)}.$$

The period $T = \dfrac{2\pi}{\omega}$;

$$\therefore \; \underline{T = 2\pi\sqrt{(x_2^2 - x_1^2)/(u_1^2 - u_2^2)}.}$$

(ii) From the equation $\dfrac{u_1^2}{\omega^2} + x_1^2 = a^2$,

$$a^2 = u_1^2\left(\frac{x_2^2 - x_1^2}{u_1^2 - u_2^2}\right) + x_1^2 \; ;$$

$$\therefore \; \text{amplitude,} \; \underline{a = \sqrt{\frac{u_1^2(x_2^2 - x_1^2) + x_1^2(u_1^2 - u_2^2)}{u_1^2 - u_2^2}} = \sqrt{\frac{u_1^2 x_2^2 - u_2^2 x_1^2}{u_1^2 - u_2^2}}.}$$

(i) Since $u = \omega a \cos \omega t$, the maximum value of u occurs when $\cos \omega t = 1$.

∴ Maximum velocity $= \omega a$

$$= \sqrt{\frac{u_1^2 x_2^2 - u_2^2 x_1^2}{x_2^2 - x_1^2}}.$$

EXAMPLE 2.—What is meant by Simple Harmonic Motion ?

A test-tube of weight 6 gm. and of external diameter 2 cm. is floated vertically in water by placing 10 gm. of mercury at the bottom of the tube. The tube is depressed a small amount and then released. Find the time of oscillation.   O. & C.H.S.C.

Total mass, m, of tube and mercury $= 16$ gm.

To depress the tube 1 cm. from the floating position displaces

$$\pi \times 1^2 = \pi \text{ c.c. of water,}$$

and the upward thrust on this account is πg dynes. (See p. 168.)

∴ Restoring force for unit displacement $= \mu = \pi g$ dynes.

∴ Period of oscillation

$$= 2\pi \sqrt{\frac{m}{\mu}} \quad \text{(p. 88)}$$

$$= 2\pi \sqrt{\frac{16}{\pi g}} = 2 \sqrt{\frac{\pi \times 16}{981}}$$

$$= \underline{0.453 \text{ sec.}}$$

Phase.—It is not necessary to measure time from the instant at which the body passes the middle of its path. For example, if t is reckoned from the instant at which P (Fig. 59) is at R, where OR makes an angle α with OY, then

$$OQ = OP \sin OPQ,$$

or $\qquad x = a \sin (\theta + \alpha)$

$$= a \sin \left(\sqrt{\frac{\mu}{m}} t + \alpha \right).$$

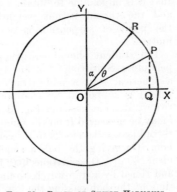

FIG. 59.—PHASE OF SIMPLE HARMONIC MOTION.

The angle α is known as the **phase** of the vibration.

Simple pendulum.—A body, hanging by a light thread, constitutes a simple pendulum when the body is small enough to be considered as a point. If OA (Fig. 60) represents the pendulum when hanging at rest, then with the bob of the pendulum drawn aside to B so that the thread makes an angle β with the vertical, the weight mg of the bob

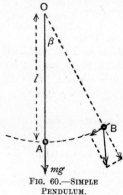

FIG. 60.—SIMPLE PENDULUM.

is no longer in the direction of the thread. It will have a component $mg \sin \beta$ at right angles to the thread. B is therefore urged along the circle towards A. The free motion of B will therefore not be strictly simple harmonic, because the force directed towards A is not proportional to the distance from A. But if β does not exceed a few degrees, β and $\sin \beta$ differ by a very small amount, and on substituting β for $\sin \beta$ the force on B perpendicular to OB is $mg\beta$. Also arc AB is βl;

$$\therefore \text{ force for unit displacement} = \frac{mg\beta}{\beta l} = \frac{mg}{l}$$
$$= \mu.$$

Hence it is seen that the time of vibration of the pendulum is $2\pi\sqrt{\dfrac{ml}{mg}}$ (from p. 88); that is, $T = 2\pi\sqrt{\dfrac{l}{g}}$.

The simple pendulum affords a method of measuring g, but it is not very accurate on account of the fact that it is impossible to obtain a point mass and the thread is not weightless. Also the point of suspension is not very definite.

The student should construct a simple pendulum consisting of a fine thread with a spherical lead weight attached. If the thread is supported by clamping between two wooden blocks, as in Fig. 61, the length l may be measured from the point where the thread leaves the blocks to the centre of the bob. On giving the bob a small displacement, 50 or 100 oscillations may be counted and timed by a stop-watch, to find T. The time of the bob passing the lowest point of its path and travelling in the same direction should be taken as the beginning of each swing.

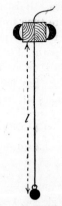

FIG. 61.—EXPERIMENT WITH SIMPLE PENDULUM.

When the results have been tabulated, T should be plotted against l, when a parabola will be obtained. On plotting T^2

against l a straight line should be obtained, whose slope is $\frac{g}{4\pi^2}$. g can then be calculated.

Using one length of thread, determinations of T should be made for various arcs of swing. It will be found that when the arc is large, T is not independent of the arc.

Compound pendulum.—A rigid body suspended by a horizontal axis such as a knife edge will vibrate in the same manner as a simple pendulum, and it is necessary now to find its time of vibration. If O is the axis (Fig. 62) and G the centre of gravity, the rest position is with G vertically under O. On displacing the body through angle β, there will be a couple $mgl \sin \beta$ tending to restore it to its original position, where $l = $ OG and m is the mass of the body. This couple will produce an angular acceleration $\frac{d^2\beta}{dt^2}$, and is expressible in the form $I\frac{d^2\beta}{dt^2}$, where I is the moment of inertia of the body about the axis of rotation O. Since the restoring couple is always in the opposite direction to β,

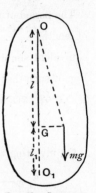

$$I\frac{d^2\beta}{dt^2} = -mgl \sin \beta,$$

or

$$I\frac{d^2\beta}{dt^2} + mgl \sin \beta = 0.$$

FIG. 62.—COMPOUND PENDULUM.

For small values of β the same approximation may be used as on p. 94, that is, β is written for $\sin \beta$, and thus,

$$\frac{d^2\beta}{dt^2} + \frac{mgl}{I}\beta = 0.$$

This equation, with different constants, was solved on p. 87, and a comparison shows that

$$\beta = a \sin \sqrt{\frac{mgl}{I}}\, t,$$

and the periodic time T is given by

$$T = 2\pi \sqrt{\frac{I}{mgl}}.$$

Writing I_g for the moment of inertia about the centre of gravity G,

$$I = I_g + ml^2, \quad \text{(p. 69)}$$

and

$$I_g = mk^2,$$

where k is the radius of gyration about G,

$$T = 2\pi \sqrt{\frac{mk^2 + ml^2}{mlg}}$$

$$= 2\pi \sqrt{\frac{k^2 + l^2}{lg}}.$$

The period of vibration is thus the same as for a simple pendulum of length $\dfrac{k^2 + l^2}{l}$. Since k^2 is always greater than zero, this length of equivalent simple pendulum is greater than l. Take a point O_1 in Fig. 62 such that $OO_1 = \dfrac{k^2 + l^2}{l}$, then O_1 is called the **centre of oscillation**. If $O_1G = l_1$, $OO_1 = l + l_1$, and

$$T = 2\pi \sqrt{\frac{l + l_1}{g}}.$$

On inverting the pendulum and suspending it from O_1, the time

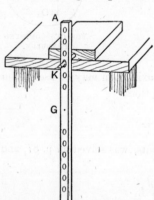

FIG. 63.—BAR PENDULUM.

of vibration is $2\pi \sqrt{\dfrac{k^2 + l_1{}^2}{l_1 g}}$. But $\dfrac{k^2 + l^2}{l} = l + l_1$, or $k^2 = ll_1$. Thus the time of vibration is

$$2\pi \sqrt{\frac{ll_1 + l_1{}^2}{l_1 g}} = 2\pi \sqrt{\frac{l + l_1}{g}}.$$

That is, the time of vibration is the same, whether the body is suspended from O or O_1; i.e. the centres of suspension and oscillation are interchangeable, and T is the time of vibration of a simple pendulum of length $l + l_1$.

Bar pendulum.—A simple and convenient form of compound pendulum consists of a brass bar AB (Fig. 63). Holes are drilled in the bar, so that it may rest on the knife edge K. These holes are symmetrically arranged about the mid-point G of the bar. The time of vibration, for the bar resting with each hole from A to G, upon the knife edge, is found. It is not necessary to take the times with the bar inverted and the holes from G to B employed, because of the symmetry of the holes with respect to the centre of gravity of the bar. When the times of vibration have been obtained they are plotted against the distance of the knife edge from the end A of the bar. A curve such as ABC (Fig. 64) is obtained. The periodic time de-

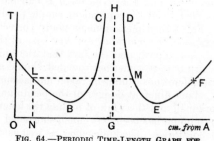

FIG. 64.—PERIODIC TIME-LENGTH GRAPH FOR
BAR PENDULUM.

creases at first and then increases, becoming infinite as the mid-point G of the bar is reached.

The branch DEF is then drawn symmetrically about the line GH, which corresponds to the middle of the bar. If then a horizontal line LM is drawn to cut both branches of the curve, the length LM is the length of simple pendulum which would have the time of vibration LN, and g may be calculated from the relation

$$T = 2\pi\sqrt{\frac{l+l'}{g}},$$ where $l+l' = $ LM and $T = $ LN. It is

well not to use points near B and E, because it is difficult to decide exactly the length of LM between the intercepts. Also it should be noted that points such as L and F may not be used because, owing to the symmetry of the bar, L and F are, for the purpose of calculation, the same point.

Kater's pendulum.—The principle of the reversible pendulum was employed by Kater in 1817. Two knife edges A and B (Fig. 65) are fixed to a bar in such a way that the pendulum may be suspended from either A or B. The heavy bob C is fixed to the bar, but the two weights D and E can slide along and may be clamped to it. The larger weight D ensures that the centre of mass of the pendulum lies between A and B. It is moved to various positions, until one is found for which the periodic time of the pendulum is nearly the same when suspended from either A or B. The fine

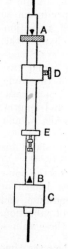

FIG. 65.—KATER'S
PENDULUM.

adjustment is made by moving the smaller weight E by means of a micrometer screw, until the times of swing are as nearly equal as is attainable. The distance between the edges of A and B is measured and the value of g is calculated, using this distance as the length of the equivalent simple pendulum.

For refined measurement many corrections must be made. For example, the buoyancy and viscosity of the air, the want of rigidity of the support, and the fact that the knife edges are not perfectly sharp but are somewhat rounded, should all be allowed for, but these considerations cannot be taken into account here.

Many different designs of the pendulum have been used since the original, and the work of finding the length of the equivalent simple pendulum has been very much shortened by a device found in many laboratories. The knife edges, as well as a heavy bob, are adjustable in position. Then by movement of the bob, a position may be found for which the time of oscillation is roughly the same for suspension about each knife edge. A further adjustment may be made by moving one of the knife edges, the appropriate direction being determined by noticing whether the period is greater with the bob at the top or the bottom. For example, in Fig. 65, a displacement of A towards the centre of gravity will shorten the period when the pendulum is suspended from A much more than it will when the pendulum is suspended from B. When equality is very nearly attained, a position may be found for which a slight displacement of A changes the longer period from the upright to the inverted position. Four readings of the time are then made, two before displacing A and two

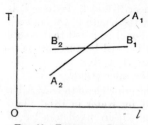

FIG. 66.—FINDING OF PERIOD OF VIBRATION OF KATER'S PENDULUM.

after, the distance between the knife edges being measured in each case. On plotting these periods and lengths (Fig. 66) to a very large scale, A_1 and A_2 being the lengths and times for oscillation about A, and similarly for B, and joining A_1A_2 and B_1B_2 the intersection of these lines gives the point whose coordinates are the length of the equivalent simple pendulum and its corresponding period of vibration. g may be calculated from these values.

EXAMPLE.—Describe, with the help of a rough graph, how the time period of oscillation of a uniform bar pendulum will vary as the point of suspension is moved from one end of the bar to the other.

Prove that the time period of oscillation of a thin, circular hoop, about an axis through the circumference and perpendicular to the plane of the hoop, is the same as that of a simple pendulum of length equal to the diameter of the hoop.   J.M.B.H.S.C.

For the answer to the first part, see p. 97.

If m is the mass of the hoop and r its radius, the moment of inertia about its centre, the axis being perpendicular to its plane, is mr^2. Hence I about a point in the circumference is $mr^2 + mr^2 = 2mr^2$.

Then
$$T = 2\pi\sqrt{\frac{I}{mgl}} \quad \text{(p. 95)}$$

$$= 2\pi\sqrt{\frac{2mr^2}{mgr}}$$

$$= 2\pi\sqrt{\frac{2r}{g}}.$$

That is, the period of oscillation is the same as that of a simple pendulum of length $2r$.

Torsional vibration.—A very important example of simple harmonic motion is that of a body suspended by a wire. If the body is given a rotation with the wire as axis, it will vibrate in a horizontal plane. When one end of a wire is fixed and the other end rotated through an angle θ, the twist in the wire produces a restoring couple proportional to θ for quite large angles of twist, provided that the wire is fairly thin (see p. 141). Calling this couple $c\theta$, c is the couple for one radian twist. Then if I is the moment of inertia of the suspended body, $I\dfrac{d^2\theta}{dt^2}$ is the couple acting on it (p. 64), and the equation of motion is found as on p. 95 :

$$I\frac{d^2\theta}{dt^2} + c\theta = 0;$$

solving it as before,

$$\theta = \theta_0 \sin\sqrt{\frac{c}{I}}\,t,$$

where θ_0 is the angular amplitude of vibration, and

$$T = 2\pi\sqrt{\frac{I}{c}}.$$

The great importance of this type of motion lies in the fact that moments of inertia may be compared. In making the measurements, a wire AB (Fig. 67) is used, soldered above to a piece of thick wire held by a clamp, and soldered below to a lug and screw shown at C.

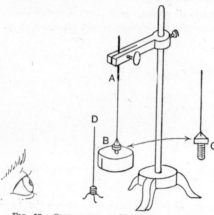

FIG. 67.—COMPARISON OF MOMENTS OF INERTIA.

One of the bodies is suspended by screwing C into it, and a rod D is placed near the body. The eye, or a telescope, is moved about until D appears in line with some feature of the suspended body. A mark may be placed on it if necessary. The body is now given a twist and released. The times of the first and last passages for, say, 100 oscillations are observed, as described on p. 94. The time T_1 of one oscillation is thus found.

The body is then replaced by the second, and T_2 found in the same way. If I_1 and I_2 are the respective moments of inertia of the bodies,

$$T_1 = 2\pi\sqrt{\frac{I_1}{c}} \quad \text{and} \quad T_2 = 2\pi\sqrt{\frac{I_2}{c}};$$

$$\therefore \frac{I_1}{I_2} = \frac{T_1^2}{T_2^2}.$$

It should be noticed that the amplitude of oscillation need not be small, as in the case of the pendulum, because the restoring couple is proportional to θ, up to large values of θ. Also that the small moment of inertia of the support C (Fig. 67) has been neglected; but this is justified when fairly large moments of inertia are being compared.

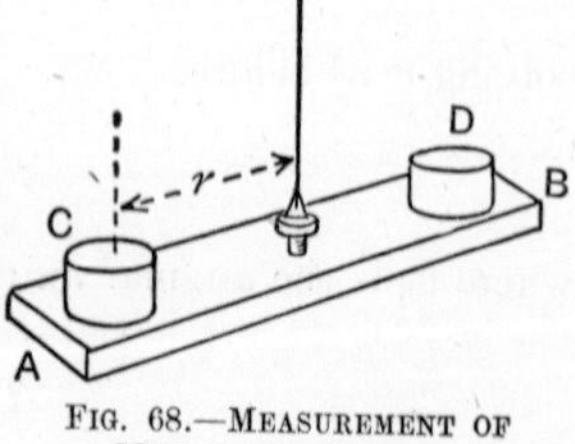

Absolute Determination of moment of inertia.—When the actual value of the moment of inertia of a body is required, it may be possible to calculate it from its mass and shape when the body is of regular form. But in any case the

FIG. 68.—MEASUREMENT OF MOMENT OF INERTIA.

moment of inertia can be found experimentally by adding to the body another of known moment of inertia. Consider a bar AB (Fig. 68), or body of any shape, upon which two cylinders may be placed symmetrically as at C and D. The mass of each cylinder being m and its radius a, the moment of inertia of each about its own axis is $\frac{1}{2}ma^2$, and about the suspension wire as axis is $\frac{1}{2}ma^2 + mr^2$. The moment of inertia of the two together is thus

$$ma^2 + 2mr^2 = m(a^2 + 2r^2) = I_1.$$

If I is the moment of inertia of AB and its supporting lug, the total moment of inertia when the cylinders are in place is $I + I_1$.

The times of vibration of the system are found with the cylinders in place (T_1) and with the cylinders removed (T_2).

Then
$$T_1 = 2\pi\sqrt{\frac{I + I_1}{c}},$$

$$T_2 = 2\pi\sqrt{\frac{I}{c}};$$

$$\therefore \frac{I + I_1}{I} = \frac{T_1^2}{T_2^2},$$

$$\frac{I_1}{I} = \frac{T_1^2 - T_2^2}{T_2^2},$$

and
$$I = I_1 \frac{T_2^2}{T_1^2 - T_2^2}.$$

If the cylinders are moved and a third body or pair of bodies of moment of inertia I_2 be placed on the bar with its horizontal balance preserved, and the time of oscillation T_3 is observed,

$$T_3 = 2\pi\sqrt{\frac{I + I_2}{c}};$$

$$\therefore \frac{T_2^2}{T_3^2} = \frac{I}{I + I_2},$$

$$\frac{T_2^2}{T_3^2 - T_2^2} = \frac{I}{I_2},$$

and
$$I_2 = I \frac{T_3^2 - T_2^2}{T_2^2}.$$

so that
$$I_2 = I_1 \frac{T_3^2 - T_2^2}{T_1^2 - T_2^2}.$$

Conical pendulum.—If a body in the form of a simple pendulum is given such a motion that the bob describes a horizontal circle of

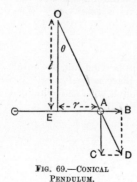

FIG. 69.—CONICAL
PENDULUM.

radius r (Fig. 69) with circumferential velocity v, the centrifugal force AB will be $\dfrac{mv^2}{r}$ and the weight AC is mg. The resultant of these, AD, must act along the string.

Then

$$\frac{CD}{AC} = \frac{AE}{OE} = \frac{r}{l} = \tan\theta,$$

$$\frac{mv^2}{rmg} = \tan\theta,$$

$$v^2 = rg\tan\theta,$$

$$v = \sqrt{rg\tan\theta}.$$

The time T of one travel round the circle is

$$\frac{2\pi r}{v} = 2\pi \frac{r}{\sqrt{rg\tan\theta}}.$$

$$\therefore T = 2\pi\sqrt{\frac{r}{g\tan\theta}}$$

$$= 2\pi\sqrt{\frac{l}{g}}.$$

That is, the periodic time is that of a simple pendulum of length l equal to the axial height of the cone. If θ is very small l becomes very nearly the length of the string, and the periodic time is nearly independent of θ, so that the period is the same whether the path of the bob of the pendulum is circular or linear.

Representation by sine curve.—The projection of a uniformly rotating vector on any straight line is a simple harmonic motion (p. 90). If the axis OY is chosen as the straight line and OA (Fig. 70) the rotating vector, then $y = AP = a_1 \sin\omega t$, where angle AOP is ωt. On plotting angles $0°$ to $360°$ along the axis of X, and at each appropriate angle erecting the ordinate equal to $y = a_1 \sin\omega t$, the sine curve CDE is obtained. This curve goes through a cycle while OA makes one revolution. This method of representation lends itself very well to the study of combined simple harmonic motions.

Combination of simple harmonic motions.—When two simple harmonic motions take place in the same direction about the same point, the resultant displacement is the sum of the separate displacements. If, in addition, the periods of the separate motions are the same, there may still be a difference in their phases and amplitudes.

If the two are represented by the projection of the vectors OA and OB (Fig. 70) on the axis of Y, then the first has equation

$$y = a_1 \sin \omega t,$$

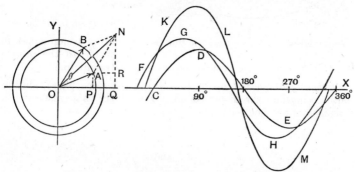

FIG. 70.—SINE CURVES OF SIMPLE HARMONIC MOTION.

where $\omega t = $ AOP, and the second has equation $y = a_2 \sin(\omega t + \theta)$, where $\omega t + \theta = $ BOP. The sine curve for the first oscillation may be plotted in the form CDE, and for the second oscillation the curve is FGH.

On adding ordinates, the curve KLM is obtained, and this is the same as would have been obtained if the resultant ON of the rotating vectors OA and OB had been found and the sine curve for the rotation on ON had been plotted. For, NQ is equal to the projection of ON upon OY, and,

$$NQ = AP + NR$$
$$= a_1 \sin \omega t + a_2 \sin(\omega t + \theta).$$

Thus if two simple harmonic motions in the same direction are combined, the rotating vectors which define them may be added by the ordinary law of vector addition (p. 3). It also follows that a simple harmonic motion may be resolved into two, since its rotating vector may be resolved into two, as on p. 11, each component vector giving rise to a simple harmonic motion.

Harmonic motions at right angles.—When the motions take place at right angles to each other, the body describes a curve in the plane containing the two motions. If one of the oscillations is in the line OX (Fig. 71) its equation may be written

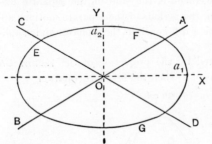

$$x = a_1 \sin (\omega t + \theta_1),$$

and if the other is parallel to OY its equation may be written

$$y = a_2 \sin (\omega t + \theta_2),$$

FIG. 71.—COMBINED SIMPLE HARMONIC MOTIONS. x and y being equal in magnitude to the projections of two rotating vectors on a single straight line.

If $\theta_1 = \theta_2 = 0$ the two oscillations are in the same phase, and for both oscillations the displacement is zero at the same instant. At this instant the body actually passes through O.   Then

$$x = a_1 \sin \omega t \quad \text{and} \quad y = a_2 \sin \omega t ;$$

$$\therefore \frac{x}{a_1} = \frac{y}{a_2}, \quad \text{and} \quad \frac{x}{y} = \frac{a_1}{a_2}.$$

This is the equation of the line AB, which is the path of the body.

If $\theta_1 = 0$ and $\theta_2 = \pi$, the phases of the two vibrations differ by 180° and

$$x = a_1 \sin \omega t \quad \text{and} \quad y = - a_2 \sin \omega t ;$$

$$\therefore \frac{x}{y} = - \frac{a_1}{a_2},$$

and the path of the body is the line CD.

Again, if $\theta_1 = 0$ and $\theta_2 = \frac{\pi}{2}$,

$$x = a_1 \sin \omega t, \quad \text{and} \quad y = a_2 \sin \left(\omega t + \frac{\pi}{2} \right)$$

$$= a_2 \cos \omega t ;$$

$$\therefore \frac{x^2}{a_1{}^2} + \frac{y^2}{a_2{}^2} = \sin^2 \omega t + \cos^2 \omega t$$

$$= 1.$$

The path of the body is then the ellipse EFG, and the direction of motion of the body round the ellipse is clockwise.   This may be seen from the fact that for the right-hand half of the figure x is positive and $\sin \omega t$ is positive. But $y = a_2 \cos \omega t$, and $\dfrac{dy}{dt} = -\omega a_2 \sin \omega t$, so that $\dfrac{dy}{dt}$ is negative. This means that the velocity of y is directed downwards in the figure.

Again, if $\theta_1 = 0$ and $\theta_2 = -\dfrac{\pi}{2}$,

$$y = a_2 \sin \left(\omega t - \frac{\pi}{2} \right)$$

$$= -a_2 \cos \omega t.$$

The figure is still the ellipse, but the travel of the body is anti-clockwise around it.

If, in addition, $a_1 = a_2$, the equation of the figure is $x^2 + y^2 = a_1{}^2$ and the figure is a circle.

Thus two simple harmonic motions compound into a straight line motion when they have the same phase, and into an ellipse or circle when the phases differ by $\dfrac{\pi}{2}$.

For any other difference in phase the motion is still an ellipse, but its major and minor axes are inclined to the directions of the component vibrations.

Its equation may be found by resolving the first simple harmonic motion into two components, one in phase with, and the other component 90° in phase from, the second simple harmonic motion. By combining the two in phase a linear motion results, and this combined with the component whose phase is 90° from it results in an elliptical motion. The axes of the ellipse are no longer the same as the original axes.

EXERCISES ON CHAPTER IV

SIMPLE HARMONIC MOTION AND SIMPLE PENDULUM

1. Explain what is meant by simple harmonic motion. Obtain an expression for the relation between the velocity and the displacement for such motion.

A vertical spiral spring of negligible mass supports a heavy particle which stretches it through a length L cm. Show that the period of the vertical oscillations of the system is the same as the period of a simple pendulum of length L cm.   O. & C.H.S.C.

2. Find an expression for the period of a simple pendulum, and give the condition under which the period is independent of the amplitude.

If a seconds pendulum is increased 1 per cent. in length, how many beats will it lose in a day ?   C.W.B.H.S.C.

3. Prove that the time of a small oscillation of a simple pendulum of length l is $2\pi\sqrt{(l/g)}$.

If the time of oscillation is 20 sec., find the length of the pendulum ; and if the velocity of the bob at its lowest position is 2 ft. per second, find the amplitude of the swing.   C.W.B.H.S.C.

4. Define *simple harmonic motion*, and obtain the relation between the velocity and the displacement from the mean position in such a motion.

A particle describing simple harmonic motion executes 100 complete vibrations per minute, and its speed at its mean position is 15 feet per second. What is the length of its path ?

What is its velocity when it is half-way between its mean position and an extremity of its path ?   C.W.B.H.S.C.

5. A mass of 12 lb. is suspended from a fixed point by a light spring. In the position of equilibrium the spring is extended 6 inches. The mass is then pulled down a further 4 inches, and released from rest. Find the time of a complete oscillation, and find the greatest kinetic energy of the mass.   C.H.S.C.

6. Define the *frequency* and *phase* of a simple harmonic motion.

A particle is moving in a straight line with simple harmonic motion. Its velocity has the values 5 ft./sec. and 4 ft./sec. when its distances from the centre point of its motion are 2 ft. and 3 ft. respectively. Find the length of the path, the frequency of the oscillation, and the phase of the motion when the point is at the distance 2 ft. from the centre.   L.H.S.C.

7. A particle moves in a straight line with simple harmonic motion of period $2\pi/n$ and amplitude a. Show that the velocity of the particle at a distance x from the middle point of the path is $n\sqrt{(a^2 - x^2)}$.

A particle, moving in a straight line with simple harmonic motion of period $2\pi/n$ about a centre O, is observed to have a velocity $bn\sqrt{3}$ when at a distance b from O. If the particle is moving away from O at that instant, show that it will travel a further distance b in time $\pi/3n$ before coming to rest.   J.M.B.H.S.C.

8. The space-time equation for a simple harmonic motion is

$$s = a \sin (pt + \beta).$$

Prove that the velocity v and the acceleration f at any instant of the motion are connected by the equation

$$p^2v^2 + f^2 = a^2p^4.$$

Hence or otherwise prove that if at any stage of the motion the kinetic energy is suddenly increased by a blow in the ratio $1 + \alpha : 1$, the amplitude of the swing is increased in the ratio

$$\sqrt{1 + \frac{\alpha v^2}{a^2 p^2} : 1}.$$

    C.W.B.H.S.C.

9. A particle moves with simple harmonic motion ; if its velocities at distances of 4 feet and 5 feet from the centre are 13 feet per second and 5 feet per second respectively, find the period and amplitude.

The motion of a particle is compounded of a simple harmonic motion along the x-axis and a simple harmonic motion, with the same centre and of the same period, along the y-axis, the amplitude of the latter being twice that of the former and its phase one quarter of a period different. Show that the path of the particle is an ellipse and that the maximum velocity is twice the minimum velocity. C.H.S.C.

10. Explain how the period of small oscillations of a simple pendulum depends on the length of the pendulum and the acceleration due to gravity.

A simple pendulum has a period of 4 seconds. After *shortening* the pendulum by one metre, its period is found to be 3·46 seconds. Calculate the value of the acceleration due to gravity. Lond. Int. Sc.

COMPOUND PENDULUM

11. What are the characteristics of simple harmonic motion ?

Obtain from first principles an expression for the time of oscillation of a compound pendulum. How would you use such a pendulum to determine the acceleration due to gravity ? C.H.S.C.

12. What is meant by the moment of inertia of a body about an axis ? Show how the moment of inertia is related to the kinetic energy of a rotating rigid body and to its angular acceleration ?

A disc of radius a cm. oscillates as a pendulum about an axis perpendicular to the plane of the disc through a point $\dfrac{a}{2}$ from its centre. Calculate the periodic time. O.H.S.C.

13. Explain how the length of the simple pendulum which has the same period as a given compound pendulum may be found experimentally.

A uniform cube is free to turn about one edge which is horizontal. Find, in terms of a seconds' pendulum, the length of the edge of the cube so that it may execute a complete oscillation in 2 sec. C.W.B.H.S.C.

14. Discuss the conditions which determine the sensitivity of a balance. How is it that, in practice, the sensitivity of a balance is usually found to vary with the load ?

The beam of a balance weighs 150 gm. and its moment of inertia is 5000 gm.-cm.^{2}. Each arm of the balance is 10 cm. long. When set swinging the beam makes one complete oscillation in 6 seconds. How far is the centre of gravity of the beam below its point of support, and through what angle would the beam be deflected by a weight of one milligram placed in one of the scale pans ? C.H.S.C.

15. A uniform thin rod AB of mass m and length l can rotate in a vertical plane about A as a pendulum. A particle of mass $2m$ is also fixed on the rod at a distance x from A. Find x so that the periodic time of a small swing may be a minimum. L.H.S.C.

16. Find the period of the small oscillations of a rigid body free to turn about a fixed horizontal axis, and also find a formula for the length of the equivalent simple pendulum.

Three particles of the same mass m are fixed to a uniform circular hoop of mass M and radius a at the corners of an equilateral triangle. The hoop is free to move in a vertical plane about the point on the circumference opposite to one of the masses m. Prove that the equivalent simple pendulum is equal in length to the diameter of the circle.   L.H.S.C.

17. A simple pendulum consists of a light rod of length l suspended at one end, and carrying a particle of mass m at the other end. Find the period of small oscillations.

If a second particle of the same mass can be attached to the rod at any point, show that for every position of this second particle, except at the ends, the period of the small oscillations of the resulting pendulum will be shorter than that of the original pendulum.

Find the value of the shortest possible period of small oscillations.

J.M.B.H.S.C.

18. Show that, when a rigid body is allowed to swing about a fixed horizontal axis, the motion is the same as that of a simple pendulum of a suitable length.

A uniform square lamina of side $2a$ is hung up by one corner and swings in its own plane, which is vertical. Find the length of the equivalent simple pendulum.   C.H.S.C.

19. A heavy rigid body, of mass M, is swinging freely about a fixed horizontal axis which is distant h from G, the centre of mass of the body. The moment of inertia of the body about an axis through G, parallel to the axis of suspension, is Mk^2. Compare the motion of the heavy body with that of a simple pendulum, and, if the oscillations are small, find the period.

Find the moment of inertia of a uniform rectangular lamina of sides $2a$, $2b$ about an axis through its centre of mass, perpendicular to the lamina. Obtain the period of the swing when the oscillations are small, if the lamina swings in its own vertical plane about the mid-point of one of its shorter sides $(b < a)$.   L.H.S.C.

20. Give the theory of Kater's pendulum and find an expression for the acceleration of gravity in terms of two nearly equal periods of oscillation about the two parallel knife edges.

Indicate the sources of error in an experimental determination of " g."

Lond. B.Sc.

CHAPTER V

GRAVITATION

Historical.—Up to the time of Galileo, it was thought that heavy bodies fall more rapidly than light ones. He showed that bodies all fall at the same rate, apart, of course, from air friction. The significance of this fact was not seen at the time, but really it proves that the weight of a body is proportional to its mass. For if all bodies have the same acceleration when falling freely, and acceleration $=\dfrac{\text{force}}{\text{mass}}$; it follows that the force, in this case gravitational force, is proportional to the mass. Then followed the observations of the motion of the planets by Tycho Brahe, from which observations Kepler deduced definite laws, the most important of which is that the planets move in ellipses round the sun, which is situated at one focus of the ellipses. The reason for Kepler's laws was unknown, and it remained for Sir Isaac Newton to show that they are consistent with the fact that every particle of matter attracts every other particle of matter with a force which varies directly as the product of the masses of the particles and inversely as the square of the distance between them.

The fact that Newton showed that the moon is attracted by the earth with a force which is in accordance with this law has already been referred to (p. 79).

Constant of gravitation.—So long as the bodies may be considered as points, the attraction between them is easily calculated. If m_1 and m_2 are the masses of two point bodies and d is the distance between them, then according to Newton's law the force on each is proportional to $\dfrac{m_1 m_2}{d^2}$. This proportionality may be expressed as follows :

$$\text{force of attraction} = \mathsf{G}\,\frac{m_1 m_2}{d^2}\,.$$

109

The quantity G is a constant for any system of units employed, and its experimental determination will be described (p. 115). It is known as the constant of gravitation.

Potential.—If the distribution of matter in any system is known, it is possible to find the gravitational force on any body due to this distribution. If the body has unit mass, the force on it is called the strength of gravitational field at the point. It is possible to calculate the gravitational field at every point of the system, but the calculation may be difficult. The process may be simplified very much by considering a new quantity defined by the equation, $F = \dfrac{dV}{dx}$, where F is the gravitational field at a point and V is a quantity called the gravitational potential at the point. The equation may be expressed in words : the gravitational field at any point is the rate of change with distance of the gravitational potential.

The difference in potential between two points is the work done on account of gravitational force, when a unit mass moves from one point to another.

Thus $F = \dfrac{dV}{dx}$ may be written $dV = F\,dx$. $F\,dx$ is the work done for the infinitesimal displacement dx. If then a unit mass moves from a point A to a point B, $\displaystyle\int_A^B F\,dx = V_B - V_A$, where V_B is the potential at B and V_A that at A.

If there is no other force than the gravitational force acting on the unit mass, the work $\displaystyle\int_A^B F\,dx$ is converted into kinetic energy. If the velocity of the body when at point A is v_A, and that when at B is v_B, the change in kinetic energy in passing from A to B is $\frac{1}{2}v_B^2 - \frac{1}{2}v_A^2$. If then the potential is a measure of the potential energy of the mass, the potential decreases when the kinetic energy increases, and the sum of the two must be constant ;

$$\therefore \quad \tfrac{1}{2}v_A^2 + V_A = \tfrac{1}{2}v_B^2 + V_B = \text{Const.},$$

or $$\tfrac{1}{2}v_A^2 - \tfrac{1}{2}v_B^2 = V_B - V_A.$$

Potential due to a point mass m.—If the mass m is situated at O (Fig. 72) and a unit mass is placed at P, the force on the unit mass is directed towards O and its value is $\dfrac{Gm}{x^2}$. If the unit mass travels from B to A in the direction of this force, its kinetic energy increases and the potential decreases.

$$\text{Work done} = \int_B^A \frac{Gm}{x^2}\, dx$$

$$= -\left[\frac{Gm}{x}\right]_B^A$$

$$= -Gm\left(\frac{1}{a} - \frac{1}{b}\right),$$

and this is the difference of potential between A and B.

At an infinite distance from O, the gravitational force due to m is zero, and the work done in moving a mass about at infinity is zero,

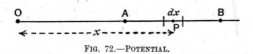

FIG. 72.—POTENTIAL.

so that the potential at all points at infinity is the same. It is usual to take this potential as zero, and the potential of A reckoned from this zero is found by putting $b = \infty$;

$$\therefore \text{ potential at } A = -\frac{Gm}{a}.$$

Thus gravitational potential is an essentially negative quantity because it is zero at infinity and decreases in travelling from infinity towards an attracting mass.

Potential due to hollow spherical shell.—Consider the point P near a uniform hollow shell whose mass is σ per unit area of surface and whose radius is a. Join OP (Fig. 73 (a)) and draw a slice QR so that the element of circumference at Q or R subtends an angle $d\theta$ at O. Then the area of the slice is $2\pi a \sin\theta \cdot a\, d\theta = 2\pi a^2 \sin\theta\, d\theta$, and its mass is $2\pi a^2 \sigma \sin\theta \cdot d\theta$, if the slice is very thin. Also let AP $= r$.

Since every point of the slice is at distance r from P, the potential at P due to the slice is

$$\frac{2\pi Ga^2\sigma \sin\theta \cdot d\theta}{r},$$

omitting, for a moment, the negative sign.

The element AB is drawn on a larger scale in Fig. 73 (*b*). AD is drawn parallel to OP, BC perpendicular to PA. C, D are joined. Remem-

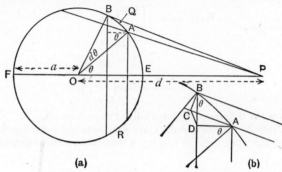

FIG. 73.—POTENTIAL DUE TO SPHERICAL SHELL.

bering that AB is really very small, it may be taken as a straight line and $AC = dr$. Since $\widehat{BCA}$ and $\widehat{BDA}$ are right angles, ABCD is a cyclic quadrilateral, and therefore $\widehat{ABD} = \widehat{ACD} = \theta$. Also $\widehat{CAD} = \widehat{APO}$ (*a*), so that triangle ADC in (*b*) is similar to PAO in (*a*) ;

$$\therefore \frac{OP}{AP} = \frac{AC}{AD}.$$

Now $AB = a\,d\theta$; $\therefore AD = a \sin \theta . d\theta$, and $AC = dr$;

$$\therefore \frac{d}{r} = \frac{dr}{a \sin \theta . d\theta}, \quad \text{or} \quad \frac{a \sin \theta . d\theta}{r} = \frac{dr}{d},$$

and the potential at P due to the slice,

$$\frac{2\pi G\sigma a^2 \sin \theta . d\theta}{r}, \text{ becomes } \frac{2\pi G\sigma a\, dr}{d}.$$

Since every term is constant except dr, the potential due to the whole sphere is

$$\frac{2\pi G\sigma a}{d} \int_{r=EP}^{r=FP} dr = \frac{2\pi G\sigma a}{d} . 2a = \frac{4\pi a^2 \sigma G}{d}.$$

But the mass m of the sphere is $4\pi a^2 \sigma$;

$$\therefore \text{ potential due to sphere is } \frac{Gm}{d}.$$

That is, the potential is the same as though the mass of the sphere were concentrated at its centre.

The geometrical part of the above proof may be avoided by noting that in Fig. 73

$$r^2 = a^2 + d^2 - 2ad \cos \theta ;$$

$$\therefore \ 2r \, dr = 0 + 0 + 2ad \sin \theta \, d\theta,$$

or

$$\frac{dr}{a \sin \theta \, d\theta} = \frac{d}{r} .$$

If P is situated at E, the potential is given by

$$\frac{2\pi G \sigma a}{d} \int_0^{2a} dr = \frac{2\pi G \sigma a}{d} . 2a$$

$$= \frac{4\pi a^2 G \sigma}{d} .$$

and since $d = a$;

$$\therefore \ V = \frac{Gm}{a} .$$

Again, if P is situated inside the sphere,

$$V = \frac{2\pi G \sigma a}{d} \int_{(a-d)}^{(a+d)} dr .$$

The lower limit is $+ (a-d)$ and not $- (a-d)$, because r increases continuously in the travel from E to F ;

$$\therefore \ V = \frac{2\pi G \sigma a}{d}(a+d-a+d) = \frac{2\pi G \sigma a}{d} \ (2d)$$

$$= \frac{4\pi G \sigma a^2}{a} = \frac{Gm}{a} ,$$

or, restoring the negative sign (p. 111),

$$V = - \frac{Gm}{a} ;$$

It is therefore the same at all points inside the spherical shell. Hence, since $F = \dfrac{dV}{dx}$ and V is constant, $\dfrac{dV}{dx} = 0$, and the field in the interior of a spherical shell, due to the shell, is zero.

Potential due to a solid sphere.—If the sphere consists of a material of density ρ, its mass m is $\frac{4}{3}\pi a^3 \rho$. It may be considered as a number of infinitely thin concentric shells, and each of these will produce a potential at P (Fig. 74), as though its mass were concentrated at O. The potential at P due to the whole sphere is the sum of the potentials due to the separate shells, and is therefore $\dfrac{Gm}{d}$.

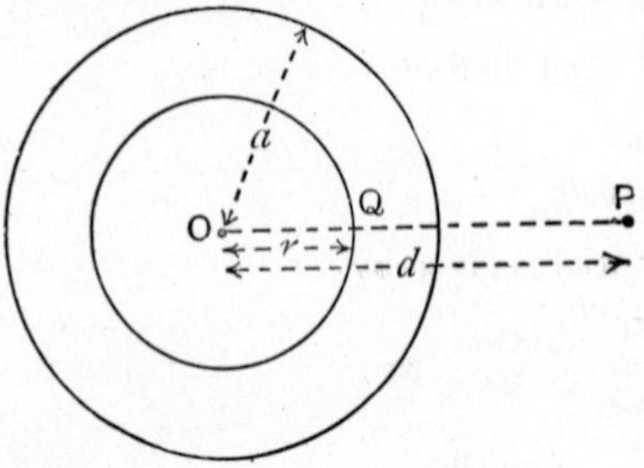

At an internal point such as Q, the potential due to the sphere of radius $OQ = r$ is

$$G\tfrac{4}{3}\frac{\pi r^3 \rho}{r} = \tfrac{4}{3}\pi r^2 \rho G.$$

FIG. 74.—SOLID SPHERE.

Imagine the remaining part of the sphere to be split up into concentric shells of radius x and thickness dx. The mass of one shell is $4\pi x^2 \rho\, dx$, and the potential it produces within itself is

$$\frac{G \cdot 4\pi \rho x^2 dx}{x} \quad \text{(p. 113),}$$

that is, $G \cdot 4\pi \rho x\, dx$. The potential at Q due to all these shells is therefore

$$\int_r^a G \cdot 4\pi \rho x\, dx = G \cdot 4\pi \rho \left[\frac{x^2}{2}\right]_r^a = G \cdot 4\pi \rho \left(\frac{a^2}{2} - \frac{r^2}{2}\right) = G \cdot \tfrac{4}{3}\pi \rho \left(\frac{3a^2}{2} - \frac{3r^2}{2}\right).$$

The total potential is therefore

$$G \cdot \tfrac{4}{3}\pi \rho \left(r^2 + \frac{3a^2}{2} - \frac{3r^2}{2}\right) = G \cdot \tfrac{4}{3}\pi \rho \left(\frac{3a^2 - r^2}{2}\right) = G \cdot \tfrac{4}{3}\pi a^3 \rho \left(\frac{3a^2 - r^2}{2a^3}\right)$$

$$= Gm\left(\frac{3a^2 - r^2}{2a^3}\right);$$

or, remembering the negative sign (p. 111),

$$\text{potential} = -Gm\left(\frac{3a^2 - r^2}{2a^3}\right).$$

Gravitational field due to solid sphere.—Having established that the potential outside a sphere is the same as though the mass of the sphere were concentrated at its centre, it follows that the same assumption may be applied to the gravitational field. This field may, however, be obtained by direct differentiation of the potential. Since $F = \dfrac{dV}{dx}$, and $V = -\dfrac{Gm}{x}$,

$$F = \frac{d}{dx}\left(-\frac{Gm}{x}\right) = \frac{Gm}{x^2}.$$

Inside the sphere, at distance x from the centre,

$$F = \frac{d}{dx}\left(-\mathsf{G}m\,\frac{3a^2 - x^2}{2a^3} \right)$$

$$= \frac{x\mathsf{G}m}{a^3}.$$

This varies from zero at the centre of the sphere, where $x=0$, to $\frac{\mathsf{G}m}{a^2}$ at the surface, where $x=a$.

Determination of G by Cavendish.—When two masses m_1 and m_2 situated a distance d apart exert a force f upon each other, then, if m_1, m_2, d and f can be measured, G is known from the relation $f = \mathsf{G}\frac{m_1 m_2}{d^2}$. The method was employed by Cavendish in 1798. He used two lead spheres A and B (Fig. 75), each 2 inches in diameter, suspended from a deal rod about 6 ft. long, and strengthened by two wires running from the ends to a vertical rod in the middle. The system is supported by a wire EF of silvered copper. This suspended system could then execute torsional oscillations of period $T = 2\pi\sqrt{\dfrac{I}{c}}$ (p. 99). T was about 7 minutes,

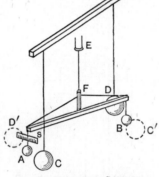

FIG. 75.—METHOD OF CAVENDISH FOR FINDING G.

so that it could be measured with considerable accuracy. I being known from a separate experiment (p. 100), c, the couple exerted by EF for one radian twist of the beam, is known.

Two lead spheres C and D, each 8 inches in diameter, are suspended so that their centres are in the same horizontal plane as those of A and B, and the distance d between the centres of A and C, B and D is known. There is then an attraction between A and C of value $\mathsf{G}\dfrac{m_1 m_2}{d^2}$, and a similar force between B and D. These two forces give rise to a couple of moment $2\mathsf{G}\dfrac{m_1 m_2}{d^2}l$, where l is half the length of the beam. If this couple produces an angular deflection of θ,

$$2\mathsf{G}\frac{m_1 m_2}{d^2}l = c\theta,$$

from which G can be calculated. The deflection is observed by means of the scale *s*, which is divided into twentieths of an inch. When one deflection has been observed, the spheres C and D, which are carried on a rotatable framework, are moved to the position C'D', giving a deflection in the reverse direction to the first. Half the difference between the first and last readings was used in finding θ. No attempt was made to allow the beam to come to rest, but in finding the position of rest three consecutive turning points were taken and the mean value found.

As the result of twenty-nine measurements, Cavendish found a mean value for G, which on the c.g.s. system is 6.562×10^{-8}.

Determination of G by Sir Charles Vernon Boys.—Many modifications of the Cavendish method have been made, but that of

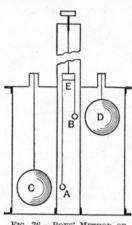

FIG. 76.—BOYS' METHOD OF FINDING G.

Boys in 1895, employing the same principle as Cavendish, eradicated most of the uncertainties of the earlier measurements. The attracting spheres CD (Fig. 76) are of lead and are $4\frac{1}{2}$ inches in diameter, and the attracted spheres AB are of gold and are 0·2 inch diameter. A and B are suspended from the sides of a mirror E, which acts as the torsion bar and also serves for measuring the deflection by means of a reflected beam of light. The mirror is suspended by a torsion fibre of fused quartz. This has great strength and almost perfect elastic properties. Its strength enables a very fine fibre to be used, so that great sensitiveness is obtained, even with a great reduction in size of the apparatus. This reduction in size produced a large decrease in the disturbance due to the movement of the air caused by temperature variation.

One of the uncertainties in the Cavendish apparatus is caused by the fact that each fixed ball attracts both the moveable ones. This effect is very much reduced in the Boys apparatus by arranging the pairs to be on different levels. The spheres C and D were always placed to exert maximum moment on the suspended system. The mean result was $G = 6.6576 \times 10^{-8}$.

Determination of G by Poynting.—The direct weighing of the attraction between two lead spheres by means of a balance has been made by several investigators; the best measurement is probably that of Poynting in 1893. The arrangement is shown diagrammatically in

Fig. 77. The attracting sphere C is of lead and weighs about 350 lb.
It is carried on a platform that can rotate about an axis O, so that the
sphere may be brought in turn
under either of the lead spheres
A or B, which weigh about 50 lb.
each. C is counterpoised on the
platform by the weight D, so that
the base of the instrument is not
disturbed when the platform is
rotated. The deflection of the
beam of the balance is so small
that it is magnified many times
by an optical arrangement, not
shown, attached to the pointer
of the balance. If θ_1 is the deflection produced by moving C
from the A to the B position and

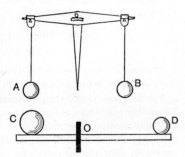

FIG. 77.—POYNTING'S METHOD OF
FINDING G.

l is the length of one arm of the balance, the couple for unit
deflection is $\dfrac{2G\,m_1 m_2\,l}{d^2\theta_1}$, where d is the vertical distance between the
centres of A and C, m_1 being the mass of A and m_2 that of C. The
balance is calibrated by moving a centigram rider a distance l_1 along
an arm of the balance, so producing a deflection θ_2. The couple for
unit deflection is thus $\dfrac{0\!\cdot\!01gl_1}{\theta_2}$. As these couples are equal,

$$\frac{2G\,m_1 m_2\,l}{d^2\theta_1} = \frac{0\!\cdot\!01gl_1}{\theta_2},$$

$$G = \frac{0\!\cdot\!01gl_1 d^2\theta_1}{2m_1 m_2 l\theta_2}.$$

The mean value obtained was $6\!\cdot\!6984 \times 10^{-8}$.

Density of the earth.—When the value of G is known, as well as
the gravitational acceleration of a body at the earth's surface, the
mean density of the earth can be found. For the force acting on a
mass m is mg dynes. It is also $\dfrac{GMm}{r^2}$ dynes, if M is the mass of the
earth. The volume of the earth is $\frac{4}{3}\pi r^3$ and $M = \frac{4}{3}\pi r^3\rho$, where ρ is its
mean density ;

$$\therefore \ \frac{4}{3}\frac{\pi r^3\rho G}{r^2} = g,$$

$$\rho = \frac{3g}{4\pi r G}.$$

This gives 5·448 gm. cm.$^{-3}$ from Cavendish's value for G, 5·5270 from Boys', and 5·4934 from Poynting's.

Later determinations have not improved much on these results, and the most probable values to date are

$$G = 6·6607 \times 10^{-8} \text{ c.g.s. units,}$$
$$\rho = 5·5247 \text{ gm. cm.}^{-3}.$$

EXAMPLE.—State the Law of Gravitation, and give a brief account of the facts which led to its discovery.

A spherical mass of 20 kgm., situated at the earth's surface, is attracted by another spherical mass of 150 kgm., with a force equal to the weight of 0·25 milligramme, when the centres of the masses are 30 cm. apart. Calculate, by the aid of this result, the approximate mass and mean density of the earth, assuming the earth's radius to be 6×10^8 cm.   C.W.B.H.S.C.

For answer to first part of question, see p. 109.

Force between spherical masses $= G \dfrac{m_1 m_2}{d^2}$

$$= G \frac{20000 \times 150000}{30^2}.$$

In the question, force $= 0·25 \times 0·001 \times g$;

$$\therefore \ 0·25 \times 0·001 \times g = G \frac{30 \times 10^8}{30^2} = G \frac{10^7}{3},$$
$$G = \frac{0·00025 \times g \times 3}{10^7}$$
$$= 7·5g10^{-11}.$$

If the earth has mass M :

Force on 1 gm. at surface $= G . \dfrac{M}{r^2} = g$;

$$\therefore \ M = \frac{r^2 \times g}{G}$$
$$= \frac{(6 \times 10^8)^2 . g}{7·5g10^{-11}}$$
$$= \frac{(6 \times 10^8)^2}{7·5 \times 10^{-11}} = \underline{4·8 \times 10^{27} \text{ gm.}}$$

Mean density of the earth $= \dfrac{\text{mass}}{\text{volume}}$

$$= \frac{(6 \times 10^8)^2}{7·5 \times 10^{-11} \times \frac{4}{3}\pi(6 \times 10^8)^3}$$
$$= \frac{3 \times 10^3}{4 \times 7·5 \times \pi \times 6} = \frac{100}{6\pi}$$
$$= \underline{5·30 \text{ gm. cm.}^{-3}.}$$

Kepler's laws.—The first of Kepler's laws has been given on p. 109. There are in all three, and since they all afford evidence of the inverse square law of attraction of masses, they are now given in full.

(i) Every planet moves in an ellipse, the sun being situated at one focus.

(ii) The radius vector from the sun to the planet describes equal areas in equal times ; that is, its areal velocity is constant.

(iii) The square of the period of revolution of the planet about the sun is proportional to the cube of the major axis of the ellipse.

EXAMPLE.—Given that the distance of the planet Jupiter from the sun is 5·20 times the earth's distance, find the period of Jupiter's revolution round the sun in earth years.

$$\left(\frac{T_J}{T_E}\right)^2 = \left(\frac{5\cdot20}{1}\right)^3, \quad T_J = (5\cdot20)^{\frac{3}{2}} = \underline{11\cdot9 \text{ earth years.}}$$

Radial and transverse acceleration.—To extend the result on p. 76 to the case in which r changes in any way whatever. Let the path of the body be PQ (Fig. 77A) and at P the radial and transverse velocities be v_r and v_t, which change in the interval of time δt to $v_r{}'$ and $v_t{}'$ at Q. At Q draw the dotted lines parallel and perpendicular to OP.

At Q the velocity parallel to OP is

$$v_r{}' \cos \delta\theta - v_t{}' \sin \delta\theta,$$

so that the change in velocity parallel to OP in time δt is

$$v_r{}' \cos \delta\theta - v_t{}' \sin \delta\theta - v_r$$

and the acceleration parallel to OP is

$$\frac{v_r{}' \cos \delta\theta - v_t{}' \sin \delta\theta - v_r}{\delta t}.$$

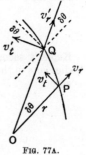

FIG. 77A.

If the radial velocity has changed by δv_r in time δt and the transverse velocity by δv_t :

$$v_r{}' = v_r + \delta v_r, \text{ and } v_t{}' = v_t + \delta v_t,$$

and the acceleration parallel to OP is

$$\frac{(v_r + \delta v_r) \cos \delta\theta - (v_t + \delta v_t) \sin \delta\theta - v_r}{\delta t}.$$

In the limit when δt becomes infinitesimal this quantity is the radial acceleration ($\cos \delta\theta = 1$, $\sin \delta\theta = \delta\theta$) and becomes

$$\frac{v_r + dv_r - v_t d\theta - dv_t \cdot d\theta - v_r}{dt}.$$

Neglecting $dv_t . d\theta$ which is a quantity of the second order of smallness,

$$\text{Radial acceleration} = \frac{dv_r}{dt} - v_t \frac{d\theta}{dt}.$$

But $v_t = \dfrac{r\, d\theta}{dt}$ and $v_r = \dfrac{dr}{dt}$; $\therefore$ radial acceleration $= \dfrac{d^2r}{dt^2} - r\left(\dfrac{d\theta}{dt}\right)^2$.

In a similar manner, the change in velocity perpendicular to OP is

$$v_t{}' \cos \delta\theta + v_r{}' \sin \delta\theta - v_t,$$

or
$$(v_t + \delta v_t) \cos \delta\theta + (v_r + \delta v_r) \sin \delta\theta - v_t,$$

and the transverse acceleration is

$$\frac{(v_t + \delta v_t) \cos \delta\theta + (v_r + \delta v_r) \sin \delta\theta - v_t}{\delta t},$$

which, in the limit becomes

$$\frac{dv_t}{dt} + v_r \frac{d\theta}{dt} = r \frac{d^2\theta}{dt^2} + \frac{dr}{dt} \cdot \frac{d\theta}{dt} + \frac{dr}{dt} \cdot \frac{d\theta}{dt} = r \frac{d^2\theta}{dt^2} + 2 \frac{dr}{dt} \cdot \frac{d\theta}{dt}.$$

This may be written in the more compact form

$$\text{transverse acceleration} = \frac{1}{r} \frac{d}{dt}\left(r^2 \frac{d\theta}{dt}\right).$$

Kepler's second law.—The gravitational attraction between two bodies acts in the line joining them. Thus the transverse acceleration is zero;

$$\therefore \frac{1}{r} \frac{d}{dt}\left(r^2 \frac{d\theta}{dt}\right) = 0,$$

or
$$\frac{d}{dt}\left(r^2 \frac{d\theta}{dt}\right) = 0; \quad \therefore r^2 \frac{d\theta}{dt} = \text{constant}.$$

To give a meaning to this constant, note that in passing from P to Q (Fig. 77B) the radius vector sweeps out the area OPQ. If the interval of time taken is sufficiently small,

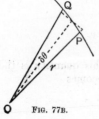

$$\text{area OPQ} = \tfrac{1}{2}r \, d\theta \,.\, r = \tfrac{1}{2}r^2 \, d\theta,$$

and the areal velocity is therefore $\tfrac{1}{2}r^2 \dfrac{d\theta}{dt}$. Calling this areal velocity h, it follows that $r^2 \dfrac{d\theta}{dt} = 2h$, and the area swept out by the radius vector in equal times is constant. This is Kepler's second law.

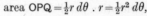

FIG. 77B.

Equation of orbit.—It was seen on p. 118B that the radial acceleration of the planet is $\dfrac{d^2r}{dt^2} - r\left(\dfrac{d\theta}{dt}\right)^2$. This is also $\dfrac{\text{G}M}{r^2}$, since the force on the planet is $\dfrac{\text{G}Mm}{r^2}$, where M is the mass of the sun and m that of the planet ;

$$\therefore \ \frac{d^2r}{dt^2} - r\left(\frac{d\theta}{dt}\right)^2 = -\frac{\text{G}M}{r^2}.$$

The negative sign is taken for $\dfrac{\text{G}M}{r^2}$, because the acceleration is towards the sun and r is directed from the sun.

Then

$$r^3\frac{d^2r}{dt^2} - r^4\left(\frac{d\theta}{dt}\right)^2 = -r\text{G}M.$$

But

$$r^2\frac{d\theta}{dt} = 2h ; \quad \therefore \ r^3\frac{d^2r}{dt^2} - 4h^2 = -r\text{G}M.$$

This equation may be put into a more convenient form by substituting $\dfrac{1}{u}$ for r, since

$$\frac{1}{u^2}\frac{d\theta}{dt} = r^2\frac{d\theta}{dt} = 2h,$$

and

$$\frac{dr}{dt} = -\frac{1}{u^2}\cdot\frac{du}{dt} = -\frac{1}{u^2}\cdot\frac{du}{d\theta}\cdot\frac{d\theta}{dt} = -2h\frac{du}{d\theta},$$

$$\frac{d^2r}{dt^2} = -2h\frac{d^2u}{d\theta^2}\cdot\frac{d\theta}{dt} = -4h^2u^2\frac{d^2u}{d\theta^2}.$$

The equation then becomes,

$$\frac{1}{u^3}\left(-4h^2u^2\frac{d^2u}{d\theta^2}\right) - 4h^2 = -\frac{1}{u}\text{G}M, \text{ or, } \frac{d^2u}{d\theta^2} + u = \frac{\text{G}M}{4h^2}.$$

On making the substitution $p = u - \dfrac{\text{G}M}{4h^2}$ the equation becomes

$$\frac{d^2p}{d\theta^2} + p = 0,$$

which is of the same form as the last equation on p. 86 and may be solved in the same way.

That is,

$$p = \text{A}\epsilon^{+\sqrt{-1}\theta} + \text{B}\epsilon^{-\sqrt{-1}\theta}.$$

Since A and B are constants of integration they may have any value we please, without altering the shape of the p, v curve.

E

Let $\quad$ $A = B = \dfrac{C}{2} \cdot$

Then $\quad$ $p = C \dfrac{\epsilon^{+\sqrt{-1}\theta} + \epsilon^{-\sqrt{-1}\theta}}{2} = C \cos \theta$, and since $\quad p = u - \dfrac{GM}{4h^2}$,

$$u = \frac{GM}{4h^2} + C \cos \theta, \text{ or, } \frac{1}{r} = \frac{GM}{4h^2} + C \cos \theta,$$

$$\frac{\dfrac{4h^2}{GM}}{r} = 1 + \frac{4h^2 C}{GM} \cos \theta.$$

The polar equation of an ellipse is found in works on Conic Sections * to be

$$\frac{l}{r} = 1 + \epsilon \cos \theta,$$

where l is the semi-latus rectum of the ellipse (Fig. 77c) and ϵ is the

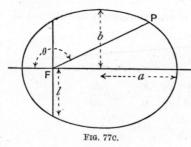

FIG. 77c.

eccentricity of the ellipse, the origin of coordinates $(r = 0)$, being situated at one focus F of the ellipse.

This establishes Kepler's first law, for, with the sun at F, the planet P describes an ellipse of eccentricity $\dfrac{4h^2 C}{GM}$ and semi-latus rectum $\dfrac{4h^2}{GM} \cdot$

Now the semi-latus rectum of an ellipse is $\dfrac{b^2}{a}$ and the area of the ellipse is πab, where a and b are the semi-axes. The time of one complete orbital revolution is therefore $\dfrac{\pi ab}{h} = T$, since h is the areal velocity;

$$\therefore T^2 = \frac{\pi^2 a^2}{h^2} \cdot b^2. \quad \text{But} \quad \frac{b^2}{a} = \frac{4h^2}{GM};$$

$$\therefore T^2 = \frac{\pi^2 a^2}{h^2} \cdot \frac{4ah^2}{GM} = \frac{4\pi^2}{GM} \cdot a^3.$$

This is Kepler's third law, that the square of the periodic time is proportional to the cube of the major axis of the ellipse described by the planet.

* C. Smith, *Conic Sections*.

Determination of g.—The most accurate method of determining the acceleration of gravity is that of the compound pendulum (p. 97), but there have been several other methods devised which are of interest. We will consider Atwood's machine, and the falling plate.

Atwood's machine.—Two equal masses m_1 and m_2 (Fig. 78) hang by a fine silk cord, which passes over a pulley P. The axle of P should rest on wheels in order to reduce the frictional resistance to its motion. m_1 and m_2 will not move until a small weight m is placed on one of them. The system will then have an acceleration much less than the gravitational acceleration. This can be measured by the use of a stop-watch or metronome. The weights of m_1 and m_2 balance, but the weight of m, that is mg, produces an acceleration a in the system, m_2 moving down and m_1 up. The total mass moved is $m_1 + m_2 + m$;

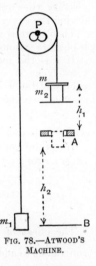

FIG. 78.—ATWOOD'S MACHINE.

$$\therefore \ (m_1 + m_2 + m)\,a = mg,$$

$$a = \frac{m}{m_1 + m_2 + m}\,g.$$

There are many devices for measuring a, but the simplest is to provide a ring A through which m_2 passes without touching, which ring catches the small weight m after it has descended the distance h_1. A movable platform B is placed so that m_2 strikes it after a measured interval of time, usually one second or an exact number of seconds. The clicks of m striking A and m_2 striking B can be arranged to coincide with the beats of a seconds pendulum.

If v is the velocity of the bodies when m strikes A, $v^2 = 2ah_1$. The system now moves with constant velocity v while m_2 passes from A to B. If this time is t, $v = \dfrac{h_2}{t}$;

$$\therefore \ \frac{h_2{}^2}{t^2} = 2ah_1,$$

or

$$a = \frac{h_2{}^2}{2h_1 t^2}.$$

On substituting in $a = \dfrac{m}{m_1 + m_2 + mg}\,g$, g can be found from

$$g = \frac{(m_1 + m_2 + m)h_2{}^2}{m\,2h_1 t^2}.$$

Apart from the difficulty of measuring the times with accuracy, there are several imperfections in the experiment. First there is the fact that there must always be some friction at the bearings of the pulley. By making fresh observations with different weights this friction may be eliminated, but a simpler method is to load m_2 with a small weight which will just keep the system moving with constant velocity when once started. This small weight must then be retained during the experiment, but ignored in the calculation.

Then there is the effect of moment of inertia of the pulley, which is of more serious consequence.

If I is the moment of inertia of the pulley and ω its angular velocity as m strikes A, its kinetic energy is $\frac{1}{2}I\omega^2$. The kinetic energy of the weights is $\frac{1}{2}(m_1 + m_2 + m)v^2$, and the work done on the system from the start is mgh_1;

$$\therefore \ mgh_1 = \tfrac{1}{2}I\omega^2 + \tfrac{1}{2}Mv^2,$$

where M is written for $m_1 + m_2 + m$.

If r is the radius of the groove of the pulley in which the silk cord runs, $v = r\omega$;

$$\therefore \ mgh_1 = \tfrac{1}{2}I\frac{v^2}{r^2} + \tfrac{1}{2}Mv^2$$

$$= \frac{1}{2}\left(\frac{I}{r^2} + M\right)v^2.$$

The effect of the moment of inertia of the pulley is therefore equivalent to adding a mass $\dfrac{I}{r^2}$ to the moving system. This quantity may be found by increasing the mass m by an amount m' and redetermining h_1 and h_2, whose new values are h_1' and h_2'. Remembering that

$$v^2 = \frac{h_2^2}{t^2},$$

the levels of A and B being adjusted until t is the same as before, the original equation

$$2mh_1t^2g = \left(\frac{I}{r^2} + M\right)h_2^2$$

becomes, with m increased by m',

$$2(m + m')h_1't^2g = \left(\frac{I}{r^2} + M + m'\right)h_2'^2 ;$$

$$\therefore \ \frac{m}{m + m'}\frac{h_1}{h_1'} = \frac{\dfrac{I}{r^2} + M}{\dfrac{I}{r^2} + M + m'} \cdot \frac{h_2^2}{h_2'^2}.$$

All the quantities are known except $\dfrac{I}{r^2}$, which can therefore be calculated, and added to M in the original equation for g.

Determination of g by dropping plate.—A falling body has too great an acceleration to be timed by an ordinary stop-watch, but a tuning-fork may be used as a standard of time if its frequency is known. If a glass plate which has been covered on one side with smoke from a flame is suspended by a thread A (Fig. 79), it may be

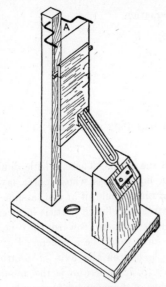

FIG. 79.—DROPPING PLATE METHOD   FIG. 80.—TRACE MADE BY TUNING-
FOR DETERMINING g.   FORK ON DROPPING PLATE.

released by burning the thread at A, and will then fall freely with acceleration g. The tuning-fork is provided with a style of aluminium the point of which rests upon the smoked surface. If the fork is set in vibration and the plate allowed to fall, a trace will be made upon the plate of a character seen in Fig. 80. If then two lengths of the trace such as BC and CD are measured, which contain equal numbers of waves of the trace, the time t for the interval of the plate passing the style from B to C is the same as that from C to D, and if n is the frequency of the fork this number of waves in BC or CD is $nt = n_1$, and the time of fall from B to C, or C to D, is $t = \dfrac{n_1}{n}$.

If u is the velocity of the plate as B passes the style.

$$d_1 = ut + \tfrac{1}{2}gt^2 \; ;$$

also,

$$d_1 + d_2 = 2ut + \tfrac{1}{2}g \cdot 4t^2$$
$$= 2ut + 2gt^2.$$

Multiplying the first equation by 2,

$$2d_1 = 2ut + gt^2,$$

and subtracting from the second equation,

$$d_2 - d_1 = gt^2,$$

or

$$g = \frac{d_2 - d_1}{t^2}$$

$$= \frac{(d_2 - d_1)n^2}{n_1^2}.$$

d_1 and d_2 may be measured by a travelling microscope, and n_1 is counted.

Variations in g on the surface of the earth.—There is little doubt that the earth was at one time a liquid mass whose outer layer solidified on cooling. Such a liquid mass would, if at rest, assume a spherical form on account of the attraction of each particle for every other particle. Every particle would be attracted towards the centre, and from symmetry the resulting form would be a sphere. But if the mass is rotating, every particle not on the axis of rotation experiences a centrifugal force $m\omega^2 r$ (p. 78) where ω is the angular velocity of rotation and r the distance of the particle of mass m from the axis of rotation. This centrifugal force is therefore greatest at the equator, and may be calculated. Taking the earth's equatorial radius as 3963 miles or $6\cdot378 \times 10^8$ cm. and remembering that it makes a complete rotation of 2π radians in one sidereal day, the centrifugal force on 1 gram $= \omega^2 r$

$$= \left(\frac{2\pi}{86164}\right)^2 6\cdot378 \times 10^8 = 3\cdot39.$$

The mean solar second is the unit of time on the c.g.s. system, and the earth makes one rotation with respect to the fixed stars in 86164 mean solar seconds, because the earth makes one revolution round the sun in $365\tfrac{1}{4}$ solar days or $366\tfrac{1}{4}$ sidereal days. A rotation with respect to the fixed stars takes place in $86400 \times \dfrac{365\frac{1}{4}}{366\frac{1}{4}} = 86164$ mean solar seconds.

$\therefore$ centrifugal force on 1 gm. $= 3\cdot 39$ dynes.

The value of g at the equator is $978\cdot 03$ cm./sec.^{2}, that is, the centrifugal effect at the equator is $\dfrac{3\cdot 39}{978\cdot 0} = \frac{1}{288}$ of the whole acceleration.

At a point A in latitude θ (Fig. 81) the centrifugal force for 1 gm. is $\omega^2 . AB = \omega^2 r \cos \theta$. The resultant force at A is perpendicular to the surface, since the liquid earth would not otherwise be in equilibrium. Owing to the oblate form assumed on account of rotation, the normal AC cuts the equatorial plane at C. If g is the observed acceleration of gravity at A, take a point D on CO, such that

$$\frac{CD}{CA} = \frac{\omega^2 r \cos \theta}{g}.$$

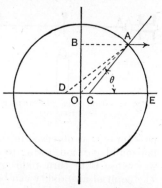

FIG. 81.—DIRECTION OF RESULTANT WEIGHT AT ANY POINT ON THE EARTH.

Then ADC may be taken as a triangle of forces, and AC is the resultant of AD and DC. AD therefore represents the component of gravity at A due to the attraction of the earth. Since AC is less than AD, it follows that the weight of a body is always diminished by the rotation of the earth. Further, the latitude of A as measured by the direction of the vertical is $\overset{\frown}{ACE}$. This is greater than the geocentric latitude θ.

There is still another reason why the acceleration of gravity varies from place to place. Owing to the ellipticity of the earth, points in high latitude are nearer the centre of the earth than points near the equator. On this account the attraction on any body at the surface increases towards the poles.

The value of g has been determined by the pendulum method at a great many places, and the result is that at the sea-level,

$$g = 978\cdot 03(1 + 0\cdot 00531 \sin^2\theta) \text{ cm./sec.}^2,$$

where θ is the latitude of the place.

Gravity balance.—Since the weight of a body is proportional to the acceleration of gravity, it might be expected that a spring balance could be used to measure the variations of gravity at different places. Since the force applied for a given stretch of spring depends upon the properties of the spring alone, the reading of the balance when supporting a mass is proportional to g. The method only fails because of the want of sensitiveness of the ordinary spring balance. Threlfall and Pollock in 1899 devised a balance in which the couple required to twist a quartz thread is used instead of the force required to extend a spring.

A fine quartz thread AB (Fig. 82) is stretched between A and B, A being fixed while B can turn. A small rod C is attached to the thread, and is so designed that the centre of gravity of the rod is at one side of the thread. C is brought into a horizontal position by twisting B. About three whole turns of B are necessary, and a vernier V moving over a circular scale fixes the position of B. A very small movement of V alters the

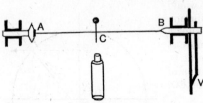

FIG. 82.—THRELFALL AND POLLOCK GRAVITY BALANCE.

position of C as observed in the microscope. As C is unstable in its horizontal position, owing to the fact that a slight movement of V will cause C to turn right over, a stop is placed to prevent this. The point of unstability can be found readily.

The instrument is calibrated by making readings at two places where g has been found by the pendulum method. Its variation with temperature must be determined at one station. It is then possible to make a survey of g by carrying the instrument from place to place, the various positions of the pointer V indicating the values of g. This is much more expeditious than making observations with the pendulum at all the stations.

EXERCISES ON CHAPTER V

1. Outline a method for determining the mass of the earth.

Assuming that a sphere of mass 40 kilos is attracted by a second sphere of mass 80 kilos, when their centres are 30 cm. apart, with a force equal to the weight of $\frac{1}{4}$ mg., calculate the constant of gravitation.   J.M.B.H.S.C.

2. Describe the most accurate experiment you know by which the earth's mean density has been determined.

If the constant of gravitation in the c.g.s. system is $6 \cdot 7 \times 10^{-8}$, the mean radius of the earth is $6 \cdot 4 \times 10^{8}$ cm., and the mean density of the earth is $5 \cdot 5$, calculate the acceleration due to gravity at the earth's surface, assuming that the earth behaves as if its mass were concentrated at its centre.

C.W.B.H.S.C.

3. Give a brief survey of the evidence that led Newton to formulate his Law of Gravitation.

A small satellite revolves round a planet of mean density 10 gm. per c.c., the radius of the satellite's orbit being *very little* greater than the radius of the planet. If the constant of gravitation is 6.66×10^{-8} c.g.s. units, calculate the time of revolution of the satellite. J.M.B.H.S.C.

4. Prove that a body falling from the surface of the earth through a hole passing through the earth's centre will travel with simple harmonic motion, if frictional effects are inappreciable and the density of the earth is uniform. Find the period of the motion if the value of g at the surface is 981 cm. sec.$^{-2}$ and $r = 6.38 \times 10^6$ metres.

5. Show that the periodic time of the body in question 4 is the same if its path is any straight line which need not pass through the centre of the earth. The body may be considered to slide without friction through a straight tube.

6. Define the Newtonian constant of gravitation. Assuming the earth to be a sphere of uniform density, explain how the intensity of gravity varies in passing from the surface of the earth to the centre.

Describe one laboratory method by which the constant of gravitation has been accurately measured. Lond. B.Sc.

7. Give a statement of Newton's law of gravitation, and define the Newtonian gravitation constant.

Show that the gravitational intensity due to a uniform spherical shell of matter at a point inside the shell is zero, and write down a simple expression for the intensity at a point outside. Lond. B.Sc.

8. What is meant by the intensity of gravity and by the gravitational constant ? Deduce an approximate relation between the intensity of gravity at the earth's surface, its mass, radius and the gravitational constant.

Assuming that the whole variation of the weight of a body with its position on the earth's surface is due to the rotation of the earth, find the difference in the weight of a gram as measured at the equator and at the pole. (Radius of the earth = 6.4×10^8 cm.) Lond. B.Sc.

CHAPTER VI

ELASTICITY

Strain.—All bodies can be deformed by suitably applied forces. There are, however, many ways in which the deformation may take place. The simplest form is a compression equally in all directions, giving rise to a change in volume of the body without any change in its shape. All bodies, solid or fluid, are capable of this bulk or volume compression. Another case is that of the stretch of a wire or the longitudinal compression of a rod. This is confined to solids, as is the bending of a beam or the shearing of a block.

In all these cases the change per unit amount, or the ratio of the total change to the total amount, is called the **strain**. Thus, for a stretched wire of original length L, if the change in length is l,

$$\text{strain} = \frac{l}{L}.$$

For a body of volume V which changes in volume by v, the volume strain $= \dfrac{v}{V}$. Shearing strain will be considered later (p. 128).

Stress.—Strains are produced by suitably applied forces, which forces are distributed over definite areas of the strained bodies. The amount of force per unit area of its application is called the **stress** acting upon the body. Thus if f is the force acting over an area a, stress $= \dfrac{f}{a}$. In the case of a stretched wire the stress is usually applied by a weight suspended by the wire, while in the case of a volume strain the stress may be the pressure of a fluid applied over the surface of the body.

Hooke's law.—Provided that the strain is small, **it is proportional to the stress producing it.** This is known as **Hooke's law.** If the stress is removed, under these conditions, the strain disappears, the body

126

returning to its original condition. When the stress is continually increased, in the case of solid bodies, a point is reached at which the strain increases more rapidly than is indicated by Hooke's law. The point at which this begins is called the elastic limit. If the body is a wire under stretch, it will not regain its original length on being unloaded, if the elastic limit has been passed. On loading beyond the elastic limit, a point at which the extension begins to increase rapidly is reached. This is called the yield point, and this extension is permanent. After a great extension the breaking point is reached. Some substances, such as lead, have a long range between the yield point and the breaking point ; they are said to be plastic.

Elasticity.—Within the limits to which Hooke's law is applicable, the ratio of stress to strain is called the modulus of elasticity. There are three moduli in common use. For the stretching of a wire or rod, there is no stress on the sides, the stress being in the form of a longitudinal tension, f/a. The ratio of stress to strain in this case is called Young's modulus of elasticity (e). Then

$$e = \frac{\text{stress}}{\text{strain}} = \frac{f}{a} \div \frac{l}{L} = \frac{fL}{al}.$$

Since the stresses and strains within the limits for which Hooke's law is true are always very small quantities, this relation may best be expressed as a differential coefficient. Thus, $\frac{\delta f}{a}$ being the stress and $\frac{\delta l}{L}$ the strain,

$$e = \frac{\delta f}{a} \div \frac{\delta l}{L} = \frac{L}{a} \cdot \frac{\delta f}{\delta l},$$

which in the limit becomes

$$e = \frac{L}{a} \frac{df}{dl}.$$

The dimensions of e are given by

$$[e] = [\text{L} . \text{L}^{-2} . \text{MLT}^{-2} . \text{L}^{-1}]$$
$$= [\text{ML}^{-1}\text{T}^{-2}].$$

It should be noted that the expression " Modulus of elasticity of a string " is sometimes used. This quantity is the ratio of the whole force stretching the string to the strain it produces. It is not Young's modulus of elasticity. Its dimensions are $[\text{MLT}^{-2}]$.

When an external pressure p compresses a body, the ratio of stress to strain is called the **bulk modulus of elasticity** (k).

Thus,
$$k = p \div \frac{v}{V} = \frac{pV}{v}.$$

Or expressed as a differential coefficient,
$$k = \delta p \div \frac{\delta v}{V} = V \frac{\delta p}{\delta v};$$

and in the limit,
$$k = V \frac{dp}{dv}.$$

Also, the dimensions of k are given by
$$[k] = [L^3 \cdot ML^{-1}T^{-2} \cdot L^{-3}]$$
$$= [ML^{-1}T^{-2}].$$

The third case occurs when the shape of the body is changed. This takes place by the movement of the layers, one over the other.

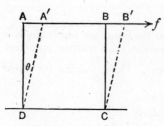

FIG. 83.—SIMPLE SHEAR.

In Fig. 83, consider the cube ABCD with the face DC fixed to a plane, and a force f applied in the plane of the face AB. The cube is then distorted into the position A'B'CD, and the angle θ through which AD or BC is turned is the strain. The stress is f/a, where a is the area of the upper face AB over which f is applied. In this case the cube is said to be **sheared**, and the strain is a **shearing** strain. The ratio of stress to strain is called the **modulus of rigidity**, or the **simple rigidity** of the body (n).

$$n = \frac{\text{stress}}{\text{strain}} = \frac{f}{a} \div \theta,$$

$$= \frac{f}{a\theta};$$

or, more exactly,
$$n = \frac{1}{a} \frac{df}{d\theta},$$

and
$$[n] = [L^{-2}MLT^{-2} \cdot LL^{-1}] = [ML^{-1}T^{-2}].$$

It will be noticed that when the body undergoes simple shear, its volume is unchanged, because the area of ABCD is equal to that of A'B'CD, and the thickness of the cube from back to front is unchanged.

Shear is equivalent to compression and extension.—In Fig. 83 it is clear that the diagonal DB has been increased to length DB', and at the same time AC has been diminished to A'C. If it is remembered that the amount of shear in any practical case is always extremely small, this extension and compression may be expressed in terms of θ. In Fig. 84 the angle θ is greatly exaggerated, so that, in reality, the triangles AFA' and BEB' are right-angled, 45° triangles.

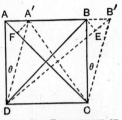

FIG. 84.—EQUIVALENCE OF SHEAR TO COMPRESSION AND EXTENSION.

$$\therefore \ EB' = \frac{BB'}{\sqrt{2}}.$$

If AB $= l$, then

$$DB = DE = l\sqrt{2} \ ;$$

$\therefore$ extension strain along diagonal

$$= \frac{EB'}{DB} = \frac{BB'}{\sqrt{2}} \cdot \frac{1}{l\sqrt{2}}$$

$$= \frac{BB'}{2l}.$$

But

$$\theta = \frac{BB'}{l} \ ;$$

$$\therefore \ \text{extension strain} = \frac{\theta}{2}.$$

Expressed as differentials, writing angle ADA' as $\delta\theta$, if BB' (Fig. 84) is δx, $\delta\theta = \dfrac{\delta x}{l}$, and B'E $= \dfrac{\delta x}{\sqrt{2}}$.

$\therefore$ Extension strain along DB is $\dfrac{B'E}{DB} = \dfrac{\delta x}{\sqrt{2}} \div l\sqrt{2}$

$$= \frac{\delta x}{2l} = \frac{\delta\theta}{2}.$$

Similarly there is a compression

$$\frac{AF}{AC} = \frac{AA'}{AC\sqrt{2}} = \frac{l\theta}{l\sqrt{2}\,\sqrt{2}} = \frac{\theta}{2},$$

in the direction of the diagonal AC. Thus a simple shear θ is equivalent to a compression and extension at right angles to each other, each of value $\theta/2$.

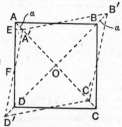

The converse statement that simultaneous equal compression and extension at right angles to each other are equivalent to a shear is true. In Fig. 85 imagine the cube ABCD to be compressed along the diagonal AC, so that the new diagonal becomes A′C′ and AA′ $=\alpha$. At the same time let the extension along DB move B to B′ and D to D′ where BB′ $=\alpha$. Then

$$AB = l, \quad OA = \frac{l}{\sqrt{2}}, \text{ and } OA' = \frac{l}{\sqrt{2}} - \alpha.$$

FIG. 85.—EQUIVALENCE OF COMPRESSION AND EXTENSION TO SIMPLE SHEAR.

Similarly $OB' = \dfrac{l}{\sqrt{2}} + \alpha$;

$$\therefore \ (A'B')^2 = \left(\frac{l}{\sqrt{2}} + \alpha\right)^2 + \left(\frac{l}{\sqrt{2}} - \alpha\right)^2$$
$$= l^2 + 2\alpha^2.$$

In an actual case $2\alpha^2$ is extremely small in comparison with l^2, and may be neglected. Therefore A′B′ $= l =$ AB. Thus the figure A′B′C′D′

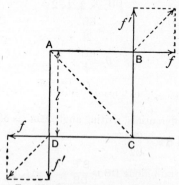

FIG. 86.—COUPLES ACTING ON CUBE.

may be rotated through the angle AFA′ and at the same time D′C′ be made to coincide with DC. A′D′ would then make angle 2AFA′ with AD, so that the angle of shear is

$$2AFA' = 2 \, \frac{EA'}{EF} = 2 \, \frac{\alpha}{\sqrt{2}} \div \frac{l}{2} = 4 \, \frac{\alpha}{\sqrt{2}\,l} = 2 \, \frac{\alpha\sqrt{2}}{l} \, .$$

But the compression strain along AC is $\dfrac{\alpha}{AO} = \dfrac{\alpha\sqrt{2}}{l}$. That is, the angle of shear is twice the compression. This is the same statement as that compression $= \dfrac{\theta}{2}$.

The compression and extension may be considered to be produced by a pressure and a tensile stress equivalent to the shearing forces acting on the body. For if the force f acts in the plane of the face AB of the cube ABCD (Fig. 86), the cube would move unless there is an equal and opposite force. As the cube is supposed to be fixed at the plane CD, there must be a force f in this plane. Hence there is now a couple fl acting on the cube, and it will be tilted off the plane unless held by an equal and opposite couple $f'l$, again supplied by the plane. $f = f'$. The resultant of f and f' at B is $f\sqrt{2}$. Since the half ABC of the cube is in equilibrium, there must be a force $f\sqrt{2}$ acting over the face AC, and as the area of this face is $l^2\sqrt{2}$, there must be a tensile stress $\dfrac{f\sqrt{2}}{l^2\sqrt{2}} = \dfrac{f}{l^2}$ in the material in the direction DB. This tensile stress is equal to $\dfrac{f}{l^2} = \dfrac{f}{a}$, the simple shearing stress which produces the shear θ (p. 128).

In a similar manner it may be shown that there is a pressure $\dfrac{f}{l^2}$ parallel to AC, which produces the compression in this direction.

Thus a simple shear is in all ways equivalent to two equal strains, a compression and an extension at right angles to each other.

Measurement of Young's modulus.—The measurement of Young's modulus of elasticity, in the case of a wire, may be carried out by measuring directly the extension of the wire produced by a given load. The wire AB is soldered at its upper end to a brass plate screwed to an overhead beam (Fig. 87). As the supporting beam may sag with increasing load, a second wire CD is soldered alongside of A. CD carries a scale S clamped to it, and AB the vernier V, so that if the beam gives, the scale and vernier are both affected to the same extent. The reading of the vernier for different loads at B is observed, and the increase

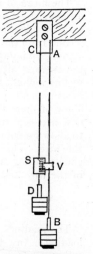

FIG. 87.—YOUNG'S MODULUS MEASUREMENT.

in length of the wire between A and V for given loads is thus found.

The weights D and B must be sufficiently great to keep the wires taut from the beginning. B may then be increased a kilogram at a time, the vernier readings for each load being observed. The results should be tabulated as follows :

Increase in Load.	Vernier Reading.		Mean.	Elongation for 3 Kilos.
	Loading.	Unloading.		
1	a_1	a_2	a	
2	b_1	b_2	b	
3	c_1	c_2	c	
4	d_1	d_2	d	$d-a$
5	e_1	e_2	e	$e-b$
6	f_1	f_2	f	$f-c$

The mean of the numbers in the last column is the elongation for an increase of load of 3 kilos. In finding the elongation it is necessary to take the first vernier reading from the fourth $(d-a)$, the second from the fifth, and so on. If the first had been taken from the second, giving $(b-a)$, $(c-b)$, $(d-c)$, etc., then on adding up to take the average, all the readings would cancel except a and f, and might just as well not have been taken. This procedure is followed in most measurements of elasticity. Of course, if the wire and supports will allow of more loads to be used, the table may be extended. It is now necessary to know the length AV, which length should be great, to allow for sufficient stretching ; also to measure the cross-section of the wire. The diameter may be found by means of a micrometer gauge, taking the mean of a number of readings. If r is the radius of the wire and l the extension for load W,

$$e = \frac{WgL}{\pi r^2 l} .$$

The readings on unloading should be very nearly the same as on loading. Any difference is probably due to bends in the wire being taken out on loading. If the differences are great the series should be repeated until concordance is attained.

There are several modifications of this method. In one of them, due to Searle, the extension of the wire is measured by means of a spirit level and micrometer. Two frames AB and CD (Fig. 88) are pivoted at G and H, one frame being attached to each wire. A spirit level L rests on a support at E and on the point of the micrometer screw at F. There is a second bar, corresponding to GH, at the far side of the apparatus, which cannot be seen in the diagram. When the load is placed on the pan S, the frame CD sinks, owing to the extension of the wire. This is seen by the travel of the bubble of the spirit level towards E. The bubble is restored to its central position by raising the end F by means of the micrometer screw M. The extension of the wire is thus given by the movement of the micrometer M. Successive loads are placed in the pan S and the adjustment of the level made for each load. The corresponding

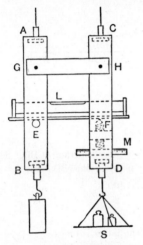

FIG. 88.—SEARLE'S EXTENSOMETER.

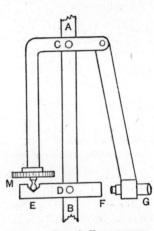

FIG. 89.—EWING'S EXTENSOMETER.

readings of the micrometer M are then entered in tabular form, as on the previous page, and the extension of the wire C for given stretching force is calculated.

For thick bars, Ewing's **extensometer** is used. The rod AB is stretched by means of a testing machine. Two arms are attached to it at C and D (Fig. 89) by screws with pointed ends, so that they can revolve about C and D. A microscope G is focussed on a fine mark on F, and when the rod is extended, the travel of the image of the mark over a fine transparent scale in the eyepiece gives the travel of the mark at F. This is $\dfrac{EF}{ED}$ times the extension of the portion CD of the rod. The micrometer screw M serves to set the mark F in a convenient position and to calibrate the scale in the eyepiece.

EXAMPLE.—What is meant by Young's modulus ?

A flexible wire, of length two metres, and area of cross-section 1 sq. mm., is stretched tight between two points A and B in the same horizontal plane. When a mass of 10 gm. is hung from the mid-point of the wire, it is found that this point is depressed a distance of 1 cm. below the line AB. Calculate Young's modulus for the material of the wire.　　C.H.S.C.

Extension of CB (Fig. 90) is $\sqrt{100^2 + 1} - 100 = 100 \cdot 0049999 - 100$

$$= 0 \cdot 005 \text{ cm.}$$

Note that the diagram is not drawn to scale.

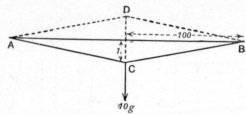

FIG. 90.—PROBLEM.

To find the tension T in BC complete the parallelogram ACBD. Then CBD serves as the triangle of forces for the point C, since BD ∥ AC,

$$\therefore \quad \frac{T}{10g} = \frac{BC}{CD} = \frac{\sqrt{100^2 + 1}}{2} = \frac{100}{2} = 50,$$
$$T = 500g.$$

10000 is so great compared with 1, that the latter is omitted ;

$$\therefore \quad \text{stress} = \frac{T}{a} = \frac{500g}{\cdot 01} = 50000g, \quad \text{strain} = \frac{0 \cdot 005}{100} ;$$
$$\therefore \quad e = \frac{50000g \times 100}{0 \cdot 005} = \frac{5 \times 9 \cdot 81 \times 10^{11}}{5} = \underline{9 \cdot 81 \times 10^{11} \text{ dyne cm.}^{-2}.}$$

Work done in strain.—If the three principal cases are taken in order, there are :

(i) *Stretch of a wire.*—For a stretching force f, the work done for an increase in length dx is $f \cdot dx$, and for the whole stretch from 0 to x,

$$\text{work done} = \int_0^x f \, dx.$$

But　　　　　$e = \dfrac{Lf}{xa}$ (p. 127) ; $\therefore f = \dfrac{eax}{L}$;

$$\therefore \text{ work} = \int_0^x \frac{eax}{L}\, dx$$

$$= \frac{ea}{L} \cdot \int_0^x x\, dx = \frac{1}{2}\frac{eax^2}{L} = \frac{1}{2}\frac{eax}{L} \cdot x$$

$$= \tfrac{1}{2} \text{ stretching force} \times \text{stretch}.$$

The volume of the wire is La, so that the work done per unit volume of the material is

$$\frac{1}{2}\frac{eax^2}{L^2a} = \frac{1}{2}\frac{eax}{La} \cdot \frac{x}{L}$$

$$= \tfrac{1}{2} \text{ stress} \times \text{strain}.$$

(ii) *Volume strain.*—For stress p, the force over an area a is pa, and the work done for a movement dx in the direction of p, that is, normal to the surface, is $pa\,dx$. $a\,dx$ is a volume change, and taking this over the whole surface the total is dv ;

$$\therefore \text{ work done for change } dv = p\,dv.$$

$$\text{Total work done} = \int_0^v p\,dv.$$

Now $$k = \frac{pV}{v} \text{ (p. 128)} ; \quad \therefore \ p = \frac{kv}{V}.$$

$$\therefore \text{ Work} = \int_0^v \frac{k}{V} v\,dv$$

$$= \frac{1}{2}\frac{kv^2}{V} = \frac{1}{2}\frac{kv}{V} \times v$$

$$= \tfrac{1}{2}p \cdot v.$$

For unit volume,

$$\text{work done} = \tfrac{1}{2}p \cdot \frac{v}{V}$$

$$= \tfrac{1}{2} \text{ stress} \times \text{strain}.$$

(iii) *Shearing strain.*—In Fig. 83 (p. 128) let $AA' = x$. Then work for increase dx is $f\,dx$, and work done for total displacement x is $\int_0^x f\,dx$. But $n = \dfrac{f}{a\theta}$ (p. 128), $f = na\theta = nlx$; since $a = l^2$,

$$\therefore \text{ work} = \int_0^x nlx\,dx = \tfrac{1}{2}nlx^2.$$

The volume of the whole cube is l^3 ;
∴ work per unit volume is

$$\frac{1}{2}\frac{nlx^2}{l^3} = \frac{1}{2}\frac{nx}{l}\cdot\frac{x}{l}$$

$$= \tfrac{1}{2}\text{ stress} \times \text{strain}.$$

It will be seen that the work done per unit volume of the material in these three cases, in producing any strain, is of the same form, that is, $\tfrac{1}{2}$ stress × strain ; so long, of course, as Hooke's law holds good.

EXAMPLE.—Define *stress, strain, Young's modulus.* How would you determine Young's modulus for a steel wire ?

Calculate the work done in producing an extension of 2 mm. in a steel wire of length 3 metres and diameter 1 mm. [Young's modulus for steel = 2×10^{12} dynes per sq. cm.]   C.H.S.C.

$$e = \frac{Lf}{la},$$

$$2 \times 10^{12} = \frac{300 \times f}{l \times \pi(0\cdot 05)^2},$$

$$f = \frac{2 \times 10^{12} \times \pi(0\cdot 05)^2}{300} l = \frac{\pi 10^8}{6} l.$$

$$\text{Work done} = \int_0^{0\cdot 2} f\, dl$$

$$= \int_0^{0\cdot 2} \frac{\pi 10^8}{6} l\, dl$$

$$= \frac{1}{2}\cdot\frac{\pi 10^8}{6}(\cdot 2)^2$$

$$= \frac{\pi \times 10^6}{3}$$

$$= 1\cdot 047 \times 10^6 \text{ ergs.}$$

EXAMPLE.—Explain the meaning of *stress* and *strain.* In what circumstances is their ratio known as Young's modulus ? What meaning can be attached to their product ?

A uniform wire 300 cm. long weighing 21·0 gm. elongates 2·4 mm. when stretched by a force of 5·0 kilos wt. The density of the metal is 8·8 gm. per c.c. Determine (a) the value of Young's modulus for the metal, (b) the energy stored in the wire. State the units in which each result is expressed.   J.M.B.H.S.C.

On p. 134 it is shown that the energy per unit volume of the wire is $\frac{1}{2}$ stress × strain. Therefore stress × strain is twice the work done in producing the strain, for unit volume of the material.

Volume of wire $\qquad = \dfrac{21 \cdot 0}{8 \cdot 8} = 300 \times a$;

$\qquad \therefore$ cross-section $a = \dfrac{21}{8 \cdot 8 \times 300}$.

(a) Young's modulus $\quad = \dfrac{300}{0 \cdot 24} \times \dfrac{5000 \times 981 \times 8 \cdot 8 \times 300}{21}$

$\qquad\qquad\qquad\qquad = 7 \cdot 71 \times 10^{11}$ gm. cm.$^{-1}$ sec.$^{-2}$.

(b) Energy per c.c. of wire $= \frac{1}{2}$ stress × strain

$\qquad\qquad\qquad\qquad = \dfrac{1}{2} \dfrac{5000 \times 981 \times 8 \cdot 8 \times 300}{21} \times \dfrac{0 \cdot 24}{300}$;

$\qquad \therefore$ total energy $=$ energy per c.c. × volume

$\qquad\qquad\qquad\qquad = \dfrac{1}{2} \dfrac{5000 \times 981 \times 8 \cdot 8 \times 0 \cdot 24}{21} \times \dfrac{21}{8 \cdot 8}$

$\qquad\qquad\qquad\qquad = 5000 \times 981 \times 0 \cdot 12$

$\qquad\qquad\qquad\qquad = 5 \cdot 89 \times 10^5$ ergs.

Relation between e, k and n.—Consider a cube of unit edge with pulls or pressures perpendicular to its faces as in Fig. 91. This may

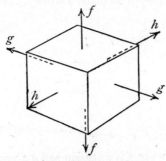

FIG. 91.—STRESSES ON CUBE.

be an elementary cube in the interior of a substance, or it may be a separate cube. In either case, if $g = h = 0$ the cube is strained, and its elongation is $\dfrac{f}{e}$ where e is Young's modulus. At the same time the sides perpendicular to f are shortened by an amount which we will write μf. If the material has the same elastic properties in all directions, that is, if it is isotropic, the shortening of all the edges perpendicular to f will be the same, *i.e.* μf.

Now let g and h be applied. The effect produced by f is the same as before, but now g produces an extension $\dfrac{g}{e}$ in its own direction and contractions μg in both directions perpendicular to itself. In the same way h will produce extension $\dfrac{h}{e}$ and contractions μh. Thus the total extension in the direction of f is $\dfrac{f}{e} - \mu g - \mu h$. If now $f = g = h$, the total extension parallel to any one set of edges is $\dfrac{f}{e} - 2\mu f$ and the new volume is

$$\left\{ 1 + \left(\frac{f}{e} - 2\mu f \right) \right\}^3.$$

Now $\left(\dfrac{f}{e} - 2\mu f \right)$ is always extremely small, so that its square and cube may be neglected in comparison with unity. Thus the new volume may be written $1 + 3\left(\dfrac{f}{e} - 2\mu f \right)$, and the increase in volume is

$$3\left(\frac{f}{e} - 2\mu f \right).$$

This is also the volume strain under a stress f. The bulk modulus k (p. 128) is therefore $\dfrac{f}{3\left(\dfrac{f}{e} - 2\mu f \right)}$.

That is,
$$k = \frac{1}{\dfrac{3}{e} - 6\mu},$$

or
$$\frac{1}{k} = \frac{3}{e} - 6\mu.$$

Again, let $h = 0$, while f is a tension and g a pressure. The total extension parallel to f is now $\dfrac{f}{e} + \mu g$, and the total compression parallel to g is $\dfrac{g}{e} + \mu f$. If in addition g is numerically equal to f, the extension is $\dfrac{f}{e} + \mu f$ and the compression is also $\dfrac{f}{e} + \mu f$. The strain in this case is a shear, the angle of shear θ being $2\left(\dfrac{f}{e}+\mu f\right)$, as shown on p. 129. The **rigidity** n is $\dfrac{f}{\theta}$, so that

$$n=\frac{f}{2\left(\dfrac{f}{e}+\mu f\right)},$$

or

$$n=\frac{1}{\dfrac{2}{e}+2\mu}$$

$$\frac{1}{n}=\frac{2}{e}+2\mu,$$

$$\frac{3}{n}=\frac{6}{e}+6\mu.$$

This, combined with the equation, $\dfrac{1}{k}=\dfrac{3}{e}-6\mu,$

gives,

$$\frac{3}{n}+\frac{1}{k}=\frac{9}{e}.$$

Thus e, k and n are not independent of each other, and any of them can be calculated for any solid when the other two are known.

Poisson's ratio.—When a tensile stress is applied to a wire, the ratio of the lateral contraction strain to the elongation strain is called Poisson's ratio. It will be seen that it may be found from the elastic constants of the material. In the above case μf (Fig. 91) is the lateral strain and f/e is the longitudinal strain, and the ratio (σ) is Poisson's ratio ;

$$\therefore \quad \sigma=\frac{\mu f}{\dfrac{f}{e}}=\mu e.$$

If this value for μ be written in the equation $\dfrac{1}{n}=\dfrac{2}{e}+2\mu$, we have

$$\frac{1}{n}=\frac{2}{e}+\frac{2\sigma}{e},$$

or

$$1+\sigma=\frac{e}{2n}.$$

Torsion.—It has been seen that if two of the principal moduli of elasticity, can be measured, the third can be calculated. The bulk modulus is very difficult to measure directly, but Young's modulus can be measured, in many cases, with fair accuracy. If then the modulus of rigidity can be measured, the bulk modulus becomes known. The most convenient method of measuring the modulus of rigidity is to determine the couple, when a wire of the material is subjected to torsion; that is, one end is fixed and the other end is twisted through an angle about the axis of the wire.

Consider a section of the wire (Fig. 92). This may be considered to be divided into cylindrical layers of radius r and thickness dr.

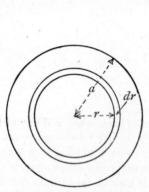

FIG. 92.—SECTION OF WIRE.

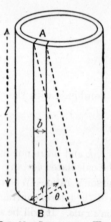

FIG. 93.—STRAIN IN A WIRE UNDERGOING TORSION.

When one end of the wire is rotated, each cylindrical layer undergoes a shear which gives rise to a couple tending to restore the cylinder to its original form. The sum of these couples for the whole cross-section is the resultant couple due to the torsion in the wire.

In order to find the couple for each elementary cylinder, consider a strip AB of the cylinder (Fig. 93). If the upper end is fixed and the lower end is rotated through angle θ, the end of the strip moves through the linear distance $r\theta$, and the strip is sheared through the angle $\dfrac{r\theta}{l}$. If f is the force applied circumferentially, at B, the shearing stress acting on the strip is $\dfrac{f}{b \cdot dr}$, where b is the width of the strip measured along the circumference and dr is its radial thickness. Hence

$n = \dfrac{f}{b\,dr} \div \dfrac{r\theta}{l}$ (p. 128), $n = \dfrac{fl}{r\theta \cdot b\,dr}$, or $f = \dfrac{nr\theta b\,dr}{l}$. The moment of this

force about the axis of the cylinder is $fr = \dfrac{nr^2\theta b\,dr}{l}$. This, together

with the force due to a similar strip on the opposite side of the cylinder, will constitute a couple $\dfrac{2nr^2\theta \cdot b\,dr}{l}$. Taking all the strips round half the cylinder, $b = \pi r$;

$$\therefore \text{ total couple} = \frac{2\pi n\theta r^3 dr}{l} = dc.$$

Returning to Fig. 92, it is seen that the resultant couple c for all the elementary cylinders is $\displaystyle\int_0^a dc$,

that is
$$c = \int_0^a \frac{2\pi n\theta r^3 dr}{l}$$
$$= \frac{2\pi n\theta}{l}\left[\frac{r^4}{4}\right]_0^a$$
$$= \frac{\pi n\theta a^4}{2l}.$$

It will be noticed that in Figs. 92 and 93 the diameter of the wire has been greatly exaggerated. For a fairly long wire of small diameter the shearing strain is very small, although θ may be large. Thus the couple is proportional to the torsional angle θ, even when this is considerable.

Measurement of n by torsional vibration.—The method of measuring moment of inertia described on p. 100 is applicable to the determination of the torsional rigidity of the wire. If the body of known moment of inertia I is suspended by the wire and allowed to vibrate torsionally and T determined, the couple c for one radian twist is known.

$$T = 2\pi\sqrt{\frac{I}{c}}.$$

But
$$c = \frac{\pi n a^4}{2l} \text{when } \theta = 1;$$

$$\therefore c = \frac{4\pi^2 I}{T^2} = \frac{\pi n a^4}{2l},$$

or
$$n = \frac{8\pi l I}{a^4 T^2}.$$

l and a are measured in the usual way. It should be noted that the greatest care must be used in measuring a, because it enters into the result to the fourth power. Any uncertainty in the value of a gives therefore an uncertainty four times as great in the result.

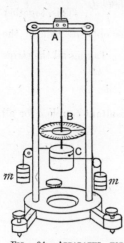

FIG. 94.—APPARATUS FOR STATICAL METHOD OF MEASURING MODULUS OF RIGIDITY.

Statical method of measuring n.—If a couple which can be measured is applied to the lower end of a wire and the twist produced is observed, the rigidity may then be calculated. The wire AB (Fig. 94) is clamped at A, and at B it is attached to a vertical rod carrying a pointer that moves over a circular scale. It also carries a cylinder C to which are attached threads passing over pulleys and supporting weights mm. If r is radius of C the couple applied to the wire is $2mgr$. The twist α degrees produced by the couple, is observed by means of the pointer and scale. The twist θ in radians is then $\dfrac{\pi\alpha}{180}$, and the couple for one radian twist is $\dfrac{2mgr}{\theta}=c$. From the equation $c=\dfrac{\pi na^4}{2l}$, n may then be calculated (p. 141).

The precautions described on p. 132 for applying the load in steps and tabulating the resulting scale readings should be observed.

The results for rigidity obtained by the statical method are slightly lower than those obtained by the dynamic method, because with most substances the twist produced by a torsional couple is not quite independent of the time for which the couple is applied. When the load is applied in the statical method the twist increases with time, giving an increased twist. With the dynamical method the time of vibration is too short for this yield to be produced.

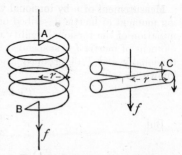

FIG. 95.—EXTENSION OF A SPRING.

Extension of the flat spiral spring.—Provided that a spiral spring is of small pitch in comparison with the radius, an expression for its extension in terms of the stretching force may be found. Let the spring be bent inwards at A and B (Fig. 95), so that the force f causing its elongation may be applied along the axis of the spiral. The force f has a moment fr at the wire, and this is balanced by a couple due to the twist in the wire produced by the extension of the spring. If the section C of the wire is vertical, the couple due to twist must equal fr, and this condition is approximately fulfilled when the wire is nearly horizontal, that is, when the spiral is a flat one. Also from p. 141 this couple is related to the twist in unit length of the wire by the equation $fr = \dfrac{\pi n \theta a^4}{2}$. This twist θ lowers every part of the spring situated below the section considered, by the amount $r\theta$. Thus B is lowered by the amount $r\theta$ for every unit of length of wire of the spring, so that if the total length of wire in the spring is l, the total extension of the spring is $lr\theta = h$;

$$\therefore \ h = lr \cdot \frac{2fr}{\pi n a^4}$$

$$= \frac{2lr^2}{\pi n a^4} f.$$

If the extension is caused by hanging a load m by the spring, $f = mg$ and

$$h = \frac{2lr^2}{\pi n a^4} mg.$$

It should be noticed that a is the radius of the wire, and r is the radius of the spiral into which the wire is bent.

By measuring the extension for various loads by the procedure on p. 132, n may be found.

As an alternative, the mass m may be set in vertical vibration, when

$$T = 2\pi \sqrt{\frac{m}{\text{force per unit extension}}} \quad \text{(p. 88)}$$

$$= 2\pi \sqrt{m \div \frac{mg}{h}} \quad = 2\pi \sqrt{m \div \frac{\pi n a^4}{2lr^2}}$$

$$= 2\pi \sqrt{\frac{2mlr^2}{\pi n a^4}}.$$

Bending of a beam.—In this discussion a beam is taken to be a long body of uniform cross-section, subject to forces which bend it from the straight. If one end A of the beam AB is fixed

(Fig. 96) and the other end B is loaded, the beam is bent as shown. Such a beam is called a cantilever. There is difficulty in fixing such a beam at A so that the sides, at the point of entry to the support,

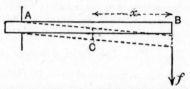

FIG. 96.—BENDING OF BEAM (CANTILEVER).

shall be horizontal, but the reasoning to be applied would be valid if the beam were of double the length, supported on a knife edge at A, and loaded with the force f at both ends (p. 147).

Limiting the problem to the case of a beam whose thickness is small in comparison with the length, any shearing stresses over a section of the beam are extremely small and will be neglected.

Consider a piece of the beam BC, where C is a right section at distance x from B. This is in equilibrium under its own weight, the the load f and certain forces which occur at the section C. The weight of the beam itself will be neglected, so that the bending due to f alone is considered.

Since BC is in equilibrium there must be a vertical force f at C, eventually due to the fixing in the wall. The forces f at B and C constitute a couple of moment fx, which would cause BC to rotate. As, however, it is at rest, there must be an equal and opposite couple acting over the cross-section at C. This cross-section may be of any shape, but it is convenient to draw it as a rectangle. It is represented enlarged by EFGH in Fig. 97. Let $d\alpha$ be a small area of the cross-section. It may be looked upon as a section of a longitudinal filament of the beam. When the beam is bent, such filaments in the upper part of the beam are stretched, and are therefore under tension. Those in the lower part are compressed. These forces of tension and compression supply the couple that balances fx and maintains the part BC (Fig. 96) in equilibrium. There must be some filaments

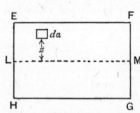

FIG. 97.—CROSS-SECTION OF BEAM.

between the upper and lower parts of the beam that are neither
stretched nor compressed. These lie in a surface called the **neutral
surface** which intersects the diagram in the line **LM**. In Fig. 98 the
upper part of the beam is represented by **ABDC**, **CD** being the neutral
surface, and **AB** a filament in the upper part, the curvature being
exaggerated in the diagram. The
lower part of the beam is not
shown. In the unbent position of
the beam the piece ab of the filament is equal in length to cd of the
neutral surface. In the bent posi-
tion $ab = (r + z)\theta$, and $cd = r\theta$;

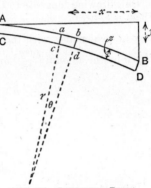

$$\therefore\ ab - cd = z\theta,$$

and the strain in ab is

$$\frac{z\theta}{r\theta} = \frac{z}{r}.$$

But $\dfrac{\text{stress}}{\text{strain}} = e$;

FIG. 98.—STRESSES IN BEAM.

$\therefore$ stress in filament $= \dfrac{ez}{r}$.

Now turning again to Fig. 97, the stress over $d\alpha$ is $\dfrac{ez}{r}$ and the force
over $d\alpha$ is $\dfrac{ez}{r}\,d\alpha$. For the whole section **EFGH**, the force is $\dfrac{e}{r}\displaystyle\int z\,d\alpha$,
and this must be zero, for there is no resultant longitudinal force
acting on the beam. Thus, looking upon the cross-section **EFGH** as a
uniform plate, its centre of gravity must lie in the neutral surface **LM**,
for $\displaystyle\int z\,d\alpha$ is zero for any axis passing through the centre of gravity
(p. 56).

Again, the force over $d\alpha$ has a moment $\dfrac{ez}{r}\,d\alpha\,.\,z = \dfrac{e}{r}z^2 d\alpha$ about **LM**,
so that for the whole section, the moment is $\displaystyle\int\dfrac{e}{r}z^2 d\alpha$, or $\dfrac{e}{r}\displaystyle\int z^2 d\alpha$. The
quantity $\displaystyle\int z^2 d\alpha$ is the moment of inertia about **LM**, considering the
section as a uniform plate (p. 64). Thus whatever the shape of the
cross-section of the beam $\left(\dfrac{e}{r} \times \text{mom. of inertia of section}\right)$ is the couple
that balances fx, or $fx = \dfrac{eI}{r}$. This couple is known as the **bending moment**
at the section, and may be found by taking the algebraic sum of all
moments not due to elastic stresses, on one side of the section.

In Fig. 98 take axes x and y as shown, measuring from the undisturbed position of the end of the beam. Remembering that the deflection is much smaller than shown, the length of the section is $ab = \delta x$;

$$\therefore \ \delta x = r\theta.$$

But, drawing tangents to the curve at a and b, the angle between them is θ, because each is at right angles to a radius. But the angle any tangent makes with the axis of x is $\dfrac{dy}{dx}$, and this increases from b to a by the amount $\left(\dfrac{d^2y}{dx^2}\right)\delta x$;

$$\therefore \ \theta = \left(\frac{d^2y}{dx^2}\right)\delta x = \frac{\delta x}{r} \ ;$$

$$\therefore \ \frac{1}{r} = \frac{d^2y}{dx^2};$$

$$\therefore \ eI\,\frac{d^2y}{dx^2} = fx.$$

Integrating this once, with respect to x,

$$eI\,\frac{dy}{dx} = \tfrac{1}{2}fx^2 + \mathsf{C}.$$

If l is the length of the beam, $\dfrac{dy}{dx} = 0$, when $x = l$, because at this point (A) the beam is horizontal;

$$\therefore \ \mathsf{C} = -\tfrac{1}{2}fl^2.$$

Hence $\qquad eI\,\dfrac{dy}{dx} = \tfrac{1}{2}fx^2 - \tfrac{1}{2}fl^2.$

Integrating again with respect to x,

$$eIy = \tfrac{1}{6}fx^3 - \tfrac{1}{2}fl^2x + \mathsf{C}'.$$

Again, $y = 0$ at A, that is when $x = l$;

$$\therefore \ 0 = \tfrac{1}{6}fl^3 - \tfrac{1}{2}fl^3 + \mathsf{C}',$$

$$\mathsf{C}' = \tfrac{1}{3}fl^3.$$

Hence $\qquad eIy = \tfrac{1}{6}fx^3 - \tfrac{1}{2}fl^2x + \tfrac{1}{3}fl^3.$

At the end B, $x = 0$;

$$\therefore \ eIy = \tfrac{1}{3}fl^3,$$

or $\qquad\qquad y = \dfrac{fl^3}{3eI}.$

For a beam of **rectangular section,** of breadth b and depth d, the moment of inertia of the strip AB (Fig. 99) about LM is $z^2b\,dz$, treating the section as a plate of unit mass per unit area, and for the whole area

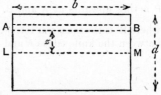

$$I = \int_{-d/2}^{+d/2} bz^2 dz$$

$$= b\left[\frac{z^3}{3}\right]_{-d/2}^{+d/2} = \frac{bd^3}{12};$$

$$\therefore\ y = \frac{4fl^3}{ebd^3}.$$

FIG. 99.—BEAM OF RECTANGULAR CROSS-SECTION.

That is, the depression of the loaded end of the beam is proportional to the cube of its length, and inversely proportional to the breadth and to the cube of the depth.

In the case of a circular beam or rod, $I = \dfrac{mr^2}{4}$ (p. 71). But $m \propto \pi r^2$. Therefore for our present purpose

$$I = \frac{\pi r^4}{4},$$

and

$$y = \frac{4fl^3}{3\pi er^4}.$$

Beam method for determining e.—By measuring the depression caused by loading a beam of known dimensions it is possible to

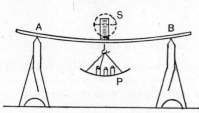

FIG. 100.—DETERMINATION OF YOUNG'S MODULUS BY BENDING OF BEAM.

determine Young's modulus for the material of the beam. It is convenient to use a beam of rectangular cross-section supported on knife edges at A and B (Fig. 100). The load is supplied by adding weights to the scale pan P, which is supported from a knife edge resting on the middle of the beam. The depression of the middle point is determined by means of a microscope with a cross wire in the eyepiece, indicated as a dotted circle in the diagram.

Readings of the scale should be taken with the load increasing by steps and then decreasing, as described on p. 132, and the ratio of deflection to load calculated.

Since the middle part of the beam is horizontal, the beam may be considered as two beams of the type shown in Fig. 96 and inverted. The bending may be considered to be produced by half the load in P acting upwards at A and B. Thus f in equation $y = \dfrac{4fl^3}{ebd^3}$ is $\frac{1}{2}Wg$, where W is the mass put into P. Again, if L is the length of the beam between the knife edges A and B, $L = 2l$ and the equation becomes

$$y = \frac{4 \cdot Wg \cdot L^3}{2 \cdot 8 \cdot ebd^3}$$

$$= \frac{WgL^3}{4ebd^3}.$$

The student should make an experiment with each of three different values of L and show that, other things being constant, the depression y is proportional to the cube of the length. Then turning the beam on edge so that breadth and depth are interchanged, it should be shown that, other things being constant, the depression varies inversely as bd^3. Finally Young's modulus e for the material should be calculated.

Beam bent by couple at each end.—It was seen on p. 145 that when a beam is bent, there is a couple $\dfrac{eI}{r}$ acting over each cross-section. This couple may be applied at A and B (Fig. 101) by holding each

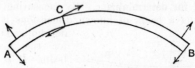

FIG. 101.—BENDING BY MEANS OF A COUPLE.

end in a vice, or by any other means, so that the couple p is applied at each end. Then a portion of the beam such as AC is in equilibrium. It follows that there must be a couple acting over the section at C, equal and opposite to p.

But the couple at C is $\dfrac{eI}{r}$ where r is the radius of curvature of the beam at C;

$$\therefore \ p = \frac{eI}{r}.$$

p, e, and I are constant if the beam is uniform. Thus r is constant. That is, the beam is bent into a circle of radius $\dfrac{eI}{p}$.

Searle's method of comparing n and e.—A very simple method of comparing the rigidity and Young's modulus for a short length of wire has been devised by G. F. C. Searle.

Two similar brass rods A and B (Fig. 102 (a)) are suspended by vertical threads. The wire C is rigidly fixed into the rods at A and B,

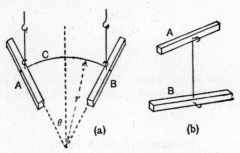

FIG. 102.—SEARLE'S METHOD OF COMPARING n AND e.

so that when C is straight A and B are parallel. On pulling two ends together slightly and releasing them the rods will vibrate, owing to the couple produced by the bending of the wire. On p. 148 it was seen that when a beam is bent by a couple it has constant radius of curvature given by $p = \dfrac{eI}{r}$, so that when A is deflected through angle θ, $p = \dfrac{eI\theta}{l}$, where l is half the length of C.

Therefore the couple for unit θ is $\dfrac{p}{\theta} = c = \dfrac{eI}{l}$.

The value of I for a circular wire is $\dfrac{\pi a^4}{4}$ (p. 147), where a is the radius of cross-section of the wire;

$$\therefore \ c = \frac{e\pi a^4}{4l},$$

and if I_1 is the moment of inertia of the bar A or B, the time of oscillation T_1 is given by

$$T_1 = 2\pi\sqrt{\frac{I_1}{c}} \quad \text{(p. 99)},$$

$$T_1{}^2 = 4\pi^2 I_1 \div c$$

$$= \frac{16\pi l I_1}{e a^4}.$$

The threads are then removed, and one bar, A or B, is supported in a clamp as in Fig. 102 (b). The lower bar is then displaced and

F

allowed to oscillate torsionally and the time of vibration T_2 observed.
In this case $c_2 = \dfrac{\pi n a^4}{4l}$ (p. 141) and $T_2 = 2\pi \sqrt{\dfrac{I_1}{c_2}}$;

$$\therefore T_2{}^2 = 4\pi^2 I_1 \div \frac{\pi n a^4}{4l}$$

$$= \frac{16 \pi l I_1}{n a^4}.$$

$$\therefore \frac{T_1{}^2}{T_2{}^2} = \frac{n}{e}.$$

The ratio of n to e is thus found. If it is desired to find the absolute value of e or n, it is necessary to measure l, I_1 and a and use the expression for T_1 or T_2.

EXERCISES ON CHAPTER VI

1. Give an account of what happens as a piece of wire is gradually stretched. Use this example to illustrate the meaning of the terms : *stress, strain, yield point, Hooke's law, elastic limit*.　　C.H.S.C.

2. Explain what are meant by *elastic limit, modulus of elasticity, Young's modulus*.

Describe how you would determine Young's modulus for a material in the form of a uniform wire, and make an estimate of the accuracy of the determination.　　O. & C.H.S.C.

3. Define Young's modulus of elasticity and describe how it may be measured in the case of a steel wire. What precautions would you take to ensure that the wire had not been overloaded during the experiment ?

　　L.H.S.C.

4. What is meant by the terms stress, strain, and modulus of elasticity ? Describe an experimental method of determining Young's modulus for steel in the form of a long thin wire.

A steel wire 2 mm. in diameter is just stretched between two fixed points at a temperature of 20° C. Determine its tension when the temperature falls to 10° C. (Coefficient of linear expansion of steel = 0·000011. Young's modulus for steel = 2·1 × 10¹² dynes per sq. cm.)　　C.W.B.H.S.C.

5. Find the force which must act on a particle that it may move with uniform speed in a circular path.

A body of mass 10 gm. fastened to one end of a rubber cord of cross-sectional area 5 sq. mm., rotates in a horizontal circle with uniform speed about the other end which is fixed. It executes 2000 revolutions per minute. If the radius of the circle described is 12 cm., find the unstretched length of the cord.

(Young's modulus for the cord is 5 × 10⁸ dynes per sq. cm.)

　　C.W.B.H.S.C.

6. Explain what you mean by the terms—bulk modulus and rigidity modulus.

Describe an experiment by which you would determine the rigidity modulus of a wire, stating clearly how you would calculate the result from your observation.

C.W.B.H.S.C.

7. A particle of mass m is attached by a light elastic string of unstretched length l to a fixed point O, from which the particle is allowed to fall freely from rest. When the particle reaches its lowest position the length of the string is $2l$; prove by considerations of energy or otherwise that its tension is then $4mg$. If in this position half the particle becomes detached, prove that the remaining mass $\frac{1}{2}m$ will rise to a height $\frac{1}{8}l(7 + \sqrt{17})$ above O.

C.H.S.C.

8. A mass m is hung at the end of an unstretched spring of negligible inertia, and released from rest. Show that the maximum tension in the spring is $2mg$. (Assume that Hooke's law is obeyed.)

If a downward blow of impulse B is given to the mass in its lowest position, find the maximum tension, given that the statical extension of the spring for unit mass is c.

C.H.S.C.

9. Find the work done in stretching an elastic string of natural length l to a length $l + x$.

A mass of 10 lb. is attached to one end B of an elastic string AB of natural length 2·25 ft. The modulus of the string is 48 lb. weight. If the end A is fixed and the mass falls from rest at A, find the extension of the string when B reaches its lowest point.

J.M.B.H.S.C.

10. A mass M hangs at rest, being supported by a light elastic string whose natural length is l. If M is displaced vertically and then released, show that it will execute simple harmonic oscillations, and find the time of a complete oscillation. Show that this time is $2\pi\sqrt{(a/g)}$, where a is the amount by which M stretches the string in the equilibrium position.

If a mass m is added to the mass M the time of oscillation is altered in the ratio 5 : 4. Compare the masses m and M.

J.M.B.H.S.C.

11. A particle, of weight w, hangs at the end of a light elastic string of unstretched length l and modulus λ. Prove that in the position in which the string is stretched by the amount x, the combined gravitational and elastic potential energy is

$$\frac{\lambda x^2}{2l} - wx + \text{const.}$$

Determine, by considering the stationary value of this expression, the position of equilibrium of the particle.

C.W.B.H.S.C.

12. Define *Young's modulus*. Is it possible for a liquid to possess this modulus? Give reasons for your answer.

A vertical wire is loaded (within the limits of Hooke's law) by weights which produce a total extension of 3 mm. and 5 mm. respectively. Compare the amounts of work necessary to produce these extensions.

Lond. Int. Sci.

13. Establish an expression for the work done in stretching a wire through l centimetres, assuming Hooke's law to hold.

Find the work done in joules in stretching a wire of cross-section 1 sq. mm. and length 2 metres through 0·1 mm., if Young's modulus for the material of the wire is 2×10^{12} dyne cm.$^{-2}$. Lond. Int. Sci.

14. Show that, for a homogeneous isotropic substance,

$$\frac{Y}{N} = 2(\sigma + 1),$$

where Y is Young's modulus, N the simple rigidity, and σ Poisson's ratio.

A gold wire, 0·32 mm. in diameter, elongates by 1 mm. when stretched by a force of 330 gm. wt. and twists through 1 radian when equal and opposite torques of 145 dyne-cm. are applied at its ends. Find the value of Poisson's ratio for gold. Lond. Schol.

15. Find an expression for the couple required to bend a uniform straight lath into an arc of a circle of small curvature.

A lath of width 2 cm. and thickness 3 mm., supported horizontally on knife edges 80 cm. apart, is loaded with weights of 10 gm. hung from its ends, which project 15 cm. beyond the knife edges. If the centre of the lath is thereby elevated 2 mm., calculate Young's modulus for the material. Lond. B.Sc.

CHAPTER VII

HYDROSTATICS

Definitions of fluid ; liquid and gas.—The shearing strain which a solid body can support indefinitely was studied in the last chapter. It is characteristic of solids that they are strained under a shearing stress, and that the strain lasts as long as the stress acts. In opposition to this, a fluid constantly and continuously yields under a shearing stress. The yield or flow may be rapid or slow. If the flow is rapid the fluid is said to be mobile ; if it is slow the fluid is viscous. Thus a fluid will take, rapidly or slowly, the shape of the vessel in which it is contained. Although the distinction between a fluid and a solid is easily made, in doubtful cases it is not so easy to decide where the border line occurs. In highly elastic solids such as quartz there is no change of shape in millions of years, as is evident from the fact that the edges of quartz crystals are as sharp as when the crystals were formed. Also a liquid such as water flows so rapidly that in a very short time any sharp edges disappear, and when in small quantity the water takes the form of a spherical drop. But if a substance such as pitch be examined, it will be found that it will break with the blow of a hammer and has the appearance of a solid. If, however, a barrel of pitch with one end removed is placed on its side and observed periodically, it will be observed that it flows out of the barrel, as water would do, but vastly more slowly. Thus the pitch is a highly viscous liquid, which at first sight might be taken for a solid. On the other hand, those wires which yield for a time under tension (p. 127) might, during the time for which the yield goes on, be considered as fluids, but on cessation of the yield they must be considered as solids.

Fluids may be classified further as liquids and gases. A gas has the property of indefinite expansion, and therefore fills completely any vessel enclosing it. A liquid, on the contrary, may not fill the vessel and can present a free surface at its upper limit. A gas never presents a free surface, and if there is any aperture in the containing vessel the gas will all escape through it.

Force and pressure.—The definition of force given on p. 27, although quite valid, must be considered carefully when dealing with fluids. The force exerted on or by a fluid is always distributed over an area. The side or bottom of a vessel may be considered as such an area, and the force exerted on unit area is called the **pressure** due to the liquid. The pressure may not be uniform, in which case the small force δf acting over a small area $\delta\alpha$ is a pressure, $\dfrac{\delta f}{\delta\alpha}$. When $\delta\alpha$ is vanishingly small, the pressure at the point is

$$p = \frac{df}{d\alpha}.$$

Pressure always at right angles to boundary surface.—At the boundary of a liquid, produced by the containing vessel, there is pressure exerted by the liquid on the wall of the vessel and an equal and opposite pressure of the wall on the liquid. This pressure must be perpendicular to the boundary surface, for if it were not, it would have a component parallel to the boundary which would cause the liquid to move. But the liquid is supposed to be at rest; hence the pressure is perpendicular to the surface.

Pressure within liquid exerted equally in all directions.—In the interior of a liquid, although there is no boundary, the idea of pressure must be extended to mean the force per unit area across any plane in the liquid. Imagine a portion of liquid ABC (Fig. 103) in the interior. Let it be in the form of a triangular prism, with vertical ends ABC and A'B'C' and horizontal edges AA', BB', CC'. The prism is exaggerated in size in the diagram in order to show the forces. It is supposed to be, in reality, so small that the depth at all parts is practically the same. If the prism of liquid is replaced by a uniform solid of the same weight and dimensions, this solid would be in equilibrium, for there is no change

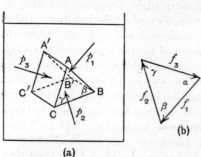

FIG. 103.—PRESSURE IN A LIQUID.

in the forces or pressures, due to the rest of the liquid, by this imaginary solidification of the prism. But it is now seen there are pressures on the faces. The dimensions of the faces are so small that the pressures on each may be looked upon as uniform, and the pressures on the end faces are equal and opposite and can therefore be neglected in considering equilibrium. Let the pressure on the face ABB'A' be p_1, and the others p_2 and p_3 as shown. If l is the length of the prism the force on the face due to p_1 is

$$f_1 = p_1 l \cdot \text{AB}.$$

Similarly the forces on the other faces are $f_2 = p_2 l \cdot \text{BC}$ and

$$f_3 = p_3 l \cdot \text{AC}.$$

Since the prism is at rest, these three forces produce equilibrium, and on drawing the triangle of forces at Fig. 103 (b) it is seen that

$$\frac{f_1}{\sin \gamma} = \frac{f_2}{\sin \alpha} = \frac{f_3}{\sin \beta}.$$

That is,

$$\frac{p_1 l \cdot \text{AB}}{\sin \gamma} = \frac{p_2 l \cdot \text{BC}}{\sin \alpha} = \frac{p_3 l \cdot \text{AC}}{\sin \beta};$$

$$\therefore \frac{p_1 \cdot \text{AB}}{\sin \gamma} = \frac{p_2 \cdot \text{BC}}{\sin \alpha} = \frac{p_3 \cdot \text{AC}}{\sin \beta}.$$

But an inspection of Fig. 103 (a) shows that

$$\frac{\text{AB}}{\sin \gamma} = \frac{\text{BC}}{\sin \alpha} = \frac{\text{AC}}{\sin \beta}.$$

The two sets of equations can only be true if $p_1 = p_2 = p_3$, that is, if the pressure on each face is the same. Since the prism may be rotated about its axis into any position and the same relation holds, it follows that **the pressure at any place in a liquid is exerted equally in all directions.**

Relation between pressure and depth in a liquid.—The pressure at any depth in a liquid, due to the liquid possessing weight, may be found by using the last proved condition. Imagine a vertical column ABDC (Fig. 104) with a horizontal base CD. Since the column is in equilibrium, the resultant of the forces

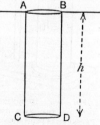

FIG. 104.—PRESSURE AT ANY DEPTH IN A LIQUID.

all over its surface must be equal and opposite to its weight. The forces over the vertical walls must have a zero resultant, since they have no component in the direction of gravity. The force over AB, due to the liquid, is zero and that over CD is $p \times a$, where p is the pressure of the liquid at CD and a is the area of CD. The weight of the liquid in the column is volume × density, that is, $ha\delta$. Therefore,

$$pa = ha\delta,$$
$$p = h\delta.$$

The question of units is important. $h\delta$ is the pressure in gravitational units, that is, in grams weight per square centimetre or pounds weight per square foot or square inch. It is frequently necessary to express the pressure in absolute units. In this case the weight of the column is $ha\delta g$, and the pressure is $h\delta g$ dynes per square centimetre or poundals per square foot or square inch.

The dimensions of pressure are those of $\dfrac{\text{force}}{\text{area}}$, that is,

$$[MLT^{-2}L^{-2}] = [ML^{-1}T^{-2}].$$

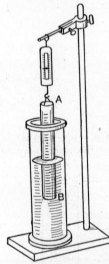

FIG. 105.—DEMONSTRA-
TION OF THE FACT THAT
PRESSURE IS PROPORTIONAL
TO DEPTH.

If there is any pressure on the upper surface of the liquid, this must be added to the pressure $h\delta g$, in order to find the pressure at any depth. This pressure is commonly due to the atmosphere or to some other liquid resting upon the first. Whatever the cause, let the pressure on the upper surface be p_1; then the force over AB due to it is p_1a, and for equilibrium

$$pa - p_1a = ha\delta g,$$
or
$$p = h\delta g + p_1.$$

An important consequence of this is that the **free surface of every liquid at rest must be horizontal.** For if it were not, the depth from the surface to a horizontal plane might differ at two places and the pressures at these places would be different. The liquid would then flow from the place of higher pressure on the horizontal plane to the place of lower pressure. The flow would continue until the pressures were the same, that is, the depths were the same. This would be attained when the free surface of the liquid is horizontal, that is, at right angles to the direction of gravity.

Experimental demonstration.—A simple experiment will show that the pressure at any depth in a liquid is proportional to the depth. A brass cylinder AB (Fig. 105), which is sealed with a disc at its lower end, is suspended by a spring balance and immersed with B at various depths below the surface of water.

The weight of AB is observed by means of the spring balance before immersion. The diminution in weight for various depths of immersion of B is observed and plotted against the depth, on squared paper. It will be found that a straight line results, and that the line passes through the origin. The diminution in weight is due to the pressure at B, which is thus seen to be proportional to the depth.

Comparison of densities.—A simple U-tube may be employed to compare the densities of two liquids, provided that the liquids do not mix. The denser liquid is first poured into one limb AD (Fig. 106) of the U-tube. The other liquid is then poured into the other limb CD and the position of B, the surface of separation of the two liquids when they come to rest, is noted. A point E on the same level as B may be found by using a second U-tube

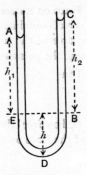

FIG. 106.—COMPARISON OF DENSITIES BY U-TUBE.

with water in it. The part EDB is occupied by the denser liquid. If δ_1 and δ_2 are the densities of the liquids, the pressure at D due to the column AD is $h_1\delta_1 + h\delta_1$, and that due to the column CD is $h_2\delta_2 + h\delta_1$. For the liquids to be at rest these pressures must be the same, so that

$$h_1\delta_1 + h\delta_1 = h_2\delta_2 + h\delta_1,$$

$$h_1\delta_1 = h_2\delta_2,$$

or

$$\frac{\delta_1}{\delta_2} = \frac{h_2}{h_1}.$$

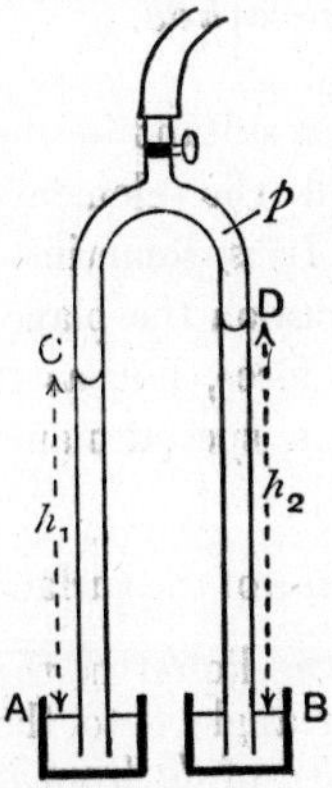

The method cannot be used if the liquids mix, but this difficulty is overcome in an apparatus due to Hare, by using separate vessels A and B (Fig. 107) for the liquids. The two tubes are united at the top and some of the air is drawn out. The liquids then rise in the tubes and the columns AC and BD are measured. If p is the reduced pressure in the tops of the tubes, the pressure at A is $h_1\delta_1 + p$. That at B is $h_2\delta_2 + p$. These are both equal to the atmospheric pressure.

FIG. 107.—HARE'S APPARATUS.

F 2

S.P.M.

Thus
$$h_1\delta_1 + p = h_2\delta_2 + p,$$
$$h_1\delta_1 = h_2\delta_2,$$
$$\frac{\delta_1}{\delta_2} = \frac{h_2}{h_1}.$$

Force on immersed plane.—The force on the horizontal bottom of a vessel containing a liquid is the simple product of the pressure and the area of the surface, because the depth of every point being the same, the pressure is constant over the surface.

Thus
$$\text{force} = \text{pressure} \times \text{area}$$
$$= pa$$
$$= h\delta a \text{ gravitational units.}$$

If, however, the plane surface is not horizontal it is necessary to find the force on an element of area da and integrate over the whole

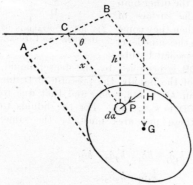

surface. The force on the element is $p\,da = \delta h\,da$, where h is the depth of the element. This force is perpendicular to the plane. The force for the whole plane is therefore

$$\int \delta h\,da = \delta \int h\,da,$$

which is the resultant of the forces on all the elements of surface. It is sometimes called the **thrust** on the plane, or the total force, but as it

FIG. 108.—FORCE ON IMMERSED SURFACE.

is simply a force it is hardly necessary to use a special name for it.

In order to find the value of $\delta \int h\,da$, imagine the plane of the surface to be produced to meet the horizontal surface of the liquid in the line AB (Fig. 108), the plane being inclined at an angle θ to the horizontal. Taking AB as reference line, the distance of da from it being x, $h = x\sin\theta$. Then the total force F on the surface is given by

$$F = \delta \int h\,da = \delta \sin\theta \int x\,da.$$

If the surface be considered as a uniform plate of area a and its centre of gravity to be situated at G, a distance X from AB.

$$\int x\, da = aX \quad \text{(p. 56)};$$

$$\therefore F = \delta \,.\, \sin \theta \,.\, aX,$$

Also if H is the depth of the point G,

$$\frac{H}{X} = \sin \theta,$$

or

$$X = \frac{H}{\sin \theta},$$

and

$$F = \delta \sin \theta \,.\, a \,\frac{H}{\sin \theta}$$

$$= a\delta H.$$

Now δH is the pressure at the centre of gravity, or more correctly, centre of area of the surface, therefore

force on plane = area × pressure at centre of area.

This gives the value of the resultant force on the plane, but it is not yet known at what point of the plane this resultant force acts. In order to determine this, take moments about the line AB.

The force on the element of area da is $\delta h\, da = \delta \sin \theta \,.\, x\, da$, and the moment of this about AB is $\delta \sin \theta \,.\, x\, da \,.\, x = \delta \sin \theta x^2 da$. The total moment of all the forces is $\delta \sin \theta \int x^2 da$, where the integration extends all over the surface.

This moment must equal FX_1, where X_1 is the distance from AB at which the resultant force F acts;

$$\therefore FX_1 = \delta \sin \theta \int x^2 da.$$

The point through which F acts is called the **centre of pressure**, and if H_1 is its distance below the surface of the liquid,

$$\frac{H_1}{X_1} = \sin \theta;$$

$$\therefore \frac{FH_1}{\sin \theta} = \delta \sin \theta \int x^2 da.$$

But $h = x \sin \theta$;

$$\therefore \; H_1 = \frac{\delta \sin^2 \theta}{F} \int \frac{h^2}{\sin^2 \theta} \, da$$

$$= \frac{\delta \int h^2 da}{F}$$

$$= \frac{\delta \int h^2 da}{\delta a H}$$

$$= \frac{\int h^2 da}{a H} \, .$$

It will thus be seen that the depth of the centre of pressure below the surface of the liquid does not depend upon the density of the liquid. The integral $\int h^2 da$ or $\int x^2 da$ depends upon the shape of the plane surface.

A further useful result may be obtained by noticing that

$$X_1 = \frac{\delta \sin \theta \int x^2 da}{F} = \frac{\int x^2 da}{\int x \, da} \, .$$

Now $\int x^2 da = k^2 a$ where k is the radius of gyration (p. 65) of the surface of area a about the line AB where its plane cuts the surface of the liquid. Also $\int x \, da = x_1 a$, where x_1 is the distance of the centre of area from AB ;

$$\therefore \; X_1 = \frac{k^2 a}{x_1 a} = \frac{k^2}{x_1} \, .$$

EXAMPLE 1.—Find the force on the rectangular end of a tank of width b and depth d filled with water. Also find the centre of pressure on the end of the tank.

The centre of gravity is at depth $\dfrac{d}{2} = H$, and the pressure there is

$$\frac{d}{2} \text{ gm. wt./cm.}^2,$$

since the density of water is unity. Therefore force is area $\times$ pressure at depth $\dfrac{d}{2} = b \cdot d \, \dfrac{d}{2} = \dfrac{bd^2}{2}$ gravitational units.

In order to find the centre of pressure, note that, owing to symmetry, it is in the median vertical line. Also its depth is given by

$$H_1 = \frac{\int h^2 da}{Ha}.$$

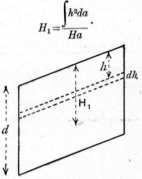

FIG. 109.—CENTRE OF PRESSURE.

In this case take a horizontal parallel strip of depth dh (Fig. 109). Then $da = b\,dh$;

$$\therefore\ H_1 = \frac{\int_0^d h^2 b\,dh}{aH}$$

$$= \frac{2b}{bd\,.\,d}\int_0^d h^2\,dh$$

$$= \frac{2}{d^2}\,.\,\frac{d^3}{3},$$

$$\underline{H_1 = \tfrac{2}{3}d.}$$

EXAMPLE 2.—What do you understand by " the pressure at a point in a liquid," and by " the centre of pressure " ?

One end of a tank full of water is a vertical rectangle 5 ft. long and 3 ft. high. Find the thrust on it.

If it were hinged at the lower edge and kept in position by bolts at each end of the top edge, find the force on each bolt.   O.H.S.C.

The depth at the centre of area is 1·5 ft. Pressure at this depth is 1·5δ lb. wt. per sq. ft. where δ = 62·3 lb. per cu. ft.

Thrust = area × pressure at centre of area

= 5 × 3 × 1·5 × 62·3

= 1402 lb. wt.

Depth of centre of pressure = $\tfrac{2}{3}$ × 3   (see above)

= 2 ft. ;

∴ centre of pressure is 1 ft. above the hinge.

Taking moments about the hinge,

$$F \times 3 = 1402 \times 1,$$

where F is the force due to both bolts,

$$F = 467 ;$$

$$\therefore \underline{\text{force due to each bolt} = 233 \cdot 5 \text{ lb. wt.}}$$

Principle of Archimedes.—When a body is at rest, the resultant vertical force on it must be zero (p. 52). If the body is immersed in

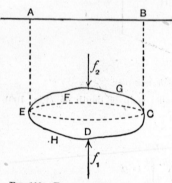

FIG. 110.—FORCE ON IMMERSED BODY.

a liquid the vertical forces acting upon it are (i) its weight (w), (ii) the force due to pressure of the liquid over its lower surface acting upwards (f_1), (iii) the force due to the pressure of the liquid over its upper surface acting downwards (f_2), and (iv) the force due to any support.

Suppose the body CHDEGF (Fig. 110) to have the same density δ as the liquid in which it is immersed. If the body were made of the liquid it would be at rest, and if we like to imagine it to become solidified without changing density, this will not change any of the forces acting on it, and it will remain at rest. In this case force (iv) above is zero. Hence for equilibrium $w + f_2 = f_1$.

Imagine a vertical line AE to travel round the body, touching it along a line CDEF. The liquid in the column ABCDEFG is supported by the forces over the upper surface of the body, and its weight is therefore f_2, which is equal to the volume × density. Similarly f_1 is the volume of ABCHE multiplied by the density. Thus $f_1 - f_2$ is the volume of the body multiplied by its density, that is, its weight in gravitational units. $f_1 - f_2$ is the resultant upward force on the body due to the surrounding liquid, and is therefore equal to the weight of the liquid, having the same volume as the body, that is, it is equal to the weight of the liquid displaced by the body.

The forces on the body due to the surrounding liquid do not depend upon the density of the body itself. Therefore the resultant upward force on the body is always equal to the weight of the liquid displaced. This is usually expressed by saying that the loss of weight of a body immersed in a liquid is equal to the weight of the liquid displaced. This is known as the principle of Archimedes.

The fact may be demonstrated by hanging a solid cylinder A (Fig. 111) and a hollow cylinder B from a spring balance. A fits closely into the interior of B, so that the external volume of A is equal to the internal volume of B. The two are weighed in air.

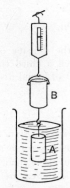

If now A is immersed in a beaker of water as shown, and at the same time B is filled with water, the reading of the spring balance is unchanged. Thus the loss of weight of A is equal to the weight of the water placed in B.

When "loss in weight" is mentioned, it must be remembered that the more exact expression would be "loss in apparent weight," because the actual weight does not change on immersion, but the upward force due to the liquid produces an apparent decrease in weight.

FIG. 111.—ILLUSTRATION OF THE PRINCIPLE OF ARCHIMEDES.

The principle of Archimedes may be more exactly expressed as follows : a body wholly or partially immersed in a fluid experiences an upward force equal to the weight of the fluid displaced, which force acts through the centre of gravity of the displaced fluid.

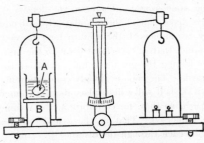

FIG. 112.—DENSITY BY DISPLACEMENT.

The last part of this statement follows from the fact that the body CHEG (Fig. 110) is in equilibrium. Its own weight acts through its centre of gravity, and if its density is the same as that of the fluid displaced, this would have had the same centre of gravity. The weight of the body and the upward force due to the fluid must be in the same line, or the body would experience a couple and would not remain at rest.

Measurement of density.—The principle of Archimedes affords one of the best methods of measuring density. The body A (Fig. 112), whose density is required, hangs by a fine thread from a hook above the pan of a balance. A bridge B is placed so that a beaker of liquid can be placed over the pan and held independently of it, and the body A is immersed in the liquid. Then A may be weighed, first without being immersed, w_1, and next when immersed in the liquid, w_2. The loss in weight is thus $w_1 - w_2$, and if the liquid is water and the density of water is taken as unity, the volume of the body is $w_1 - w_2$.

Then,
$$\text{density} = \frac{w_1}{w_1 - w_2}.$$

If the density of another liquid is required, the body may be weighed a third time, w_3, this time immersed in the liquid. The weight of liquid displaced is $w_1 - w_3$, and its volume is $w_1 - w_2$;

$$\therefore \text{ density of liquid} = \frac{w_1 - w_3}{w_1 - w_2}.$$

EXAMPLE.—State the principle of Archimedes, and describe how it may be verified experimentally.

A circular cylinder and a circular cone, of the same height and the same basal area, are hung at opposite ends of a string which passes over a pulley. The cone hangs base upwards, and, when the bodies are suspended in air, the string is in equilibrium. The cone and cylinder are now held in a trough of water so that their uppermost surfaces are in the surface of the water. What equilibrium position will the system take up if the holding forces are now removed ?   C.H.S.C.

Since the string is in equilibrium, when the bodies are in air, the cone and the cylinder must have the same weight. Therefore the density of the material of the cone is three times that of the cylinder. In order to preserve equilibrium when they are immersed, the upward force on each due to the liquid must be the same, that is, each must displace the same volume of water. The cylinder having the greater volume displaces the more water and will move upwards. The cone is already completely immersed, and when it moves downwards it will still displace its own volume of water. Volume of cone is $\frac{1}{3}\pi r^2 l$, so that, for equilibrium, the volume $\frac{1}{3}\pi r^2 l$ of the cylinder must be immersed. That is, the cylinder moves upwards and the cone downwards, each through the distance $\frac{2}{3}l$.

Correction for buoyancy in weighing.—In using a balance (p. 52) it is not generally necessary to make any allowance for the loss of apparent weight of the standard weights and the body to be weighed. When great accuracy is desired this buoyancy must be taken into account. If the body being weighed has the same density as the standard weights, they have the same volume, when equilibrium is attained, and therefore displace the same amount of air, so that no correction is necessary.

If, however, the body being weighed has density δ_1 and the weights density δ_2, while the density of air is δ_3, then if the true mass of the body is m_1 it displaces $\frac{m_1}{\delta_1}$ volume of air and its apparent weight is $\left(m_1 - \frac{m_1}{\delta_1}\delta_3\right)$, the mass of air displaced being $\frac{m_1}{\delta_1}\delta_3$. If on balancing, the standard weights required for equilibrium are m_2, their volume is $\frac{m_2}{\delta_2}$, and the mass of air displaced is $\frac{m_2\delta_3}{\delta_2}$, and their apparent weight is $\left(m_2 - \frac{m_2\delta_3}{\delta_2}\right)$. When equilibrium is obtained,

$$\left(m_1 - \frac{m_1}{\delta_1}\delta_3\right) = \left(m_2 - \frac{m_2\delta_3}{\delta_2}\right);$$

$$\therefore \; m_1 = m_2\left(\frac{1 - \delta_3/\delta_2}{1 - \delta_3/\delta_1}\right)$$

$$m_1 = m_2\left(\frac{\delta_2 - \delta_3}{\delta_2} \cdot \frac{\delta_1}{\delta_1 - \delta_3}\right) = m_2\left(1 - \frac{\delta_3}{\delta_2}\right)\left(1 - \frac{\delta_3}{\delta_1}\right)^{-1}.$$

If brass weights are used $\delta_2 = 8\cdot4$, and the density of air δ_3 is $0\cdot00123$ at $14°$ C.;

$$\therefore \; m_1 = m_2\left(\frac{8\cdot4 - 0\cdot00123}{8\cdot4} \cdot \frac{\delta_1}{\delta_1 - 0\cdot00123}\right)$$

$$= m_2\frac{\delta_1}{\delta_1 - 0\cdot00123} \text{ to within 1 in 8000}$$

$$= m_2\delta_1(\delta_1 - 0\cdot00123)^{-1}$$

$$= m_2\left(1 - \frac{0\cdot00123}{\delta_1}\right)^{-1}$$

$$= m_2\left(1 + \frac{0\cdot00123}{\delta_1} + \left(\frac{0\cdot00123}{\delta_1}\right)^2 + \ldots\right),$$

unless δ_1 is very small,

$$m_1 = m_2\left(1 + \frac{0\cdot00123}{\delta_1}\right), \text{ or more exactly } m_2\left(1 - \frac{0\cdot00123}{8\cdot4} + \frac{0\cdot00123}{\delta_1}\right).$$

Floating bodies.—If the density of a body is greater than that of the liquid in which it is immersed, its weight is always greater than that of the liquid displaced, and it will sink unless some support is provided. If the density is equal to that of the liquid, it will remain in equilibrium anywhere, provided that it is completely immersed. But with a density less than that of the liquid, the upward thrust when completely immersed, that is, $f_1 - f_2$ (p. 162) is greater than the weight of the body. It will then rise and float partly immersed. For equiiibrium, the weight of the liquid displaced is equal to the weight of the body.

Stability of floating body.—For a body to float at rest, its centre of gravity must be in the same vertical line as the centre of gravity of the displaced liquid (p. 163). If

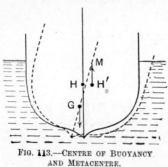

FIG. 113.—CENTRE OF BUOYANCY AND METACENTRE.

the floating body is then given a slight rotation about a horizontal axis, this rotation may or may not move the centre of gravity of the displaced liquid. If it does not, as in the case of a sphere, the body is floating in neutral equilibrium and will remain in any position.

In other cases it is necessary to consider the couple brought into play when a small rotation is given to the body, so that the same amount of fluid is displaced by it as in the undisturbed position. If G (Fig. 113) is the centre of gravity of the floating body and H the centre of gravity of the displaced fluid, the body is in equilibrium when these two are in the same vertical line. H is sometimes called the **centre of buoyancy.** When the displacement occurs, the centre of buoyancy moves to H′, the amount of movement being determined by the shape of the floating body. It is now seen that a couple acts on the body. The couple may tend to restore the body to its original position, as in the figure, in which case the equilibrium is stable. On the other hand, it may tend to displace the body still more, in which case the original equilibrium is unstable.

If a vertical line is drawn through H′ to cut the median line of the body in the point M, this point M is called the **metacentre** and MG the **metacentric height**. If the centre of gravity G is below M the equilibrium is stable, but if G is above M the equilibrium is unstable. Hence the importance of knowing the position of the metacentre in ship-designing, and of keeping the centre of gravity as low as possible.

EXAMPLE.—What is meant by " centre of pressure " and by " metacentric height " ?

A flat rectangular plate 3 ft. by 2 ft. is fixed in the vertical side of a ship of 20,000 tons displacement with the top of the longer side of the plate horizontal and at a depth of 2 ft. below the water surface.

What is the total thrust due to the water on the plate, and at what point may it be considered to act ?

If a load of 20 tons moved 50 ft. across the deck causes the ship to tilt through $\frac{1}{2}°$, what is its metacentric height ?   (1 cubic foot of water weighs 62·5 lb.)   O.H.S.C.

$$\text{Thrust on plate} = \text{area} \times \text{pressure at c.g.}$$

$$= 3 \times 2 \times 3 \times 62\cdot5$$

$$= \underline{1125 \text{ lb. wt.}}$$

$$\text{Depth of centre of pressure} = \int_2^4 \frac{3h^2 dh}{6 \times 3} \quad \text{(see p. 160)}$$

$$= \frac{1}{6}\left[\frac{h^3}{3}\right]_2^4 = \frac{1}{6}\left[\frac{64}{3} - \frac{8}{3}\right]$$

$$= \underline{\tfrac{5\,6}{1\,8} = 3\cdot11 \text{ ft.}}$$

A load of 20 tons moved 50 ft. across the deck is equivalent to the application of a couple of 50×20 ton-feet.

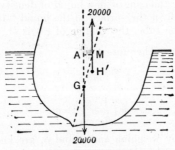

FIG. 114.—PROBLEM.

Since the ship is still in equilibrium, the weight and the upward force of the water produce a couple equal and opposite to 50×20.

$$\therefore \quad 20000 \times (\text{MA}) = 50 \times 20 \quad \text{(see Fig. 114)};$$

$$\therefore \quad \text{MA} = \tfrac{1}{2\,0} \text{ ft.}$$

But $\qquad \widehat{MGA} = \frac{1}{2}^\circ$ and $MA = MG \sin \widehat{AGM}$;

$$\therefore \quad \tfrac{1}{20} = MG \sin \tfrac{1}{2}^\circ,$$

$$0\cdot05 = MG(0\cdot0087),$$

$$MG = \frac{0\cdot05}{0\cdot0087},$$

metacentric height $= 5\cdot75$ ft.

Hydrometers.—A hydrometer is an instrument for measuring rapidly the densities of solids or liquids by using the principle of Archimedes. Only two of the various types of hydrometer will be described : (i) the **constant weight** hydrometer, and (ii) the **constant immersion** hydrometer.

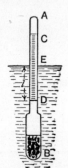

(i) An example of the constant weight type of hydrometer is illustrated in Fig. 115. A uniform tube AD terminates in a bulb B, the lower part of which contains lead shot or mercury. This weight ensures a low position for the centre of gravity of the whole, which enables the body to float in a vertical position. Suppose that the weight of the instrument is w gm., and that it floats to the level D in a liquid of density δ_1.

FIG. 115.—CONSTANT WEIGHT HYDROMETER.

The volume of the part BD is then $\dfrac{w}{\delta_1}$. On immersing it in a liquid of density δ_2, less than δ_1, it may float with E in the surface of the liquid. If a is the area of cross-section of the tube, the volume of ED is la, and the volume immersed is $\dfrac{w}{\delta_1} + la$. Therefore

$$\left(\frac{w}{\delta_1} + la\right) \delta_2 = w,$$

or $\qquad w\left(\dfrac{1}{\delta_2} - \dfrac{1}{\delta_1}\right) = la.$

If w is found by weighing and a and δ_1 are known, δ_2 may be found on observing l. It is more convenient to use two liquids of known density and observe l. Then $\dfrac{a}{w}$ can be calculated since $\dfrac{1}{\delta_2} - \dfrac{1}{\delta_1} = l \cdot \dfrac{a}{w}$. Using a third liquid of unknown density δ_3,

$$\frac{1}{\delta_3} - \frac{1}{\delta_1} = l_3 \cdot \frac{a}{w}.$$

δ_3 is known in terms of l_3. It is convenient to plot a curve connecting δ_3 and l_3 from the known values of δ_1 and $\dfrac{a}{w}$, and so construct a scale for the stem AD, so that the density of any liquid may be read off directly on immersion in it. It should be noticed that each hydrometer has a limited range, confined to the densities corresponding to the levels C and D.

The student should construct a hydrometer of a test-tube loaded with shot, with a paper scale inside it. It is loaded so that its total weight is w_1 and the mark to which it sinks in water may be noted. Some more shot is added so that the weight is w_2. If it is then depressed an additional distance l cm. on the scale, $w_2 - w_1 = la$, taking the density of water as unity. Knowing a, w_2 and δ_1, the depth of sinking for any liquid of density δ_2 may be found from

$$\frac{1}{\delta_2} - \frac{1}{\delta_1} = l \cdot \frac{w_2}{a},$$ δ_1 in this case being unity.

(ii) **Nicholson's hydrometer** is a common form of the constant immersion type. It consists of a pan A, a wire stem AB, and a float BC to which is attached a cone D, weighted with lead shot. The float and the shot together cause the hydrometer to float in an upright position. It is always loaded with weights in the pan A, so that a mark E on the stem AB is in the surface of the water. Some weights in A are removed, and the body whose density is required is placed in A, and the weights are adjusted until the hydrometer again sinks to E. If the first weight is w_1 and the second w_2, the weight of the body in air is $w_1 - w_2$. The body is now transferred to the pan formed by the top of the cone D, so that it is immersed. If the body is less dense than water it must be tied to the pan so that it cannot float. The adjustment of the weights in A is again made so that the hydrometer sinks to E. If w_3 is then the weight in A, the weight of the body in water is $w_1 - w_3$, and the density is

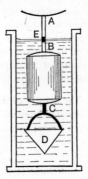

FIG. 116.—NICHOLSON'S HYDROMETER.

$$\frac{\text{weight in air}}{\text{weight in air} - \text{weight in water}} = \frac{w_1 - w_2}{(w_1 - w_2) - (w_1 - w_3)} = \frac{w_1 - w_2}{w_3 - w_2}.$$

The result obtained is, of course, the ratio of the density of the body to that of water, commonly known as the **specific gravity** of the body. For approximate purposes the density of water is taken as unity, so that the density of the body and its specific gravity have the same value on the c.g.s. system. But if the absolute density in grams per cubic centimetre is required, the specific gravity of the body as found must be multiplied by the density of the water at the temperature of the experiment as found from tables. On the British system of units the density is approximately 62·5 times the specific gravity.

If the density of a liquid is required, the experiment may be repeated, using the liquid in place of the water. The result gives the ratio of the density of the solid (δ_1) to that of the liquid (δ_2), that is $\dfrac{\delta_1}{\delta_2}$. The first experiment gives $\dfrac{\delta_1}{\delta_w}$ where δ_w is the density of the water at the temperature of the experiment. Dividing one result by the other gives $\dfrac{\delta_2}{\delta_w}$. This measurement is impossible if the liquid has such a small density that the hydrometer when unloaded sinks in it below the mark E.

EXAMPLE.—Describe and explain the mode of action of the common (constant weight) hydrometer.

A constant weight hydrometer has a mass of 20 gm. and reads 1·00 when immersed in water. A piece of brass (sp. gr. 8·4) is attached to the lower end by a brass wire, so that the total mass is increased to 22·5 gm., and the level to which the hydrometer sinks in water is noted. What is the specific gravity of the liquid in which, without the brass, the hydrometer would sink to the same level?   J.M.B.H.S.C.

The density of the water is indicated as being unity, so that the volume when immersed in water and unloaded is 20 c.c. The volume immersed when loaded with the brass is 22·5 c.c.

$$\text{Volume of brass} = \frac{2·5}{8·4} \text{ c.c.}$$

∴ Volume immersed if the brass is removed without change of level is

$$\left(22·5 - \frac{2·5}{8·4}\right) \text{c.c.}$$

As this is the volume immersed in liquid of density δ to this mark when the weight is 20 gm.,

$$\left(22·5 - \frac{2·5}{8·4}\right)\delta = 20,$$
$$(22·5 - 0·298)\delta = 20,$$
$$\delta = \frac{20}{22·2}$$
$$= \underline{0·901}.$$

The siphon.—A useful application of liquid pressure is afforded by the siphon. If it is required to remove water or other liquid from a vessel without tilting the vessel, a bent tube ABCD (Fig. 117), filled with water, or the liquid, is placed as shown. The pressures at A and D are both atmospheric, so that at the highest point of the tube B the pressure is less than atmospheric on the C side by the pressure due to the column BCD, and on the A side by that due to the shorter column AB. In other words, the pressure is greater at A than at C. Thus the flow in the direction ABCD takes place, and will continue so long as the discharge orifice D is below the level A, the tube, of course, being completely filled with liquid.

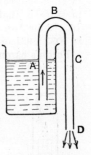

FIG. 117.—SIPHON.

Gases.—It was pointed out (p. 153) that gases are fluids of infinite expansibility. The pressure due to the weight of a column of gas at rest is the same as that of a liquid, but the column may, as in the case of the atmosphere, have variable density and not possess a measurable height. Nevertheless, an experiment due to Torricelli illustrates the effect of atmospheric pressure. If a glass tube AB (Fig. 118), closed at A and open at B, is filled with clean, dry mercury and inverted without allowing any mercury to escape or air to enter, and the open end placed under the surface of mercury in a vessel, the mercury in the tube will fall until a definite height of mercury BC remains. The upper part AC of the tube remains empty, and is called the Torricellian vacuum.

FIG. 118.—TORRICELLIAN VACUUM.

On considering a horizontal plane at B which contains the surface of the mercury in the dish, it will be seen that the pressure on the mercury over this plane must be constant (p. 156), both inside and outside the tube. The pressure inside the tube is due to the column of mercury CB. The only pressure upon the surface of the mercury in the dish outside is that of the atmosphere. Thus the atmospheric pressure may be measured by finding the pressure due to the column of mercury CB. This is equal to $h\delta g$ dynes per sq. cm., or

$h\delta$ gm. wt. per sq. cm. Mercury being such a convenient liquid for measuring pressures, it is a common practice to measure pressures in their equivalent columns of mercury. The average atmospheric pressure is that of 76 cm. of mercury column. This is equal to $76 \times 13\cdot596$, or 1033 gm. wt. per sq. cm. In absolute measure this is 1033×981 or $1\cdot013 \times 10^6$ dynes per sq. cm.

Fortin's barometer.—The vertical tube of mercury affords a rough but reliable means of measuring atmospheric pressure in terms of

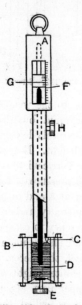

FIG. 119.—FORTIN'S
BAROMETER.

height of mercury column. It is, however, desirable to have some more accurate method of measuring the height of this column. This is afforded by many instruments, of which a common and efficient form is Fortin's barometer, illustrated diagrammatically in Fig. 119, the lower part of which is in section. The barometric tube AB is enclosed in a brass tube, which is hung from a firm support. This carries the reservoir of mercury D, into which AB dips. In order to obtain a constant level for the surface of the mercury in D a fixed pointer C is provided, and the level of mercury can be raised or lowered by the screw E, which pushes in the wash leather bottom of the tank, until the free surface of the mercury is seen to touch C. The fixed scale F has its zero at C. The height of the column is observed by means of the vernier G, which can be raised or lowered by a rack and pinion moved by H, until the bottom of the vernier appears to touch the surface of the mercury column. Parallax is avoided by means of a dummy vernier at the back of the tube, which moves with the real vernier. A thermometer is provided on the case of the instrument for measuring the temperature of the barometer at the time of making the observation.

If the temperature varies much from $0°$ C. a correction should be made, because the density of the mercury is not the standard density and the scale has not the length at which it is calibrated. The density of the mercury is $1/(1 + \beta t)$ of its normal value, where β is the coefficient of expansion of mercury. Hence on this account the column is $(1 + \beta t)$ times too long, and should be divided by $(1 + \beta t)$. Since the scale has expanded when the temperature is above $0°$ C., the column appears too short, as read by this scale. The observed reading should therefore be multiplied by $(1 + \gamma t)$, where γ is the linear coefficient of expansion of the scale. Thus if H_t is the observed height of the barometer at t° C. and H_0 the height reduced to standard conditions,

$$H_0 = H_t \frac{1 + \gamma t}{1 + \beta t}$$

$$= H_t \{1 - (\beta - \gamma)t\},$$

neglecting the squares and higher powers of the coefficients of expansion. For mercury $\beta = 0.000181$, and for brass, which is usually employed for the scale, $\gamma = 0.000019$;

$$\therefore \quad H_0 = H_t (1 - 0.000162t).$$

Aneroid barometer.—The mercurial barometer as an instrument of precision requires adjustment whenever a reading is to be made, and clearly it must not be liable to disturbance. For rapid readings, where great accuracy is not required, the aneroid barometer has been devised. It is shown diagrammatically in Fig. 120. The essential

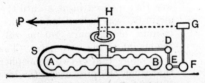

FIG. 120.—ANEROID BAROMETER.

part is a drum AB, made of flexible metal and evacuated as thoroughly as possible. Its flexibility is increased by making circular corrugations in its walls. It is kept distended against the atmospheric pressure by a strong spring S. Any movement of the upper face due to variation in the atmospheric pressure is communicated by the levers DE, EF and FG to a light chain which is wrapped round the axle H, to which is attached a pointer P, which indicates atmospheric pressure on a circular scale. A hair spring keeps the chain taut. Attempts are made in the construction of its parts to compensate for temperature changes. These are only partially successful, and if great reliability is required the aneroid barometer should be frequently checked by means of a mercurial barometer.

Expansion and compression of gases ; Boyle's law.—Although the free surface presented by a liquid distinguishes it from a gas, there are two other differences, although these tend to vanish in border-line cases. Thus, gases are generally much less dense than liquids, and they are much more easily compressed. This compressibility was first investigated by Boyle, who gave the law connecting the pressure and volume of any constant quantity of gas. This law is that **the volume varies inversely as the pressure**, provided that the temperature remains constant, and is known as Boyle's law.

He established it by the use of a bent tube, now known as a Boyle's tube. The tube ABC (Fig. 121) has a long limb AB open at the top,

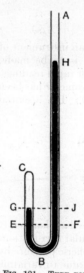

and a short limb BC sealed at the top. Mercury poured into the tube seals off a certain amount of air in BC, and in the original experiment this amount was manipulated until the levels of mercury surface in the two limbs were the same, as at E and F. Since the pressure at the surface of mercury at F is the atmospheric pressure, that of the air in CE must be the same, since the mercury EBF is in equilibrium. Mercury was then poured in at A until the volume of the air in BC was halved, and it was found that the column of mercury HJ in AB was equal to the height of the barometer. The pressure at J is therefore that of two atmospheres. It follows that when the pressure of the air enclosed in BC is doubled its volume is halved.

The student should perform the experiment, but instead of making the preliminary manipulation to get the level EF, the heights should always be measured from the base B, by means of a metre scale. The difference of the heights of H and G will then give the column of mercury, which, added to the height of the barometer, is the pressure on the air in CG. The length CG is taken as the volume of the air, since its absolute volume is not required. An allowance for the curved end at C may be made if desirable. On taking a number of readings it will be found that

$$\text{pressure} \times \text{volume} = \text{constant.}$$

that is, that the volume varies inversely as the pressure. Instead of multiplying pressure and volume, a graph may be plotted connecting pressure and volume, which will be a rectangular hyperbola, or if p is plotted against $\dfrac{1}{v}$ a straight line, which if produced would pass through the origin, is obtained.

FIG. 121.—TUBE FOR PROVING BOYLE'S LAW.

A more elaborate apparatus for establishing Boyle's law consists of an inverted burette AB (Fig. 122), in which the air is compressed, and a reservoir of mercury C which can be raised and lowered. A side tube D, which moves over a ver-tical scale, serves as a gauge for mercury level. With the tap A open, the level at D is that corresponding to atmos-pheric pressure, and on closing A the volume of air is indicated by the reading on the burette and its pres-sure by the height of mercury at D above or below the level in AB. The burette is first calibrated by run-ning water from it, step by step, and weighing the water in the ordinary manner. It is then thoroughly dried and placed in position, and air drawn into it through drying tubes by raising and lowering C. The law may then be proved for pressures less than that of the atmosphere, as well as for greater pressures.

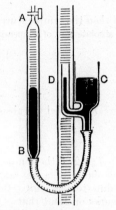

FIG. 122.—APPARATUS FOR THE INVESTIGATION OF BOYLE'S LAW.

Permanent gases ; perfect gas.—Many gases, such as oxygen, nitrogen, hydrogen, air, obey Boyle's law very nearly. They are often called the **permanent** gases, because it was at one time believed that they could not be liquefied. It is true that they cannot be liquefied by pressure alone at ordinary temperatures but by sufficient lowering of the temperature all gases may be liquefied. At high pressure it is found by accurate measurement that the permanent gases depart slightly from Boyle's law. It is convenient for indicating their departures from the law to imagine a gas which would obey Boyle's law exactly, that is, under all con-ditions its volume will, at constant temperature, vary exactly as the inverse of the pressure. Such an ideal gas is called a **perfect gas.**

Temperature.—At constant pressure, the volume of a quantity of gas varies considerably as its temperature changes. The study of this change belongs to the books on Heat, and will not be dealt with here. But a summary of the results is useful. Thus, **Charles' law** states that a permanent gas increases in volume at constant pressure by a constant amount for each degree rise in temperature. This amount is found by experiment to be approximately 1/273 of its volume at 0° C. for each degree centigrade ;

$$\therefore V_t = V_0\left(1 + \frac{t}{273}\right).$$

If then the temperature is reckoned from $-273°$ C., which is called the **absolute zero of temperature**,

$$V_T = V_0\left(1 + \frac{T-273}{273}\right)$$

$$= \frac{V_0 T}{273},$$

where T is called the absolute temperature ;

$$\therefore \frac{V_T}{T} = \frac{V_0}{T_0},$$

since $T_0 = 273$, the temperature of 0° C. on the absolute scale. Thus the volume of a gas at constant pressure is proportional to the absolute temperature. Combining this with Boyle's law, it is shown in works on Heat that

$$\frac{P_T V_T}{T} = \frac{P_0 V_0}{T_0},$$

or

$$\frac{P_1 V_1}{T_1} = \frac{P_2 T_2}{T_2} = R,$$

where R is a constant ;

$$\therefore PV = RT.$$

This is known as the characteristic equation of a perfect gas.

Elasticity of a gas.—It was seen on p. 128 that any volume elasticity is $v \cdot \dfrac{dp}{dv}$. It is now possible to find from Boyle's law an expression for this elasticity in the case of a gas at constant temperature.

For $\qquad pv = c \quad$ (p. 174),

and differentiating this,

$$p \cdot dv + v\, dp = 0,$$

c being a constant ;

$$\therefore \frac{dp}{dv} = -\frac{p}{v}.$$

But $\qquad$ elasticity $= v\dfrac{dp}{dv}$

$$= p.$$

Thus **the elasticity of a perfect gas is the pressure under which it exists.**

The negative sign occurs above because an increase of pressure is always accompanied by a decrease in volume : that is, dp and dv always have opposite signs, so that $\dfrac{dp}{dv}$ is essentially negative.

This assumes constant temperature, and is called the isothermal elasticity of a gas. When no heat is allowed to enter or leave, the temperature changes. Under these conditions the elasticity is different (Chap. XIII).

EXAMPLE.—State the conditions which must be fulfilled in order that a body may float wholly or partly submerged.

An inflated thin-walled rubber balloon containing a little mercury floats in a lake of fresh water with half its volume immersed. Show that there is a second possible position of equilibrium for the balloon, and show further that the equilibrium in the second case is unstable. Assume that the balloon remains spherical throughout.   C.H.S.C.

If V is the volume of the balloon when floating and w its weight,

$$\frac{V}{2} = w,$$

taking the density of water as unity.

The pressure is atmospheric, and taking this as equivalent to a column P of water, $P = 13 \cdot 6 \times$ height of mercurial barometer.

Let the balloon be now pushed down to a depth H; the pressure is $P + H$ cm. of water, and the new volume V_1 is given by

$$(P + H)V_1 = PV \quad \text{(Boyle's law)},$$

and
$$V_1 = \frac{PV}{P + H}.$$

If now the volume V_1 of water displaced is equal to w the weight of the balloon, there is equilibrium, and

$$w = V_1 = \frac{PV}{P + H} = \frac{V}{2} \quad \text{or} \quad H = P.$$

A slight vertical displacement dH causes a change in volume dV_1, where

$$\frac{dV_1}{dH} = -\frac{PV}{(P + H)^2},$$

P, V and $(P + H)^2$ are all essentially positive ;

$$\therefore \quad \frac{dV_1}{dH} \text{ is negative,}$$

that is, if H is decreased to less than P, V_1 increases, and the body will therefore continue to rise.

If H increases, V_1 decreases, and the body will then displace less water and will sink. It is therefore in unstable equilibrium.

McLeod gauge.—It is of great importance to be able to measure the very low pressures that occur in so-called vacuum tubes. When

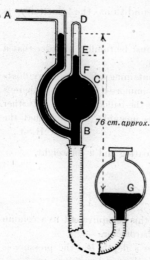

the pressure is less than that due to a column of mercury a millimetre high, the use of such a column is impossible, especially as pressures of less than 0·001 mm. of mercury may have to be measured. There are now many devices for indicating such pressures, but they suffer from the defect that they do not give the absolute value of the pressure. Such devices may, however, be calibrated by using the McLeod gauge, which depends upon Boyle's law for its use.

The tube A (Fig. 123) is sealed on to the pump or other apparatus in which the gas pressure is to be measured. At B is a T-piece leading to A, to the bulb C, and to a reservoir of mercury G. When G is lowered until the mercury falls below B, A is put in communication with C, which is then filled with the gas whose pressure, P, it is required to

FIG. 123.—THE McLEOD GAUGE.

measure. On raising G, A is cut off, and as the mercury rises in C the gas is compressed until eventually it is all contained in the capillary tube FD. The difference of level at E between the mercury in A and in DF is then noted; call this p. By a previous determination, the volume V of C measured from the joint B, and the volume v of the compressed gas in ED, from a calibration of the tube DF, are known.

Then from Boyle's law, $PV = (p + V)V$, or approximately,

$$PV = pv,$$

or
$$P = \frac{pv}{V}.$$

If the ratio V/v is large, then a very small pressure P may be multiplied up to a pressure p which can readily be measured. The calibration of FD and of C must be performed carefully before the apparatus is set up, by weighing in them a liquid of known density.

It should be noted that since the pressure is nearly zero in the gauge, while the pressure in G is atmospheric, these two must differ in level by the barometric height.

EXERCISES ON CHAPTER VII

FLUID PRESSURE AND CENTRE OF PRESSURE

1. Prove that the difference of the pressures at two points in a heavy liquid is proportional to the difference of their depths.

A hollow right circular cone of height h and semi-angle α rests with its base on a horizontal table. If the cone is filled with water and the weight of the empty cone is equal to the weight of the water it contains, find the thrust of the water on the base of the cone and the pressure of the cone on the table, explaining briefly why the second result is not double the first.   J.M.B.H.S.C.

2. Show that the depth of the centre of pressure for a plane area immersed in homogeneous fluid is $\dfrac{k^2}{h}$, where k is the radius of gyration of the area about the surface line and h is the depth of its C.G. measured in the plane of the area.

A cube, with edges of length $2a$, is immersed in a liquid and has one edge in the surface and the two faces through that edge equally inclined to the vertical. Find the centres of pressure of all the faces.   L.H.S.C.

3. A rectangular lamina is just immersed in water with one of its edges in the surface and its plane vertical. Find the position of its centre of pressure.

A square lamina with sides 2 ft. long is just immersed vertically in water with an edge in the surface and is then lowered 10 ft. Find the distance of the centre of pressure in the new position from the centre of the square.

(Neglect the pressure of the atmosphere in each case.)   J.M.B.H.S.C.

4. Find the position of the centre of pressure of a rectangle immersed in a liquid, one edge being in the free surface.

One end of a trough of rectangular cross-section 3 ft. wide by 4 ft. deep is hinged along its lower edge and is kept in position by a horizontal force P lb. wt. applied to the mid-point of its upper edge. If the trough is just filled with water, find the least value of P necessary to prevent water flowing out. (The density of water $= 62\cdot5$ lb. per cubic foot.)   L.H.S.C.

5. Find the centre of pressure of a rectangular sheet a inches long and b inches wide, of uniform thickness, immersed in liquid of uniform density with one side of length b inches in the surface, the plane of the rectangle being inclined at an angle θ to the vertical.

If the rectangular sheet remain in the same position with respect to the vessel containing the liquid, and the depth of the liquid be increased by h inches, find the new position of the centre of pressure.   L.H.S.C.

6. Neglecting atmospheric pressure, find the depth of the centre of pressure of a circular lamina just completely immersed with its plane vertical in an incompressible liquid.

A circular door in the vertical side of a tank is hinged at the top and opens inwards, and the tank contains water to a height just sufficient to cover the door. If the diameter of the door is 2 ft., find the magnitude of the force that must be applied normally to the centre of the door in order just to open the door. Find also the reaction at the hinge when this force is being applied. C.H.S.C.

THE PRINCIPLE OF ARCHIMEDES AND HYDROMETERS

7. Describe how you would determine the specific gravity of a small piece of metal by means of Nicholson's hydrometer.

A piece of an alloy of copper and tin weighs 260 gm. in water and 240 gm. in a liquid of specific gravity 1·5. Assuming that the volume of the alloy is the sum of the volumes of its constituents, find the masses of copper and tin in the given piece of alloy. Specific gravity of copper = 8·9; of tin 7·3. J.M.B.H.S.C.

IMMERSION AND ON FLOATING BODIES

8. State the principle of Archimedes.

A thin rectangular board of specific gravity s is hinged along its shorter side to the flat bottom of a tank. Find the position assumed by the board when water is poured in to a depth h; and prove that the board assumes the vertical position when h becomes equal to $\sqrt{s}$ times the length of the board. J.M.B.H.S.C.

9. State the theorem of Archimedes, and explain what you understand by the terms "force of buoyancy," "centre of buoyancy."

A cylinder of radius 1 cm. and length 4 cm., made of material of specific gravity 0·75, is floated in water with its axis vertical. It is then pushed vertically downwards so as to be just immersed. Find (a) the work done, (b) the reduction in the force on the bottom of the containing vessel when the cylinder is subsequently taken out of the water. O. & C.H.S.C.

10. A spherical balloon 20 cm. in diameter and weighing 0·4 gm. is inflated with hydrogen, and is anchored with fine cotton. If 1 litre of hydrogen weighs 0·09 gm., and air is 14·4 times as heavy as hydrogen, find in gm. wt. the tension of the cotton. C.H.S.C.

11. State the principle of Archimedes.

A slab of ice floats on water in a cylindrical vessel. Prove that if the ice melts in such a way that the area of the slab remains fixed, only its thickness diminishing, then the level of the water in the vessel remains the same. L.H.S.C.

Boyle's Law and Barometer

12. Give a theoretical proof of the principle of Archimedes.
The volume of glass in a test-tube is 10 c.c, the internal volume 30 c.c., and the weight 30 gm. Find the depth in water to which it must be thrust, mouth downwards, in order that it may sink of its own accord. Height of water barometer 10 metres. O. & C.H.S.C.

13. Show that the difference between the pressure at a point in a liquid and the atmospheric pressure is proportional to the depth below the surface. How would you verify this result by experiment ?
A diving bell of internal volume 12 cubic metres is lowered into the sea, so that the water surface in the bell is 15 metres below the surface of the sea. What volume of water will enter the bell ? (Specific gravity of sea water $= 1 \cdot 03$.) C.H.S.C.

14. A closed hollow cylindrical can 2 ft. deep floats in water with its axis vertical. There is a hole in the lower plane face, and the quantity of air in the can is so adjusted that the can floats half-immersed and one-quarter full of water.
If the apparatus be sunk to such a depth that, on being released, it no longer rises to the surface, what will then be the least depth of the upper face ? (The height of the water barometer may be taken as 34 ft., and the weight of the contained air and the volume of the material of the can may be neglected.) C.H.S.C.

15. State Boyle's law connecting the pressure and volume of gas at a constant temperature.
The space above the mercury in a faulty barometer contains air and when a true barometer reads 30 inches the faulty barometer reads 29 inches, there being then a space of 4 inches above the mercury. Find the height of the true barometer when this faulty barometer reads $28 \cdot 75$ inches. J.M.B.H.S.C.

16. State Boyle's law.
The top of a barometer tube, of cross-sectional area 1 sq. cm., is 80 cm. above the open surface of the mercury in the trough. The mercury column in the tube stands at a height of 70 cm. above the open mercury surface. $22 \cdot 5$ c.c. of air, as measured at the pressure of the outside atmosphere, are bubbled up to the top of the mercury column. What will be the new height of the mercury column ? C.H.S.C.

17. State Boyle's law and describe how you would verify it in the case of air.
The closed end of a U-tube, whose limbs have the same cross-section, contains air at atmospheric pressure, 76 cm. of mercury, which is shut in by mercury, occupying the bottom of the tube. The length of the air column is 15 cm. The tube is now sunk in the sea until the length of the air column is 3 cm. What is the depth of the surface of the mercury in the open limb below the surface of the sea ? (Density of mercury is $13 \cdot 6$ gm. per c.c., and of sea water $1 \cdot 03$ gm. per c.c.) L.H.S.C.

18. A barometer with an imperfect vacuum stands at 29·8 and 29 inches respectively, when the true atmospheric pressures are 30·4 and 29·3 inches respectively. What would a correct barometer indicate when the reading of the faulty barometer is 29·4 inches ?   L.H.S.C.

19. Explain the construction of an aneroid barometer, and describe how you would test the accuracy of the readings of such an instrument.

What are the chief purposes for which it is employed ? What are its advantages and disadvantages ?   O.H.S.C.

20. Describe the Fortin barometer. Why is it usual to reduce the readings of the barometer to 0° C. ?

A barometer is provided with a brass scale correct at 15° C. On a day when the temperature is 25° C. the height of the mercury column is observed to be 77·50 cm. Determine to the nearest 0·1 mm. the true height at 0° C., explaining each step in the calculation. (The coefficient of linear expansion of brass is 0·000018 per degree C. and the coefficient of absolute expansion of mercury is 0·000182 per degree C.)   J.M.B.H.S.C.

21. Describe a mercury barometer suitable for accurate measurements of the atmospheric pressure, and point out the precautions necessary for its use.

A simple barometer has the glass tube attached to a spring balance. What weight does the balance record when the open end of the tube is just dipping under the surface of the mercury in the reservoir, and what changes occur when the tube is lowered so that more of it dips under the mercury ?   O.H.S.C.

22. Distinguish between the aneroid and the mercury barometer, and explain the principle of each.

The height of the barometer is 29 in. and the specific gravity of mercury is 13·6. A cylindrical metal vessel is closed at one end with a glass plate cemented on to the metal. The internal diameter of the vessel is 6 in. and the greatest weight that the glass plate will bear is 200 lb. Find the least pressure to which the air inside can be exhausted without breaking the glass. (A cubic foot of water weighs 62½ lb.)   C.W.B.H.S.C.

CHAPTER VIII

FRICTION AND VISCOSITY

Static friction.—In several problems mention has been made of smooth bodies or bodies having surfaces which will slide on other surfaces without producing any tangential force. Any force between such surfaces must therefore be normal to them where they touch. Such ideal surfaces do not exist, and they have been imagined with the object of confining attention to some other feature of the problem.

If a body rests on a horizontal plane, as in Fig. 124, there is an upward force due to the plane equal to W, the weight of the body.

On applying a small force f parallel to the plane, the body will not in general move, because at the surface of separation a force equal and opposite to f comes into existence. This is known as the force of friction. With increasing applied force, the force of friction increases up to a limit. This is known as the limiting friction, and

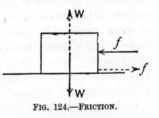

FIG. 124.—FRICTION.

directly the applied force passes this value the body moves. It is found by experiment that for any two surfaces, the limiting friction bears a constant ratio to the normal reaction W of the plane. This ratio is called the static coefficient of friction (μ). It is independent of the area of the surfaces in contact and of W, provided that this is not excessive. Thus,

$$\text{static coefficient of friction} = \frac{\text{limiting friction}}{\text{normal reaction}}.$$

$$\mu = \frac{f}{W}.$$

The student should examine this relation experimentally, and find the static coefficient of friction for a number of pairs of substances.

A slab of one substance rests upon a sheet of the other, and can be loaded until the total weight is W.

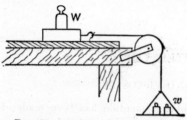

It is drawn along horizontally by a cord passing over a pulley (Fig. 125), which cord carries a scale pan and weights of total load w. For each value of W, w is increased until W begins to move; then the static coefficient of friction $= \dfrac{w}{W}$. W should be varied, and different substances should be used for the slab and the sheet and the above relation verified.

FIG. 125.—APPARATUS FOR MEASURING COEFFICIENT OF FRICTION.

Sliding friction.—There is a certain force f in each case which will maintain the body W (Fig. 124) in motion at constant velocity. In finding this value it is necessary to start the body moving when the limiting friction is approached. either by a gentle push or by tapping the board. The ratio of this value of f which will maintain W in motion without acceleration to the load W is called the **coefficient of sliding friction**. Its value is less than the static coefficient of friction, which means that a less force is required to maintain sliding at constant velocity than is required to start the body sliding. For moderate velocities the coefficient of sliding friction is constant, but at high velocity it depends slightly on the pressure.

If the force F acting upon the body parallel to the plane of sliding is greater than f, the force of sliding friction, the difference $F - f$ is the resultant which produces acceleration. As F, f and W have been taken as being in gravitational units in the above discussion, W is the mass in grammes, and the forces in dynes are Fg and fg;

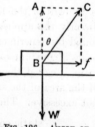

$$\therefore \text{ acceleration} = \frac{(F-f)g}{W}.$$

FIG. 126.—ANGLE OF FRICTION.

Angle of friction.—When a force f acts upon a body it may be compounded with the normal reaction of the plane to find the resultant reaction of the plane. If $\mathsf{BA} = W$ (Fig. 126) the resultant of f and BA is BC, which is inclined at an angle θ to AB. Then

$$\tan \theta = \frac{f}{W} = \mu.$$

θ is called the **angle of friction.**

Inclined plane.—If the body rests on an inclined plane, the resultant weight W may be resolved into two components,

$$R = W \cos \theta$$

perpendicular to the plane (Fig. 127) and $W \sin \theta$ parallel to the plane. For a certain inclination, θ, of the plane to the horizontal,

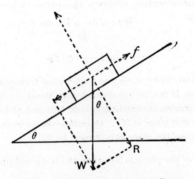

FIG. 127.—FRICTION AND INCLINED PLANE.

the position of limiting friction is reached and the body is just on the point of beginning to slide. In this condition

$$\mu = \frac{f}{R} = \frac{W \sin \theta}{W \cos \theta} = \tan \theta.$$

It is thus seen that the body is on the point of sliding when the inclination of the plane is equal to the angle of friction.

The student should measure the inclination of the plane in a number of cases, and so check the values for the static coefficient of friction found by the experiment described on p. 184.

If the body is started and slides down the plane without acceleration, the value of $\tan \theta$ is the coefficient of sliding friction.

Acceleration down inclined plane.—Let the body of mass M (Fig. 128) be situated on the plane whose inclination is θ, μ being the

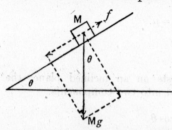

FIG. 128.—BODY SLIDING DOWN INCLINED PLANE.

coefficient of sliding friction for the body and the plane. The vertical force on M is Mg, the normal reaction of the plane being $Mg \cos \theta$, and the force down the plane $Mg \sin \theta$. If $\tan \theta$ is less than μ the body will not slide, since $Mg \sin \theta < \mu Mg \cos \theta$, where μ is the static coefficient of friction. But if $\tan \theta > \mu$,

$$Mg \sin \theta > \mu Mg \cos \theta,$$

and the resultant force down the plane is $Mg \sin \theta - \mu Mg \cos \theta$. This force produces acceleration a down the plane, where μ is now the sliding coefficient,

$$a = \frac{Mg \sin \theta - \mu Mg \cos \theta}{M}$$

$$= g(\sin \theta - \mu \cos \theta).$$

EXAMPLE 1.—State the meaning of *coefficient of friction* and describe how you would measure it for iron in contact with wood.

A body rests upon an inclined plane and will just slide down the plane when the slope of the plane is 30°. Calculate the acceleration of the body down the plane when the slope is increased to 60°. L.H.S.C.

Since the slope of the plane is 30° when the body will just slide down the plane, $\mu = \tan 30°$.

When the slope is 60°, component of weight normal to plane is $Mg \cos 60°$.

$$\therefore \text{ Force of friction} = \mu \ . \ Mg \cos 60°$$

$$= Mg \tan 30° \cos 60°.$$

Component of weight acting down plane $= Mg \sin 60°$.

$\therefore$ Resultant force down the plane $= Mg(\sin 60° - \tan 30° . \cos 60°)$;

$\therefore$ acceleration down the plane $= g (\sin 60° - \tan 30° \cos 60°)$

$$= g \left(\frac{\sqrt{3}}{2} - \frac{1}{\sqrt{3}} . \frac{1}{2} \right)$$

$$= g \frac{3-1}{2\sqrt{3}} = \frac{g}{\sqrt{3}}$$

$$= \underline{566 \text{ cm. sec.}^{-2}}.$$

EXAMPLE 2.—State the laws of sliding friction, and describe experiments you would make to illustrate them.

A rope is being used to drag a load of weight 60 lb. up a 30° slope. The coefficient of friction between the load and the slope is $\frac{1}{5}$. What is the pull in the rope when the latter is inclined at 30° to the vertical ?   O.H.S.C.

If P is the pull in the rope (Fig. 129), its component normal to the plane is P cos 60°. This does not exceed 60 cos 30° lb. wt., or the body would be lifted off the plane.

∴ Resultant force normal to plane = 60 cos 30° – P cos 60° ;

∴ force of friction = $\frac{1}{5}$(60 cos 30° – P cos 60°),

and this acts down the plane, since the body is being dragged up it.

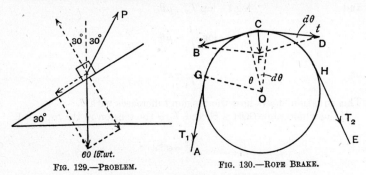

FIG. 129.—PROBLEM.   FIG. 130.—ROPE BRAKE.

If the acceleration of the body is zero, the resultant force parallel to the plane is zero ;   ∴ $\frac{1}{5}$(60 cos 30° – P cos 60°) + 60 sin 30° = P cos 30°,

$$P(5 \cos 30° + \cos 60°) = 60 \cos 30° + 300 \sin 30°,$$

$$P\left(\frac{5\sqrt{3}}{2} + \frac{1}{2}\right) = 60\left(\frac{\sqrt{3}}{2} + \frac{5}{2}\right);$$

$$P = \frac{60(\sqrt{3} + 5)}{1 + 5\sqrt{3}} = \underline{41\cdot8 \text{ lb. wt.}}$$

Rope brake.—A rope or band coiled round a cylindrical body is capable of exerting a very great couple on the body on account of the friction between the surfaces. Let the rope AGCHE (Fig. 130) leave the cylindrical surface at G and H. Consider an infinitesimal section of the rope at C, where the mean tension over this section is t, and $d\theta$ is the very small angle subtended at O.

The tensions, t, at the two ends of the section are represented by CB and CD, and their resultant is CF, and CF = CD . $d\theta$. Therefore CF = $t\,d\theta$. If μ is the coefficient of friction, $\mu t\,d\theta$ is the force of friction and is in the direction of the rope at C. This force implies a difference in tension dt in the rope at the two ends of the section;

$$\therefore\ dt = \mu t\, d\theta.$$

$$\frac{dt}{t} = \mu\, d\theta.$$

Integrating, $\log_\epsilon t = \mu\theta + k,$
where k is any constant.

If the tension at G is T_1, θ being zero,

$$\log_\epsilon T_1 = k,$$

and $\log_\epsilon t - \log T_1 = \mu\theta.$

$$\log_\epsilon \frac{t}{T_1} = \mu\theta,$$

or, $\dfrac{t}{T_1} = \epsilon^{\mu\theta}.$

This equation shows how the tension t increases with θ.

If the whole angle GOH is Θ, and T_2 is the tension in the rope at E,

$$\frac{T_2}{T_1} = \epsilon^{\mu\Theta}.$$

If the rope is coiled several times round the cylinder, Θ is very large, and the ratio T_2/T_1 may be so great that a man pulling at A can hold a ship fastened to E.

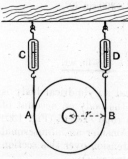

FIG. 131.—BAND BRAKE.

Band brake.—There are many forms of brake for measurement of power depending upon this principle. If a cord or band passes over a pulley AB (Fig. 131) attached to a shaft which is being driven by a motor, and the two ends are attached to spring balances, C and D, the readings being T_1 and T_2, the quantity $\dfrac{T_2}{T_1}$ or $\epsilon^{\mu\theta}$ can be found. θ may be π, 3π, 5π, etc., according to the number of times the cord passes round the drum. μ can then be calculated.

The power or rate of working of the motor can be obtained from the difference in readings of C and D. For $(T_2 - T_1)\, r$.

where r is the radius of AB, is a couple applied by friction, and

couple × angular velocity = rate of working   (p. 63).

If the axle makes n revolutions per second, angular velocity = $2\pi n$;

$$\therefore \ 2\pi n(T_2 - T_1)r = \text{rate of working.}$$

Stability due to friction.—It is not always realised that the activities of our daily life are rendered possible by friction. If there were no friction between our feet and the ground, walking would be impossible, or if motion were started it would be impossible to stop. The same applies to wheeled vehicles. Again, it would be impossible to pick anything up; it would slip through the fingers.

The stability of a body upon a plane is of importance. It was seen on p. 183 that the body will not slide unless the applied force along the plane exceeds a certain value μR. There is, however, the possibility that the body may topple over instead of sliding. The weight $W\ (=Mg)$ of the body acts through the centre of gravity G (Fig. 132).

If now a horizontal force f, less than μW, be applied at D, there will be a force of friction f' at the surface of the plane. These two produce a couple $f \times$ (AB) tending to make the body topple over. If the restoring couple $W \times$ (CB) is greater than this, the body remains at rest, and the equilibrium is stable, but if $W \times$ (CB) $< f \times$ (AB) the body topples over. To find the limiting conditions, take moments of f' and of the resultant of f and W about the point B. The moment of f' about B is zero, since its line of action passes through B. Let DK and DH represent f and W. The resultant is DE, and this cuts the plane in J. So long as CJ$<$CB the body remains upright, but if HDE exceeds the angle of friction the body will slide (p. 185). If, however, CJ$>$CB, the body will topple over.

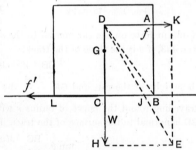

FIG. 132.—STABILITY OF BODY ON HORIZONTAL PLANE.

It may be noticed that when there is no applied force f the weight of the body is uniformly distributed over the base LB. But if f is gradually increased, the couple due to f and f' implies that the centre of reaction of the plane shifts from C towards B. Thus the force at L gets less and that at B greater, until in the limiting case the whole reaction acts through B, that at L being zero.

G 2

EXAMPLE.—Explain why a curved racing-motor track is banked up on the outside, and give an estimate of the inclination of the track for speeds of 90 M.P.H. on a curve of 800 yards' radius.

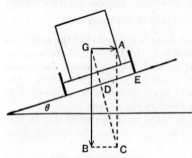

FIG. 133.—PROBLEM.

If the centres of the wheels of a car are 5 feet apart and its centre of gravity is 2 ft. 6 in. from the ground, find whether the car turning a corner on a level road will be more likely to skid or to overturn when the coefficient of friction between the wheels and the ground is 0·4.

O.H.S.C.

The reason why the curved racing-motor track is banked up on the outside is that it renders resultant force on the car normal to the surface of the track. Thus, in the Fig. 133, if θ is the slope of the track,

$$GB = W = Mg,$$

the weight of the car, and $GA = \dfrac{Mv^2}{r}$, the centrifugal force due to the car travelling round the curve of radius r with speed v. The resultant force GC is normal to the surface of the track if

$$\tan \theta = \frac{BC}{BG} = \frac{Mv^2}{r} \cdot \frac{1}{Mg} = \frac{v^2}{rg}.$$

Under this condition the car will not slip, and there is no lateral force of friction between the wheels and the ground.

$$90 \text{ M.P.H.} = \frac{90 \times 88}{60} = 132 \text{ ft. sec.}^{-1};$$

$$800 \text{ yards} = 2400 \text{ feet};$$

$$\therefore \ \tan \theta = \frac{132^2}{2400 \times 32 \cdot 2}$$

$$= 0 \cdot 2255,$$

$$\text{taking } g = 32 \cdot 2 \text{ ft. sec.}^{-2};$$

$$\therefore \ \underline{\theta = 12° \ 42'}.$$

Referring to Fig. 132, taking D to coincide with G, CG = CD = CB = 2·5 ft., since the centrifugal force acts through the centre of gravity;

$$\therefore \text{ angle CDB} = 45°,$$

or $$\tan \text{CDB} = 1.$$

Therefore the car will **not** overturn until DK/DH = 1.

If the coefficient of friction is 0·4, then tan (angle of friction)=0·4.

If then the centrifugal force increases until tan (angle CDJ)=0·4, the car is on the point of slipping. That is

$$\frac{HE}{DH} = \frac{DK}{DH} = 0·4.$$

The value of DK at which skid begins is therefore less than that for overturning. The car is therefore more likely to skid than to overturn.

Viscosity of liquids.—It was seen on p. 153 that a fluid is a substance that cannot permanently support a shearing strain. If a shearing strain is produced, the stress in the fluid disappears more or less rapidly, depending upon the nature of the fluid. Therefore if an external shearing stress is maintained, a continuous flow takes place in the fluid.

If two parallel layers in the fluid move, in the direction of their own planes, with different velocities, there is a force on each plane of a similar nature to a shearing stress.

If the fluid between the planes is moving with constant velocity, the force per unit area on the side of greater velocity is equal to the force per unit area on the side of lower velocity, but the two forces are oppositely directed. One tends to increase the velocity of the layer, the other to retard it. Thus, in

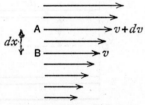

FIG. 134.—STRESS IN LIQUID.

Fig. 134, if v is the velocity of the layer B and $v+dv$ the velocity of the layer A, and dx is the distance apart of the layers, the quantity $\frac{dv}{dx}$ is called the **velocity gradient** at this part of the fluid.

The force per unit area on the layer at A is equal and opposite to that at B, and is proportional to the velocity gradient, but depends on the nature of the fluid. Calling it f,

$$f = \eta \frac{dv}{dx},$$

and η is called the **coefficient of viscosity** of the fluid. Its dimensions may be found from the relation

$$[L^{-2}][MLT^{-2}] = [\eta][LT^{-1}L^{-1}],$$
$$[\eta] = [ML^{-1}T^{-1}],$$

remembering that f is force per unit area.

The maintenance of the flow of a liquid is due to a difference of pressure between the various parts of it. In the case of flow in a tube, a difference of pressure is maintained between its ends. The liquid in contact with the wall of the tube is at rest, and the velocity increases towards the axis. This stream-line flow is found to occur only when the velocity is below a certain limit, known as the **critical velocity.** When this critical velocity is reached, the various parts of the liquid cease to travel in straight lines along the tube, but follow sinuous paths, which may be observed if a small jet of colouring matter is introduced at the inlet. With further increase of velocity all orderliness in the flow is lost and it becomes turbulent, and the colouring matter fills the whole tube, whereas in steady flow it is confined to a thin streak. A high coefficient of viscosity encourages the stream-line flow, but a high density promotes turbulence. The critical velocity may be determined by experiment.

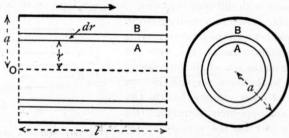

FIG. 135.—FLOW OF LIQUID IN A TUBE.

Measurement of viscosity by flow of liquid in a tube.—The most convenient method of measuring the coefficient of viscosity of a liquid is due to Poiseuille, and consists in measuring the volume of liquid flowing through a capillary tube in a given time, with known difference of pressure between its ends. Consider a cylindrical shell of the liquid of radius r and thickness dr, and that v is the velocity of the liquid at a distance r from the axis ; then $\dfrac{dv}{dr}$ is the velocity gradient at A (Fig. 135), and the force in the liquid over the inner surface of the shell is $\left(\text{area} \times \eta \dfrac{dv}{dr} \right) = 2\pi r l \eta \dfrac{dv}{dr}$, where l is the length of the capillary tube. Since the parts of the liquid near the axis are flowing more rapidly than parts nearer the walls, this stress constitutes a forward drag on the shell of liquid AB. This force changes to $2\pi r l \eta \dfrac{dv}{dr} + \dfrac{d}{dr}\left(2\pi r l \eta \dfrac{dv}{dr} \right) \times dr$ at the outer surface of the shell B, and is a drag on the shell. The difference of the two is the resultant force on the shell due to viscosity, and its value is $\frac{d}{dr}\left(2\pi r l \eta \frac{dv}{dr}\right) \times dr$. As the velocity of the shell is constant, the retarding force must be balanced by a force due to the difference of pressure P, between the ends of the capillary tube, which maintains the flow. Since the flow is everywhere parallel to the axis of the tube, the pressure over every cross-section perpendicular to the axis must be constant; otherwise there would be a radial flow. Thus the force over the section AB of the shell of thickness dr is

$$\text{area} \times P = 2\pi r \, dr \, . \, P \, ;$$

$$\therefore \ \frac{d}{dr}\left(2\pi r l \eta \frac{dv}{dr}\right) dr = 2\pi r \, dr \, . \, P,$$

or

$$\frac{d}{dr}\left(2\pi r l \eta \frac{dv}{dr}\right) = 2\pi r P.$$

Since P is independent of r P may be considered constant when integrating with respect to r;

$$\therefore \ 2\pi r l \eta \frac{dv}{dr} = \pi r^2 P + C_1,$$

where C_1 is some constant, to be determined.

$$\therefore \ \frac{dv}{dr} = \frac{rP}{2l\eta} + \frac{C_1}{2\pi l \eta r} \, .$$

Integrating again with respect to r,

$$v = \frac{r^2 P}{4l\eta} + \frac{C_1 \log r}{2\pi l \eta} + C_2.$$

In order to find C_1 and C_2 notice, in the first place, that at the axis of the tube $r = 0$, so that $\log r = -\infty$. This would make the velocity at the axis infinite. This certainly is never true, so that $C_1 = 0$, and

$$v = \frac{r^2 P}{4l\eta} + C_2.$$

Since the liquid in contact with the wall of the tube is at rest, $v = 0$ when $r = a$;

$$\therefore \ C_2 = -\frac{a^2 P}{4l\eta},$$

and

$$v = \frac{P}{4l\eta}(r^2 - a^2).$$

This would make v appear to be negative, since $a^2 > r^2$. The reason is that $\dfrac{dv}{dr}$, which is essentially negative, has been taken as positive. Reversing the sign, therefore

$$v = \frac{P}{4l\eta}(a^2 - r^2).$$

This expression gives the distribution of velocity over the cross-section of the tube. As the velocity at any point cannot be measured conveniently, it is desirable to find the total flow through the whole tube in terms of volume per unit time. The volume dV flowing through the shell per unit time is *area × velocity*;

$$\therefore dV = 2\pi r\, dr \times \frac{P}{4l\eta}(a^2 - r^2)$$

$$= \frac{\pi P}{2l\eta}a^2 r\, dr - \frac{\pi P}{2l\eta}r^3 dr;$$

$$\therefore V = \frac{\pi P a^2}{2l\eta}\left[\frac{r^2}{2}\right]_0^a - \frac{\pi P}{2l\eta}\left[\frac{r^4}{4}\right]_0^a$$

$$= \frac{\pi P a^4}{4l\eta} - \frac{\pi P a^4}{8l\eta} = \frac{\pi P a^4}{8l\eta};$$

or

$$\eta = \frac{\pi P a^4}{8lV}.$$

Experimental measurement of viscosity.—The above equation indicates clearly the measurements to be made in the determination of η for a liquid such as water, which can be obtained in large quantities. The capillary tube AB (Fig. 136) must be calibrated by placing in it, when carefully dried, a thread of mercury whose length is measured. The mercury is then run into a watch glass and weighed. Knowing the density of mercury at the temperature of the measurement, its volume can be found, and this divided by the length of thread gives the area of cross-section, from which the radius can be found, assuming the section to be circular. Since the radius enters to the fourth power into the result, it is necessary to know its value as accurately as possible. The thread of mercury should be placed in various parts of the capillary tube, and if its length varies appreciably the tube should be rejected as being too uneven for the experiment.

An upright vessel with a tube CD (Fig. 136) is kept filled with water to the level C, so that a constant head of water, h, is maintained at the end A of the capillary tube AB. Taking the pressure at

B and at C as atmospheric, the quantity P in the expression for the viscosity is equal to $h\delta g$. If water is used, $\delta = 1$ and $P = hg$. A beaker E is weighed, then catches the water which emerges in a known time, and is weighed again.

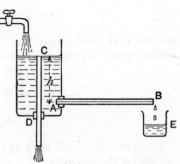

Then $V = \dfrac{m}{\delta t}$.

If l is the length of the tube,

$$\eta = \frac{\pi P a^4}{8lV} = \frac{\pi h \delta g a^4 \cdot \delta t}{8lm}$$

$$= \frac{\pi h \delta^2 g a^4 t}{8lm}.$$

If the liquid emerges at B with appreciable velocity, part of the pressure due to the head

FIG. 136.—MEASUREMENT OF VISCOSITY.

of liquid is used in creating the kinetic energy of the emergent water. This work done per unit time is the integral of $\frac{1}{2}m_1 v^2$ over the whole cross-section, where m_1 is the mass of liquid emerging per second through the cylindrical shell AB (Fig. 135). The correction is usually very small, but if required it may be made as follows.

$$m_1 = 2\pi r \, dr \cdot v\delta \,;$$

$$\therefore \; \tfrac{1}{2}m_1 v^2 = \pi \delta v^3 r \, dr.$$

And the kinetic energy produced in the whole cross-section of the tube per unit time is

$$\int_0^a \pi \delta v^3 r \, dr = \pi \delta \int_0^a v^3 r \, dr.$$

Now
$$v = \frac{P}{4l\eta}(a^2 - r^2) \quad \text{(p. 194)} \,;$$

$\therefore$ kinetic energy per second $= \dfrac{\pi P^3 \delta}{64 l^3 \eta^3} \displaystyle\int_0^a (a^2 - r^2)^3 r \, dr.$

$$\int_0^a (a^2 - r^2)^3 r \, dr = \int_0^a (a^6 - 3a^4 r^2 + 3a^2 r^4 - r^6) r \, dr$$

$$= \frac{a^8}{2} - \frac{3a^8}{4} + \frac{3a^8}{6} - \frac{a^8}{8}$$

$$= \frac{a^8}{8} \,;$$

$$\therefore \; \text{K.E. per sec.} = \frac{\pi P^3 \delta a^8}{64 l^3 \eta^3 \cdot 8}.$$

Now, $V = \dfrac{\pi P a^4}{8l\eta}$ (p. 194), and substituting V^3 for $\dfrac{\pi^3 P^3 a^{12}}{64 \cdot l^3 \eta^3 \cdot 8}$,

$$\text{K.E. per sec.} = \cdot\frac{V^3\delta}{\pi^2 a^4}.$$

But the work done in unit time by a head h_1 of liquid in creating kinetic energy is, pressure × volume moved (p. 206), that is, $gh_1\delta V$;

$$\therefore \quad \frac{V^3\delta}{\pi^2 a^4} = gh_1\delta V,$$

$$h_1 = \frac{V^2}{g\pi^2 a^4}.$$

This gives the small head h_1 that must be deducted from h in calculating the viscosity, or

$$P = h - h_1 = h - \frac{V^2}{g\pi^2 a^4}.$$

Measurement of variation of viscosity with temperature.—As it is impossible to immerse the apparatus of Fig. 136 in a bath of known

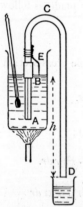

FIG. 137.—VARIATION OF VISCOSITY WITH TEMPERATURE.

temperature, it is often arranged that the capillary tube is immersed in a vessel of the liquid whose viscosity has to be found. The capillary tube AB (Fig. 137) is immersed in the liquid, and a wider tube BCD is joined to it and siphons the liquid over. It emerges at D, and is caught and weighed as described on p. 195. The bath may be maintained at any convenient temperature. The experiment is carried out exactly as in the case of the horizontal tube, but in this case the head of liquid causing flow is h, the difference of level between B and D. For if B were open to the atmosphere there would be no flow, as the columns inside and outside AB would balance. The pressure at B is lowered, due to the column of length BD when the liquid is being siphoned, so that this is the effective flow-producing head.

It is advisable to attach a bent pin E to the tube, so that, by raising the bath during the flow, the level of liquid in it may be maintained at the tip of the pin, and so a constant head of liquid preserved.

The student should measure the viscosity of water at various temperatures, and plot a graph connecting viscosity and temperature. It is a general fact that the viscosity of liquids decreases with a rise of temperature, but there is no simple and universal law connecting viscosity and temperature.

Comparison of viscosities.—There is a simple and excellent method of comparing the viscosities of two liquids, or those of the same liquid at different temperatures. A bent tube (Fig. 138) has a capillary section AB and two bulbs F and G. Marks are placed on the tube at D, A and E. One liquid is introduced into the tube, and its amount is adjusted until, with the tap T closed, the liquid will occupy the part DGA of the bent tube. If this is done for each liquid used, it is assured that the same volume of liquid is taken in each case. Having placed the liquid in the tube, its level is drawn up above the mark D by abstracting air, and the tap T is closed. On opening the tap the liquid flows from the tube DB to the tube AC. The time at which the level passes the mark D is noted, and also the time at which it passes E. The difference t_1 is the time taken for the liquid to flow from the position DA to the position EC. The retarding force due to viscosity being inversely as the fourth

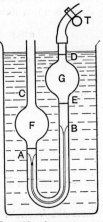

FIG. 138.—APPARATUS FOR COMPARING VISCOSITIES.

power of the radius of the tube, the wider parts will not appreciably affect the rate of flow; this is determined by the capillary portion AB. The volume passing per second is

$$V = \frac{\pi P a^4}{8 l \eta} \quad \text{(p. 194)}.$$

Although P is changing all the time the flow is taking place, it is, for every position, proportional to the density of the liquid. Therefore for every corresponding position of the two liquids $P_1 \propto \delta_1$ and $P_2 \propto \delta_2$.

Therefore for one liquid $V_1 \propto \dfrac{\pi \delta_1 a^4}{8 l \eta_1}$, and for the other $V_2 \propto \dfrac{\pi \delta_2 a^4}{8 l \eta_2}$.

Now a^4 and l are constant;

$$\therefore \frac{V_1}{V_2} = \frac{\delta_1}{\eta_1} \div \frac{\delta_2}{\eta_2} = \frac{\delta_1}{\delta_2} \cdot \frac{\eta_2}{\eta_1}.$$

Again V_1 and V_2 will vary from instant to instant during the flow, but the times for the flow of unit volume at corresponding positions vary inversely as V_1 and V_2, and the total times t_1 and t_2 must therefore do the same;

$$\therefore \frac{t_1}{t_2} = \frac{V_2}{V_1} = \frac{\delta_2}{\delta_1} \cdot \frac{\eta_1}{\eta_2},$$

or

$$\frac{\eta_1}{\eta_2} = \frac{t_1 \delta_1}{t_2 \delta_2}.$$

Thus the comparison of viscosities is made by measuring the times for corresponding flows, the densities of the liquids being known.

TABLE OF VISCOSITIES IN C.G.S. UNITS.

Temperature.			0° C.	10° C.	20° C.
Water	-	-	0·0179	0·0131	0·101
Mercury	-	-	0·0169	0·0162	0·0156
Ethyl alcohol	-	-	0·0177	0·0145	0·0119
Ether	-	-	0·00286	0·00258	0·00234

EXAMPLE.—Explain the term *viscosity*, and describe how you would compare the viscosities of water and alcohol. (The mathematical theory of the experiment is not required.)

A large bottle is fitted with a siphon made of capillary glass tubing. Compare the times taken to empty the bottle when it is filled (a) with water, (b) with petroleum of s.g. 0·8. The viscosities of water and petroleum are 0·01 and 0·02 respectively. C.H.S.C.

As in the last experiment, the conditions of the flow are the same for both liquids, apart from their densities and viscosities.

Now,

$$\frac{\eta(\text{water})}{\eta(\text{petroleum})} = \frac{\text{time}(\text{water})}{\text{time}(\text{petroleum})} \cdot \frac{\delta(\text{water})}{\delta(\text{petroleum})}.$$

$$\frac{0·01}{0·02} = \frac{t(\text{water})}{t(\text{petroleum})} \cdot \frac{1}{0·8};$$

$$\therefore \frac{t(\text{water})}{t(\text{petroleum})} = \frac{0·8 \times 0·01}{0·02}$$

$$= \underline{0·4}.$$

Measurement of viscosity by Stokes' method.—It was shown mathematically by Sir George Stokes that a small body falling through a viscous fluid attains a limiting velocity. On being released, the body at first has an acceleration, but on attaining a certain velocity, the upward force due to the viscosity of the liquid becomes sensibly equal to the weight of the body. The velocity of the body is then constant. This constant velocity is sooner attained when the body is small than when it is large. Stokes found that when a sphere is falling in a liquid of infinite extent, the upward force on it due to viscosity is $6\pi\eta rv$, where η is the coefficient of viscosity, r the radius of the sphere, and v is velocity. The upward force due to gravity and buoyancy is $\frac{4}{3}\pi r^3(\sigma-\rho)g$, where σ is the density of the sphere and ρ that of the fluid. Thus for the constant velocity,

$$6\pi\eta rv = \tfrac{4}{3}\pi r^3(\sigma-\rho)g.$$

This gives rise to a method of determining the viscosity of liquids of which a large quantity is available. A tall jar of fairly large diameter is filled with the liquid, and a steel sphere (from ball bearings) is dropped in. Its times of passing marks at three different levels are observed by means of a stop-watch. Thus the velocities of travel over two tracks are known. If these are the same, this velocity may be used in the above equation for finding η. If the velocity over the lower range is greater than that for the upper, a smaller sphere must be used, and the process repeated until the velocities are the same, within the limits of experimental error. For great accuracy corrections must be applied, to allow for the fact that the containing vessel is not infinite in size.

The method has also been used for finding the radius of small drops falling in air, from a knowledge of the coefficient of viscosity of air. It should be noted, however, that when the drop is so small that it becomes comparable in size to the distance between the air molecules, it falls at a greater rate than that indicated by Stokes' law. The law only applies to the case in which the sphere is large enough for the liquid to be considered as continuous.

Viscosity of gases.—The definition of viscosity on p. 191 applies to gases as well as liquids, but in the case of a gas there is a new difficulty in determining the coefficient of viscosity by Poiseuille's method. In calculating the volume of liquid flowing through a capillary tube in a second, the question of compressibility has been ignored. This is justified in the case of a liquid, because the change of density with pressure is so small that its effect on the measurements is negligible. The volume V of liquid emerging from the capillary tube may be determined by weighing and dividing by the density δ.

Such a process is not applicable in studying the flow of a gas through a tube. Unless there is accumulation at some part of the tube, the mass per second passing every cross-section must be the same for gases as for liquids. If δ_1 is the density of a gas at unit pressure, then from Boyle's law, $\dfrac{\delta}{\delta_1} = \dfrac{p}{1}$ where δ is the density at pressure p. Thus $\delta = p\delta_1$.

If V is the volume of gas passing any cross-section of the capillary tube, δV or $p\delta_1 V$ is the mass passing per second, and it is this quantity that must be constant during steady flow. Now from the definition of the coefficient of viscosity η, the expression $V = \dfrac{\pi P a^4}{8l\eta}$ (p. 194) has been obtained, under the assumption of zero compressibility. On multiplying both sides by δ or $\delta_1 p$,

$$\delta_1 p V = \frac{\pi a^4}{8\eta} \cdot \frac{P}{l} \cdot \delta_1 p.$$

Now $\dfrac{P}{l}$ is the pressure gradient in the tube, and calling this $-\dfrac{dp}{dx}$, where x is measured along the axis from O (Fig. 135), for a short element of the tube of length dx,

$$\delta_1 p V = -\frac{\pi a^4 \delta_1}{8\eta} \cdot \frac{p\, dp}{dx}.$$

The negative sign is taken for $\dfrac{dp}{dx}$, because the pressure is greatest at O and diminishes as x increases. If m is the mass per second of gas entering the element dx and emerging from it,

$$m = -\frac{\pi a^4 \delta_1}{8\eta} \frac{p \cdot dp}{dx}, \quad dx = -\frac{\pi a^4 \delta_1}{8\eta m} \cdot p\, dp,$$

$$\int_1^2 dx = -\frac{\pi a^4 \delta_1}{8\eta m} \int_{p_1}^{p_2} p\, dp,$$

$$l = -\frac{\pi a^4 \delta_1}{8\eta m} \left[\frac{p^2}{2}\right]_{p_1}^{p_2} = \frac{\pi a^4 \delta_1 (p_1{}^2 - p_2{}^2)}{16\eta m},$$

and

$$\eta = \frac{\pi a^4 \delta_1 (p_1{}^2 - p_2{}^2)}{16 lm}, \quad \text{or} \quad m = \frac{\pi a^4 \delta_1 (p_1{}^2 - p_2{}^2)}{16 l\eta}.$$

$\dfrac{m}{\delta_1}$ is the volume that the gas entering the tube would occupy if its pressure were unity. At the actual pressure p_1 the volume V would be $\dfrac{m}{\delta_1 p_1}$;

$$\therefore\ p_1 V = \frac{\pi a^4 (p_1{}^2 - p_2{}^2)}{16 l\eta}.$$

Measurement of the coefficient of viscosity of a gas.—The determination of η for a gas is attended with several difficulties, but the following serves as an illustration of the type of method employed. A tube AB (Fig. 139) of about half a metre in length and a few millimetres in diameter is sealed on to a capillary tube CD of about 0·1 mm. diameter. A thread of mercury E drives the air from AB through the capillary tube CD into the atmosphere. The time t required for the mercury to sink from the mark F to the mark G is noted. If then the atmospheric pressure is P and the mass of the thread of mercury is M, the pressure of the air in FB is $P+\dfrac{Mg-e}{\alpha}$, where α is the area of cross-section of the tube AB and e is a correction to be made on account of the sticking of the mercury to the walls of the tube. The value of e may be found from readings with different lengths of mercury thread. The volume of air driven through CD in time t is $L\alpha$ where $L=$FG.

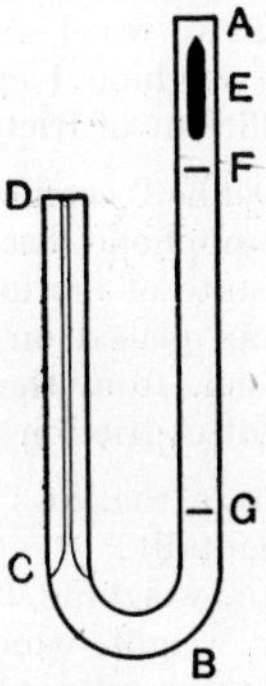

FIG. 139.—TUBE FOR MEASURING THE VISCOSITY OF AIR.

Then $$\left(P+\frac{Mg-e}{\alpha}\right)L\alpha = \frac{\pi a^4\left\{\left(P+\dfrac{Mg-e}{\alpha}\right)^2 - P^2\right\}}{16l\eta}$$

from which η can be calculated.

A great improvement was made by Rankine, who. employing this principle, joined the tubes D and A at the top, making a closed system, so that the gas is driven round the system as the mercury thread sinks. In this way small quantities of gas only are required, and the pressure in the system can be varied at will.

TABLE OF VISCOSITIES IN C.G.S. UNITS AT $0°$ C.

Air	-	-	$1·70 \times 10^{-4}$
Hydrogen	-	-	$0·86 \times 10^{-4}$
Oxygen	-	-	$1·87 \times 10^{-4}$
Nitrogen	-	-	$1·66 \times 10^{-4}$
Helium	-	-	$1·89 \times 10^{-4}$

EXERCISES ON CHAPTER VIII

1. Describe an experiment to measure the coefficient of sliding friction between two wood surfaces. Find the *least* force required to drag a heavy particle weighing 1 cwt. with constant velocity along a horizontal floor if the coefficient of friction is $\frac{1}{3}$.   Lond. Int. Sc.

2. Define " coefficient of friction " and " normal acceleration."

A gramophone disc is set revolving in a horizontal plane and reaches a steady state of motion of two revolutions per second. It is found that a small coin placed on the disc will remain there if its centre is not more than 5 cm. from the axis of rotation. Explain this, and calculate the coefficient of friction between the coin and the disc.   O. & C.H.S.C.

3. State the laws of friction and explain how you would verify them experimentally.

A man, weighing 140 lb., climbs up a uniform ladder, 20 ft. long and 70 lb. in weight, which rests against a rough vertical wall at an angle of 45°. If the coefficient of friction at each end of the ladder is 0·5, how far will the man be able to climb up the ladder before it begins to slip ?

J.M.B.H.S.C.

4. Define the *coefficient of limiting friction*.

A uniform ladder of length $2l$ and weight W rests against a vertical wall with its foot on the ground at a distance l from the wall. If the coefficient of friction between the wall and the ladder and between the ground and the ladder is 0·4, find how far up the ladder a man of weight 2W can ascend without disturbing equilibrium.   J.M.B.H.S.C.

5. Define the angle of friction.

A uniform rod rests in limiting equilibrium in contact with a horizontal floor and a vertical wall, the rod being in a vertical plane which is perpendicular to the wall. If the wall and the floor are equally rough, prove that the angle between the rod and the wall is twice the angle of friction.

L.H.S.C.

6. Show that a body can lie at rest on a rough plane inclined at an angle α to the horizontal provided that α is less than the angle of friction (λ).

If α is less than λ and W is the weight of the body, find :

    (i) the least horizontal force that must be applied to set the body moving up the plane ;

    (ii) the least horizontal force that must be applied to set the body moving down the plane ;

    (iii) the magnitude and direction of the least force that will set the body moving down the plane.   L.H.S.C.

7. A particle of mass m lies on the rough slant face of a fixed plane inclined at an angle α to the horizontal. A string fastened to the particle runs up a line of greatest slope of the plane over a small smooth pulley at the top, and carries a weight, also of mass m, suspended freely from its

other end. Prove that motion is impossible unless the angle of friction is less than $(\pi/4 - \alpha/2)$. If this condition is satisfied, find the acceleration, and prove that the tension in the string is

$$\tfrac{1}{2}mg(\sin \alpha + 1 + \mu \cos \alpha),$$

μ being the coefficient of friction.   C.W.B.H.S.C.

8. Give *two* examples from everyday life of equilibrium maintained by friction which is not limiting.

A uniform cube stands on a rough inclined plane with four edges horizontal, and is pulled up the plane by a string attached to the middle point of the uppermost edge and held parallel to the plane. The inclination of the plane is α, and $\alpha < \tfrac{1}{4}\pi$. Prove that, as the pull in the string is gradually increased, the cube will slide or topple according as the coefficient of friction between it and the plane is less than or greater than $\tfrac{1}{2}(1 - \tan \alpha)$.

Find the line of action of the normal reaction if the cube slides, and the amount of friction called into play if it topples.   O. & C.H.S.C.

9. What is meant by viscosity ? How may the viscosities of two liquids be compared ? Describe one way in which the viscosity (a) of a gas, and (b) of a liquid, is of service to mankind.   C.H.S.C.

10. State the meaning of the term " coefficient of viscosity." What are its dimensions ?

Describe carefully how you would measure the coefficient of viscosity of a liquid. (Any formula used need not be proved.)   L.H.S.C.

CHAPTER IX

FLOW OF LIQUIDS AND GASES

Incompressible mobile liquid.—The problem of the flow of liquids and gases is extremely complex. The liquid has inertia and therefore kinetic energy when in motion; it is also subject to pressure, and may have potential energy on account of its position. Also, the velocity may not be uniform throughout the liquid, in which case there are forces due to the viscosity. And lastly, the density may vary under different pressures. The viscosity is studied in Chapter VIII, with the simplifying assumption that the velocity is so small that the kinetic energy may generally be ignored. For our present purpose viscosity is ignored, so that the liquid is considered to be perfectly mobile. In addition, only those liquids with a density which does not vary appreciably with change of pressure are treated, so that the liquid is looked upon as incompressible. It remains then to find a relation between the velocity, pressure and potential energy of such a liquid.

Lines and tubes of flow.—The flow of a liquid may be turbulent (p. 192), in which case its motion is intricate and constantly varying,

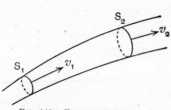

FIG. 140.—TUBE OF FLOW IN AN INCOMPRESSIBLE LIQUID.

but where the velocity at every point in the liquid remains constant the liquid is said to have stream-line flow. In this case it is possible to consider a line which is the path of any particle of the liquid. The direction of the line at any point is the direction of the velocity of the liquid at that point. Such a one is called a stream-line.

On taking a small area S_1 (Fig. 140) at right angles to the direction of flow, and drawing the stream-lines through the boundary of S_1, a tube S_1S_2 is obtained. This is a **tube of flow**. Such a tube has certain important properties. Since the side of the tube is everywhere in the direction of flow of the liquid, no liquid crosses the sides. Any liquid entering or leaving any section of the tube must therefore do so through the ends. If the tube is narrow enough to consider the velocity constant over a section, the volume entering through S_1 is S_1v_1 per sec., and the volume leaving through S_2 is S_2v_2 per sec. The mass per second passing through S_1 is $S_1v_1\rho_1$ and that through S_2 is $S_2v_2\rho_2$, where ρ_1 is the density of the liquid at S_1, and ρ_2 that at S_2. When the flow is steady,

$$S_1v_1\rho_1 = S_2v_2\rho_2 ;$$

and if, in addition, the liquid is incompressible, $\rho_1 = \rho_2$;

$$\therefore \ S_1v_1 = S_2v_2.$$

Energy possessed by liquid.—There are three possible forms of energy concerned with the flow of a liquid. The other forms of energy, such as heat, do not affect the flow of the liquid directly, although they may indirectly by causing expansion and so altering the distribution of pressure. The three forms referred to are **pressure energy, potential energy,** and **kinetic energy.**

(i) *Pressure energy.*—Consider a tank of liquid (Fig. 141) with surface AB. At the level CD there is a certain pressure p. If more liquid is to be introduced into the tank at this pressure it must be forced in. If the pipe ED of cross-section α is provided with a piston, the force on the piston is $p\alpha$. If then the piston is pushed inwards through distance x the work done is $p\alpha x$, and a volume αx or mass $\alpha x\rho$ of liquid enters the tank. If the operation takes place very slowly, the velocity is infinitesimal and any kinetic energy is negligible. The work $p\alpha x$ is energy possessed by the mass $\alpha x\rho$ of liquid in

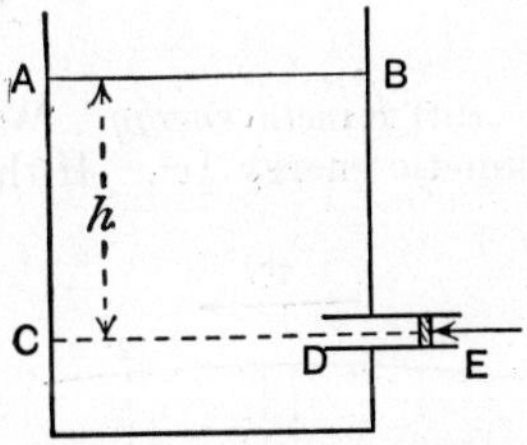

FIG. 141.—PRESSURE ENERGY IN A LIQUID.

the tank, because it is capable of performing the same amount of work in pushing the piston back and escaping from the tank.

$$\therefore \text{ Pressure energy of unit mass} = \frac{p\alpha x}{\alpha x\rho}$$

$$= \frac{p}{\rho}.$$

(ii) *Potential energy.*—The connection between the pressure at a point in a liquid due to the column of liquid above the point has already been seen (p. 156) to be

$$h\rho g = p \; ;$$

$$\therefore \; hg = \frac{p}{\rho}.$$

Since $\frac{p}{\rho}$ is energy per unit mass of the liquid, hg must likewise be energy per unit mass. Although in a liquid at rest the above equation is true, still the two sides may be considered to have different meanings. hg is the work required to lift unit mass from the level CD (Fig. 141) to the level AB, or the work done by gravity when the unit mass descends from AB to CD. It is therefore potential energy, and is actually the excess of the potential energy of unit mass at AB over its potential energy if situated at level CD. It therefore increases in an upward direction. Starting from any level, in a liquid at rest, and passing upward for a distance y, the pressure decreases by the amount $y\rho g$, and the pressure energy of unit mass therefore decreases by $\frac{y\rho g}{\rho} = yg$. But the potential energy of unit mass has increased by yg. Hence in a liquid at rest the sum of the potential and pressure energies is constant ;

$$\therefore \; \frac{p}{\rho} + hg = \text{constant.}$$

(iii) *Kinetic energy.*—When a liquid is in motion, unit mass has a kinetic energy $\frac{1}{2}v^2$. If the unit mass has constant velocity there is no resultant force acting upon it. But if it is accelerated, there is a pressure gradient in the tube of flow. Let $\frac{dp}{dx}$ be this gradient, which over a short length of tube may be taken as constant.

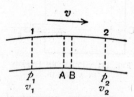

FIG. 142.—KINETIC ENERGY OF LIQUID.

Then if p is the pressure at the cross-section B (Fig. 142) of a tube of flow, the pressure at A is $\left(p + \frac{dp}{dx} \cdot \delta x\right)$, where δx is the length of the slice AB. The excess pressure at A over that at B is therefore $\frac{dp}{dx}\delta x$, and the resulting force on AB is $S\frac{dp}{dx}\delta x$ where S is the area of cross-section of the tube.

If v is the velocity of the liquid as it passes A and $\left(v+\dfrac{dv}{dx}\,\delta x\right)$ its velocity as it passes B, $\dfrac{dv}{dx}\,\delta x$ is its increase in velocity in passing from A to B. But this takes place in time $\delta t=\dfrac{\delta x}{v}$, so that $v=\dfrac{\delta x}{\delta t}$, or in the limit, $v=\dfrac{dx}{dt}$.

Now acceleration at $\text{AB}=\dfrac{dv}{dt}$, mass in the section AB is $S\rho\,\delta x$, and force on it is $S\dfrac{dp}{dx}\,\delta x$;

$$\therefore\quad -S\frac{dp}{dx}\cdot\delta x=S\rho\,\delta x\cdot\frac{dv}{dt}.$$

The negative sign occurs because the velocity increases from A to B, while the pressure falls, that is acceleration is positive for the direction in which pressure gradient is negative.

$$-\frac{dp}{dx}=\rho\cdot\frac{dv}{dt}=\rho\cdot\frac{dv}{dx}\cdot\frac{dx}{dt}$$

$$=\rho v\frac{dv}{dx},$$

$$-\frac{1}{\rho}\int_{p_1}^{p_2}dp=\int_{v_1}^{v_2}v\,dv,$$

where p_1 and v_1 are the pressure and velocity at the section 1 and p_2 and v_2 those at section 2 (Fig. 142) ;

$$\frac{p_1}{\rho}-\frac{p_2}{\rho}=\tfrac{1}{2}v_2{}^2-\tfrac{1}{2}v_1{}^2,$$

$$p_1+\tfrac{1}{2}\rho v_1{}^2=p_2+\tfrac{1}{2}\rho v_2{}^2.$$

Thus the pressure energy and kinetic energy are mutually convertible.

Bernoulli's equation.—That potential and kinetic energies are mutually convertible has already been seen (p. 110), and now pressure and kinetic energies are seen to be convertible, so that if the liquid in any stream-line undergoes any changes, the energy lost in one form is gained in another. Therefore

potential energy + pressure energy + kinetic energy = constant,

or $$hg+\frac{p}{\rho}+\tfrac{1}{2}v^2=C.$$

This is known as Bernoulli's equation, and has many important applications.

Flow of liquid from a tank.—If a hole with sharp edges is made in the side of a tank, the velocity v of the emerging jet (Fig. 143) may be found. If the tank is sufficiently wide, the velocity at AB, the surface of the liquid, may be taken as zero. Also the pressure is atmospheric. But it is also atmospheric at the emerging jet, so that the atmospheric pressure will not affect the flow and may be ignored.

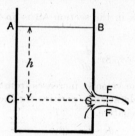 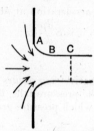

FIG. 143.—FLOW OF LIQUID　　FIG. 144.—NARROWING OF EMERGENT
FROM A TANK.　　　　JET OF LIQUID.

Consider a tube of flow which begins at AB and ends at G; at AB, $p=0$ and $v=0$, while at G. $p=0$ and $h=0$, and on applying Bernoulli's equation to this tube of flow,

$$hg + 0 + 0 = 0 + 0 + \tfrac{1}{2}v^2,$$

or $$v^2 = 2gh,$$

a result due originally to Torricelli.

If the liquid had fallen freely through a height h, its velocity would be given by $v^2 = 2gh$. This ideal velocity is never reached in the case of flow, because there is no liquid with zero coefficient of viscosity.

Also the stream-lines in the plane of the aperture are not all horizontal. Owing to their convergence upon the aperture, the momentum of the emergent liquid causes a narrowing of the jet (Fig. 144). The pressure at the outer surface of the jet is atmospheric, but is not uniform across the jet. In the plane of the aperture the pressure is below atmospheric, as the tubes of flow are narrowing and the velocity of the liquid is increasing. It is only at C, called the **vena contracta**, that the jet becomes uniform, and the velocity becomes the same throughout the jet. It is the velocity at the vena contracta that is given by Torricelli's equation.

It is found in practice that the area of the jet at the vena contracta when the orifice is circular is about 0·62 of the area of the aperture. This fraction is called the **coefficient of contraction**.

Constricted tube.—When a liquid flows through a tube of varying cross-section, the velocity varies along the tube (p. 205), and the pressure also varies. If the tube AB (Fig. 145) is constricted at C, the velocity of the liquid at C is greater than at A or B. The tube being horizontal, the equation

$$h_a g + \frac{p_a}{\rho} + \tfrac{1}{2}v_a{}^2 = h_c g + \frac{p_c}{\rho} + \tfrac{1}{2}v_c{}^2$$

becomes, since $h_a = h_c$,

$$\frac{p_a}{\rho} + \tfrac{1}{2}v_a{}^2 = \frac{p_c}{\rho} + \tfrac{1}{2}v_c{}^2 \,;$$

and as $v_c{}^2 > v_a{}^2$, it follows that $p_c < p_a$. This reduction in pressure may be shown by means of a tube ED dipping

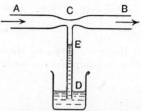

FIG. 145.—FLOW THROUGH A CONSTRICTED TUBE.

into another liquid which does not mix with the flowing liquid. The rise of liquid in DE is greater, the smaller the diameter of the tube at C.

Venturi meter.—This principle is used for measuring the amount of flow in pipes. The arrangement is known as the Venturi water meter. If two side tubes such as CD are joined to the pipe, one where the cross-section is S_1 and the other where it is S_2, then

$$S_1 v_1 = S_2 v_2 \quad \text{(p. 205),}$$

and

$$\tfrac{1}{2}v_2{}^2 - \tfrac{1}{2}v_1{}^2 = p_1 - p_2 \quad \text{(see above),}$$

ρ being unity in the case of water ;

$$\therefore \; \frac{1}{2}\frac{S_1{}^2}{S_2{}^2} v_1{}^2 - \tfrac{1}{2}v_1{}^2 = p_1 - p_2,$$

$$v_1 = S_2 \sqrt{\frac{2(p_1 - p_2)}{S_1{}^2 - S_2{}^2}},$$

$$S_1 v_1 = S_1 S_2 \sqrt{\frac{2(p_1 - p_2)}{S_1{}^2 - S_2{}^2}}.$$

$S_1 v_1$ is the volume of water passing the section S_1 per second, and therefore measures the flow in the pipe in terms of S_1, S_2 and $(p_1 - p_2)$. $(p_1 - p_2)$ is measured by uniting the vertical tubes at the base to form a manometer.

Pitot tube.—Another device using this principle for the measuring of the flow of water is that obtained by employing two vertical tubes AB and CD (Fig. 146) with small apertures situated in the water. The plane of the aperture B is parallel to the direction of flow, so that the level of the water at A measures the pressure at B. The aperture D faces the flow, so that in its plane the water is stopped, and consequently gains in pressure by the amount $\frac{1}{2}v^2$, where v is the velocity of flow. Thus the difference of level at A and C is h;

$$\therefore hg = \tfrac{1}{2}v^2; \quad \therefore v = \sqrt{2gh}.$$

Multiplying this by the area of cross-section of the pipe gives the flow in volume per second.

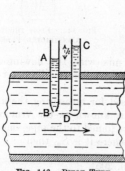

FIG. 146.—PITOT TUBE.

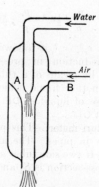

FIG. 147.—WATER PUMP.

Water pump.—A simple device is often used for producing a moderate fall in air pressure. Water from a tap issues in a jet from a small orifice A (Fig. 147). Owing to the high velocity of the jet the pressure is lowered, and air consequently enters at B. If B is connected with a vessel in which the air is originally at atmospheric pressure, the withdrawal of air by way of B soon lowers the pressure.

Flow of gas.—A liquid being nearly incompressible, its change in density can be neglected, but with a gas the change in density becomes important.

There are two cases to be considered. Either the flow is slow and the gas may be considered to have **constant temperature**, when the flow is said to be **isothermal**, or the flow is so rapid that there is no time for heat to enter or leave the gas, when the flow is said to be **adiabatic**.

When the flow is **isothermal**, Boyle's law (p. 174) may be applied, that is, $\dfrac{p}{\rho} = \text{constant} = c.$

The equation $-\dfrac{1}{\rho}\displaystyle\int_{p_1}^{p_2} dp = \int_{v_1}^{v_2} v\,dv$ (p. 207) must then be written

$$-\int_{p_1}^{p_2}\frac{dp}{\rho} = \tfrac{1}{2}v_2{}^2 - \tfrac{1}{2}v_1{}^2.$$

Now
$$\frac{dp}{\rho} = c\,\frac{dp}{p};$$

$$\therefore \ -\int_{p_1}^{p_2}\frac{dp}{\rho} = -c\int_{p_1}^{p_2}\frac{dp}{p}$$
$$= c\,(\log p_1 - \log p_2),$$

and
$$c\log p_1 - c\log p_2 = \tfrac{1}{2}v_2{}^2 - \tfrac{1}{2}v_1{}^2,$$
$$c\log p_1 + \tfrac{1}{2}v_1{}^2 = c\log p_2 + \tfrac{1}{2}v_2{}^2,$$

or
$$\frac{p_1\log p_1}{\rho_1} + \tfrac{1}{2}v_1{}^2 = \frac{p_2\log p_2}{\rho_2} + \tfrac{1}{2}v_2{}^2,$$

and Bernoulli's equation (p. 207) becomes

$$hg + \frac{p\log p}{\rho} + \tfrac{1}{2}v^2 = C.$$

If, on the other hand, the flow is adiabatic the relation between pressure and volume of a gas is $pV^\gamma = \text{constant},$[*] where

$$\gamma = \frac{\text{specific heat at constant pressure}}{\text{specific heat at constant volume}}.$$

Now $V = \dfrac{1}{\rho}$; $\therefore \ p = c\rho^\gamma,$

and instead of $\dfrac{1}{\rho}\displaystyle\int_{p_1}^{p_2} dp$ on p. 207, $\displaystyle\int_{p_1}^{p_2}\frac{dp}{\rho}$ must be written.

Now
$$dp = c\gamma\rho^{\gamma-1}d\rho;$$

$$\therefore \int_{p_1}^{p_2}\frac{dp}{\rho} = c\gamma\int_{p_1}^{p_2}\frac{\rho^{\gamma-1}d\rho}{\rho} = c\gamma\int_{p_1}^{p_2}\rho^{\gamma-2}d\rho$$

$$= \frac{c\gamma}{\gamma-1}\left[\rho^{\gamma-1}\right]_{p_1}^{p_2}$$

$$= \frac{\gamma}{\gamma-1}\left[\frac{p\rho^{\gamma-1}}{\rho^\gamma}\right]_{p_1}^{p_2}$$

$$= \frac{\gamma}{\gamma-1}\left[\frac{p_2}{\rho_2} - \frac{p_1}{\rho_1}\right];$$

[*] See Edser's *Heat*, p. 320.

and Bernoulli's equation becomes

$$hg + \frac{\gamma}{\gamma - 1} \cdot \frac{p}{\rho} + \tfrac{1}{2}v^2 = C.$$

The general form of the equation for a gas resembles that for a liquid; an increase of velocity is accompanied by a loss of pressure.

Examples of loss of pressure.—One familiar application is seen in the sprayer or atomizer. Air is blown through a tube which narrows at the aperture A (Fig. 148), by which the air leaves. A is situated over the top of the tube, dipping into the liquid B which is to be

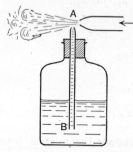

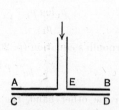

FIG. 148.—ATOMIZER.   FIG. 149.—PARADOX OF ATTRACTED DISC.

sprayed. As the air-stream emerges at high velocity at A, the corresponding reduction in pressure causes the liquid to rise in the vertical tube. As the liquid reaches the top it is blown away in the form of fine spray.

A second example is illustrated in Fig. 149. The large disc AB is arranged to be flush with the opening of the tube E. AB is placed on a cardboard disc CD. On blowing air down E, it is found that CD clings to AB, instead of being blown off as might be expected. The air escaping through the narrow space between AB and CD has increased velocity, and therefore reduced pressure. Thus the pressure above CD is less than atmospheric, so that the pressure below is greater than that above, and CD is pushed on to AB.

Liquid in rotating vessel.—If a mobile liquid is placed in a vertical cylindrical vessel, and the vessel is caused to rotate about its axis, the liquid at first will hardly move, on account of its small viscosity. There is, however, always some viscosity. The layers next the vessel will rotate with it and gradually set the inner layers in rotation. Thus the state of rotation will travel inwards, so that eventually all the liquid will rotate with the velocity of the vessel. In order to find the shape of the surface when the steady rotation is attained, it must be remembered that for equilibrium, the surface of the liquid must be at right angles to the resultant force acting on each element of liquid at the surface. In a liquid at rest the only force is gravitational, and the free surface is therefore horizontal (p. 156). But if the vessel is rotating about the vertical axis Oy (Fig. 150), the force on an element of liquid of mass m situated at P is compounded of the weight mg dynes represented by PA and the centrifugal force $\dfrac{mv^2}{x}$ represented by PB, where v is the linear speed of the mass m at P and x its distance from Oy.

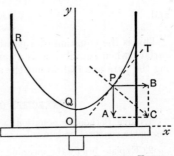

FIG. 150.—LIQUID IN ROTATING VESSEL.

Then $v = 2\pi n x$, where n is the number of revolutions per second.

$$\therefore \text{ Force PB} = \frac{m(2\pi n x)^2}{x}$$

$$= 4\pi^2 n^2 m x \text{ dynes.}$$

The resultant force PC must be at right angles to the surface at P; that is, it is at right angles to the tangent PT.

Now $\qquad \tan(\text{TPB}) = \dfrac{dy}{dx}$,

and $\qquad \widehat{\text{TPB}} = \widehat{\text{CPA}}$,

and $\qquad \tan(\text{CPA}) = \dfrac{\text{AC}}{\text{AP}} = \dfrac{4\pi^2 n^2 m x}{mg} = \dfrac{4\pi^2 n^2 x}{g}$;

$$\therefore \frac{dy}{dx} = \frac{4\pi^2 n^2 x}{g},$$

$$dy = \frac{4\pi^2 n^2}{g} x \, dx,$$

$$y = \frac{4\pi^2 n^2}{g} \tfrac{1}{2}x^2 + C$$

$$= \frac{2\pi^2 n^2 x^2}{g} + C.$$

If the origin is transferred to the point Q, then $y = 0$ when $x = 0$;

$$\therefore \; C = 0,$$

and
$$y = \frac{2\pi^2 n^2 x^2}{g}.$$

This is the equation of a parabola, so that the shape of the liquid surface when equilibrium is attained is the surface formed by rotating the parabola PQR about the axis Oy.

Exercises on Chapter IX

1. Give Bernoulli's equation, and describe how the passage of water through a constriction in a tube gives rise to a reduction in pressure.

2. Explain briefly the meaning of the words in italics in the law which states that " the *rate of change* of *momentum* is *proportional to* the acting force and *takes place in the direction* in which that force acts."

Water issues into the air from a horizontal nozzle whose area of cross-section is 0·125 sq. cm. Its speed is such that 1875 gm. emerge in one minute. The water strikes a fixed wall which is at right angles to the nozzle and 50 cm. from it, and then falls in a vertical plane.

(a) Calculate the vertical distance below the nozzle of the point where the jet strikes the wall.

(b) Calculate the force which the water exerts on the wall.

(c) Does (b) depend on (a) ? Give reasons for your answer.   C.H.S.C.

3. Water flows along a horizontal pipe, of which the cross-section is not constant. The pressure is 1 cm. of mercury where the velocity is 35 cm. sec.$^{-1}$. Find the pressure at a point where the velocity is 65 cm. sec.$^{-1}$.

4. A vertical tube of 4 mm. diameter at the bottom has water passing through it. If the pressure is atmospheric at the bottom, where the water emerges at the rate of 800 gm. per minute, what is the pressure at a place in the tube 25 cm. above the bottom, where the diameter is 3 mm. ?

5. Find an expression for the velocity of emergence of a liquid from a thin-walled orifice in a tank, and explain why the velocity in the plane of the orifice is not the same as at a short distance outside the tank.

6. If the diameters of pipe are 10 cm. and 6 cm. at the points where a Venturi meter is connected, and the pressures at the points are shown to differ by 5 cm. of water column, find the volume of water per second flowing through the pipe.

7. A Pitot tube is fixed in a main of diameter 15 cm., and the difference of pressure indicated by the gauge is 4 cm. of water column; find the volume of water passing through the main in a minute.

8. Show how Bernoulli's equation for flow of liquid must be modified for the case of a gas when the flow is (a) isothermal, (b) adiabatic.

CHAPTER X

KINETIC THEORY OF GASES

General account.—Many of the properties of matter may be studied without reference to the nature of the material itself. Thus the hydrostatic pressure due to a liquid is accounted for by its weight, and does not take into account the structure of the substance. When, however, we come to gas pressure, the property of infinite expansibility and resulting pressure on the walls of the containing vessel cannot be accounted for by the weight of the gas. The pressure may, however, be accounted for by considering the gas to consist of small bodies moving with considerable velocity and having perfect elastic properties. Such a theory is called the **kinetic theory of gases.** It was established chiefly by Clausius and Maxwell, who made successive contributions to it, and so brought it into line with many known facts.

A generation ago very little was known about the structure of atoms and molecules. They were looked upon as very minute, perfectly hard spheres, and the mechanical properties of a collection of such bodies gave a convincing and simple explanation of many of the properties of gases. Although our knowledge of the structure of atoms shows them to be very unlike the earlier simple picture of them, still the results obtained by the mechanical methods are surprisingly near the truth.

Rebound of molecules from wall.—When a molecule of mass m and velocity u meets the wall of the vessel containing the gas, and is travelling perpendicularly to the wall, it is first stopped and loses momentum mu. It then rebounds with velocity u and acquires momentum $-mu$. Its total change of momentum is $2mu$, and if n such impacts take place on each unit area of the wall in a second, the total momentum given to the molecules per second by the wall is $2nmu$. It follows that this is the pressure on the wall due to this bombardment.

215

Pressure.—If there are N molecules in unit volume of the gas, moving indiscriminately in all directions, their velocities may be resolved parallel to the three rectangular axes, x, y and z, and on adding these components of velocity for all the molecules there will be two equal and opposite components parallel to each axis, since it is considered that the gas does not move as a whole. The result is thus equivalent to $\frac{N}{6}$ mole-

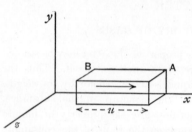

FIG. 151.—SIMPLE MOLECULAR THEORY OF PRESSURE.

cules moving along the positive direction of the x-axis, and an equal number in the opposite direction, with similar numbers parallel to the other axes.

Now consider A to be unit area of the wall perpendicular to the x-axis. All the molecules in a prism AB (Fig. 151) of length u, which are travelling towards A with velocity u, will strike A in one second, and the others will not strike it at all. This number of molecules is $\frac{N}{6}u$, which equals n in the expression $2nmu$ for the pressure;

$$\therefore \; p = 2\frac{N}{6} u \,.\, mu$$

$$= \tfrac{1}{3}mNu^2.$$

The velocity u is not necessarily the same for all the molecules, but the mean value of u^2 gives the pressure. The mean value of u^2 for all the molecules is written $\overline{u^2}$, and

$$p = \tfrac{1}{3}mN\overline{u^2}.$$

The quantity $\sqrt{\overline{u^2}}$ is called the **root mean square** velocity, and must not be confused with the mean velocity, which will be considered later.

If we write ρ for the density of the gas,

$$\rho = mN \; ;$$

$$\therefore \; p = \tfrac{1}{3}\rho\overline{u^2}.$$

It is therefore possible to find a value for $\sqrt{\overline{u^2}}$ for any gas of which the density at the atmospheric pressure is known. For hydrogen.

$\rho = 0.0896 \times 10^{-3}$ gm. per c.c. and $p = 76 \times 13.59 \times 981$ dynes per cm.^{2};

$$\therefore \quad \overline{u^2} = \frac{3 \times 76 \times 13.59 \times 981}{0.0896 \times 10^{-3}},$$

$$\sqrt{\overline{u^2}} = \sqrt{\frac{3 \times 76 \times 13.59 \times 981}{0.0896 \times 10^{-3}}} = \underline{1.84 \times 10^5 \text{ cm. sec.}^{-1}}.$$

Alternative proof.—A more exact method of finding the pressure is as follows. About a point O draw a sphere of radius r (Fig. 152).

The molecules passing through O with velocity u have paths symmetrically distributed in the space round O. Let the number of such molecules per c.c. be N_u. Take a small area $\delta\alpha$ through O and perpendicular to OP, and draw a slant cylinder with base $\delta\alpha$ and length u in the direction OA, making angle θ with OP. Then the number of molecules of velocity u in this cylinder is $N_u . u \delta\alpha . \cos\theta$. But these are travelling in all directions and $\dfrac{1}{4\pi r^2}$ of them are proceeding along AO, as though they came from unit area at A, in the direction making angle θ with OP, $4\pi r^2$

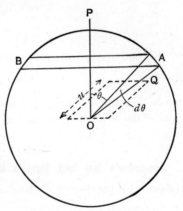

FIG. 152.—CALCULATION OF PRESSURE DUE TO A GAS.

being the area of the sphere. Therefore for all such directions as AO taken round an axis OP, the number of molecules striking $\delta\alpha$ in one second and coming from the direction of the strip AB is

$$N_u . u \delta\alpha . \cos\theta \frac{\text{area of strip}}{\text{area of sphere}} = N_u . u \delta\alpha . \cos\theta . \frac{2\pi r \sin\theta . r \, d\theta}{4\pi r^2}$$

$$= \tfrac{1}{2} N_u . u \delta\alpha . \sin\theta . \cos\theta . d\theta.$$

Each molecule has a component of velocity $u \cos\theta$ normal to $\delta\alpha$, which velocity will be reversed on impact, giving an impulse $2mu \cos\theta$, while the component of velocity $u \sin\theta$ parallel to u is not reversed.

$$\therefore \text{ Force on } \delta\alpha = \frac{2\delta\alpha N_u m u^2 \cos^2\theta . \sin\theta . d\theta}{2}.$$

Pressure on $\delta\alpha = N_u m u^2 \cos^2\theta . \sin\theta . d\theta.$

This pressure is due to the molecules with velocity u, inclined at angle θ to OP. Then, the pressure due to these molecules from the hemisphere above $\delta\alpha$ is given by,

$$\text{Pressure} = N_u m u^2 \int_0^{\frac{\pi}{2}} \cos^2\theta \, . \, \sin\theta \, . \, d\theta$$

$$= -N_u m u^2 \int_1^0 \cos^2\theta \, . \, d(\cos\theta)$$

$$= -N_u m u^2 \left[\frac{\cos^3\theta}{3} \right]_1^0$$

$$= \tfrac{1}{3} N_u m u^2.$$

Pressure due to molecules with all velocities

$$= \tfrac{1}{3} N m \overline{u^2},$$

where N is the total number of molecules per unit volume of the gas, and $\overline{u^2}$ the mean of the squares of their velocities ;

$$\therefore \quad p = \tfrac{1}{3} \rho \overline{u^2}.$$

Avogadro's law and Boyle's law.—In the expression $p = \tfrac{1}{3} \rho \overline{u^2}$ (above), ρ is the density of the gas at pressure p, so that $\rho = \dfrac{1}{v}$ where v is the volume of unit mass of the gas. Hence $p = \dfrac{1}{3} \dfrac{1}{v} . \overline{u^2}$ or $pv = \tfrac{1}{3} \overline{u^2}$. From the experiments on the mechanical equivalent of heat, it is natural to associate heat with the energy of motion of the molecules of a substance. Thus the temperature will be constant when the kinetic energy of the molecules remains unchanged. Hence at constant temperature, $\overline{u^2}$ would be constant, and from the above equation it follows that at constant temperature $pv = \text{constant}$. This is a statement of **Boyle's law** (p. 173), and it is seen that the law follows at once from the kinetic theory of gases.

If the average kinetic energy of the molecules of a gas be taken as a measure of the temperature, then Avogadro's law follows at once. Taking $p_1 = \tfrac{1}{3} m_1 n_1 \overline{u_1^2}$ to refer to one gas and $p_2 = \tfrac{1}{3} m_2 n_2 \overline{u_2^2}$ to another, and assuming the pressures to be the same,

$$p_1 = p_2,$$

or

$$m_1 n_1 \overline{u_1^2} = m_2 n_2 \overline{u_2^2}.$$

The mean kinetic energy of the molecules of the first gas is $\frac{1}{2}m_1\overline{u_1^2}$, and of the second $\frac{1}{2}m_2\overline{u_2^2}$, so that for the same temperature,

$$m_1\overline{u_1^2} = m_2\overline{u_2^2},$$

and taking the two equations together it is seen that $n_1 = n_2$.

This means that at the same temperature and pressure equal volumes of all gases contain the same number of molecules, which is Avogadro's law.

Mixtures of gases.—Where two or more gases which have no chemical action upon each other occupy the same space, the pressures exerted by the various constituents are $\frac{1}{3}m_1n_1\overline{u_1^2}$, $\frac{1}{3}m_2n_2\overline{u_2^2}$, etc., and the total pressure is

$$p = \frac{1}{3}m_1n_1\overline{u_1^2} + \frac{1}{3}m_2n_2\overline{u_2^2} + \frac{1}{3}m_3n_3\overline{u_3^2} + \text{etc.}$$

This is an expression of **Dalton's law,** that the pressure of a mixture of gases is the sum of the pressures that the individual gas would exert if occupying the same space at the same temperature.

Since the gases occupying the same space will soon acquire the same temperature, $m_1\overline{u_1^2} = m_2\overline{u_2^2} = \text{etc.} = \overline{mu^2}$;

$$\therefore \quad p = \frac{1}{3}(n_1 + n_2 + n_3 + \text{etc.})\,\overline{mu^2}.$$

Law of effusion.—When a small hole is made in the wall of a vessel containing a gas, and the wall is thin, every molecule striking the hole will pass outwards. If there is no gas outside the vessel, there will be no molecules entering through the hole.

In order to find the number of molecules per second meeting a hole of area $\delta\alpha$, refer again to Fig. 152. The number of molecules in the slant prism OQ travelling towards $\delta\alpha$ has been found to be $\frac{1}{2}\delta\alpha u N_u \sin\theta \cdot \cos\theta \cdot d\theta$ (p. 217), and these strike the wall $\delta\alpha$, or pass through the hole of area $\delta\alpha$ in a second. For all possible directions in the hemisphere, the sum will be

$$\frac{1}{2}\delta\alpha \int_0^{\frac{\pi}{2}} u N_u \sin\theta \cos\theta\, d\theta = \frac{1}{2}u N_u \delta\alpha \int_0^1 \sin\theta\, d(\sin\theta)$$
$$= \frac{1}{2}\delta\alpha u N_u \left[\frac{\sin^2\theta}{2}\right]_0^1$$
$$= \frac{1}{4}N_u \cdot u\,\delta\alpha.$$

On taking all possible values of u, the number of molecules passing through $\delta\alpha$ is $\frac{1}{4}\delta\alpha(N_{u_1}u_1 + N_{u_2}u_2 + \dots)$.

But
$$\frac{N_{u_1}u_1 + N_{u_2}u_2 + \dots}{N_{u_1} + N_{u_2} + N_{u_3} + \dots} = \bar{u},$$

where $\bar{u}$ is the average value of the velocity of the molecules of the gas. Also $N_{u_1} + N_{u_2} + \ldots = N$, so that if n is the number of molecules passing per second through unit area, $n = \frac{1}{4}N\bar{u}$.

The relation between $\bar{u}$ and $\overline{u^2}$ is not known unless the distribution of velocity amongst the various molecules of the gas is known. As a first approximation Clausius assumed that the values of the velocities of all the molecules are the same, and that their directions are uniformly distributed. In any case,

$$\overline{u^2} = \frac{N_{u_1}u_1{}^2 + N_{u_2}u_2{}^2 + \ldots}{N},$$

and if $u_1{}^2 = u_2{}^2 = u_3{}^2 = \ldots = (\bar{u})^2$,

$$\overline{u^2} = \frac{(\bar{u})^2(N_{u_1} + N_{u_2} + \ldots)}{N},$$

or

$$\overline{u^2} = (\bar{u})^2.$$

That is, the root mean square velocity is the mean velocity,

$$\sqrt{\overline{u^2}} = \bar{u}.$$

Now $$p = \tfrac{1}{3}\rho\overline{u^2} \quad \text{and} \quad n = \tfrac{1}{4}N\bar{u}.$$

Further, if ρ_1 is the density of the gas at unit pressure, $\rho = p\rho_1$;

$$\therefore\ p = \tfrac{1}{3}p\rho_1\overline{u^2},$$

or

$$\overline{u^2} = \frac{3}{\rho_1}, \quad \text{and} \quad \bar{u} = \sqrt{\frac{3}{\rho_1}}.$$

If each molecule has mass m, the mass of gas passing through the aperture per unit area is $mn = \tfrac{1}{4}Nm\bar{u} = M$;

$$\therefore\ M = \tfrac{1}{4}\rho\bar{u}$$

$$= \tfrac{1}{4} \cdot p\rho_1 \cdot \sqrt{\frac{3}{\rho_1}}$$

$$= \frac{\sqrt{3}}{4}\sqrt{\rho_1}p$$

$$= 0\cdot433\sqrt{\rho_1}p.$$

Maxwell calculated the relation between $\bar{u}$ and $\overline{u^2}$, taking the molecules to have all possible velocities in all directions, the only condition being that each group of molecules having a particular velocity will have the directions of those velocities uniformly distributed in space. This means that the gas has no motion of trans-

lation. The calculation is beyond the scope of this book. He found
that
$$\overline{u^2} = \tfrac{3}{8}\pi (\bar{u})^2.$$

Then, as before,
$$M = \tfrac{1}{4}Nm\bar{u}$$

$$= \tfrac{1}{4}\rho\bar{u}$$

$$= \tfrac{1}{4}p\rho_1 \cdot \sqrt{\frac{8\overline{u^2}}{3\pi}}$$

$$= \sqrt{\frac{1}{6\pi}}\, p\rho_1 \cdot \sqrt{\frac{3}{\rho_1}}, \text{ since } \overline{u^2} = \frac{3}{\rho_1}.$$

$$\therefore\ M = \sqrt{\frac{1}{2\pi}}\, \sqrt{\rho_1}\, p$$

$$= 0\cdot399\, \sqrt{\rho_1}\, p.$$

The simpler assumption of Clausius gives the factor $0\cdot433$, instead
of the more exact $0\cdot399$ according to Maxwell.

Law of diffusion.—According to either Clausius' or Maxwell's
assumption as regards the distribution of velocities amongst the
molecules of a gas, $(\bar{u})^2 \propto \overline{u^2}$.

That is, the mean velocity squared is proportional to the mean
square of the velocities. Now the rate of diffusion of a gas is almost
certainly proportional to the mean velocity of its molecules, that is,
to $\bar{u}$. Therefore for two gases,

$$\frac{\text{rate of diffusion of } 1}{\text{rate of diffusion of } 2} = \frac{u_1}{u_2} = \sqrt{\frac{\overline{u_1^2}}{\overline{u_2^2}}}.$$

But
$$\overline{u_1^2} = \frac{3}{\rho_1} \quad \text{and} \quad \overline{u_2^2} = \frac{3}{\rho_2};$$

$$\therefore\ \frac{\text{rate of diffusion of } 1}{\text{rate of diffusion of } 2} = \sqrt{\frac{\rho_2}{\rho_1}}.$$

That is, the rate of diffusion varies inversely as the square root of the
density of the gas. This is Graham's law of diffusion (p. 244).

Temperature and energy.—The characteristic equation of a perfect
gas is
$$pv = RT,$$

where T is the absolute temperature and R is a constant for all gases,
provided that 1 gram-molecule of the gas is considered (p. 219).

$R = 8.32 \times 10^7$ ergs per gm. mol. Now $p = \frac{1}{3} Nm\overline{u^2}$ (p. 216), where Nm is the quantity in gram-molecules in unit volume of the gas;

$$\therefore \quad p \times 1 = \tfrac{1}{3} Nm\overline{u^2} = RT,$$

$$m\overline{u^2} = \frac{3R}{N} T,$$

$$\tfrac{1}{2} m\overline{u^2} = \frac{3}{2}\frac{R}{N} T.$$

R and N are constants, so that the kinetic theory is consistent with the consideration that the absolute temperature of a gas is proportional to the mean kinetic energy of its molecules.

Mean free path.—In the simple kinetic theory of gases given above, it has been assumed that the molecules are so small that any encounter of one with another is of negligible frequency. This condition is approached as the density of the gas gets very small, so that the travel between encounters is very great in comparison with the size of the molecules themselves.

At ordinary pressures this assumption is not justified, and it is now necessary to consider modification of the theory to account for the effect of encounters between molecules.

There is no doubt that atoms and molecules are not the simple bodies they were once thought to be. To speak of the diameter of a molecule in the geometrical sense is meaningless. But there is also

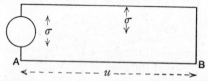

FIG. 153.—EFFECTIVE SPACE PER SEC. SWEPT THROUGH BY A MOLECULE.

no doubt that molecules do collide, and so cause each other to depart from their straight-line paths. The distance between their centres beyond which the molecules will pass without changing each other's path may be taken as the effective **diameter of the molecule**, σ. When the distance apart of the centres is less than σ, an encounter takes place.

If all the molecules of the gas are supposed to be at rest, and one molecule to move through the crowd with velocity u, the number of encounters, n per second, will equal the number of molecules whose centres lie within a cylinder AB (Fig. 153), whose length is u and whose radius is σ. The volume of the cylinder is therefore $\pi\sigma^2 u$, and the number of molecules whose centres lie inside the cylinder is $\pi\sigma^2 uN$, where N is the number of molecules per unit volume of the gas at rest within the cylinder. Of course, each encounter changes the direction of the velocity u, but this does not affect the result; the straight cylinder becomes a kinked or curved one; but its volume is still the volume swept out in one second by the disc of radius σ moving through the gas with a velocity whose value is u.

The number of encounters per second being $\pi\sigma^2 uN$, the average time between encounters is $\dfrac{1}{\pi\sigma^2 uN}$, and the average distance between encounters is

$$\text{velocity} \times \text{time} = \frac{u}{\pi\sigma^2 uN} = \frac{1}{\pi\sigma^2 N}.$$

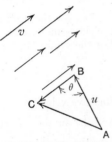

This average distance travelled between encounters is called the **mean free path** (λ) of the moving molecule;

$$\therefore\ \lambda = \frac{1}{\pi\sigma^2 N}.$$

This expression for λ has been obtained on the assumption that only one molecule of the gas is moving. The next stage is obtained by assuming the molecules all to

FIG. 154.—RELATIVE VELOCITY OF MOLECULES.

be moving in the same direction with velocity v (Fig. 154). Then let the single molecule A be projected through the crowd with velocity u. The velocity of A relative to the crowd is found, as on p. 18, by superimposing on the whole system a velocity equal and opposite to v. This reduces the crowd to rest and gives A a velocity represented by the vector AC.

Now $AC^2 = AB^2 + BC^2 - 2AB \cdot BC \cdot \cos\theta$,

where θ is the angle between the directions of u and v;

$$\therefore\ AC^2 = u^2 + v^2 - 2uv\cos\theta.$$

Imagine the whole N molecules which occupy a cubic centimetre to be divided into six groups, as on p. 216, each group travelling parallel to one of the rectangular axes, and all molecules having velocity of magnitude u. Let the single molecule at A (Fig. 155) have velocity u parallel to Ox.

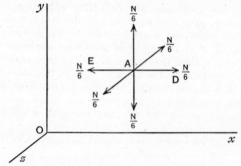

FIG. 155.—RESOLVED VELOCITIES OF MOLECULES.

Then for the first group AD there will be no encounters, because the single molecule has a velocity coinciding with that of the group. For the group AE, $\theta = 180°$;

$$\therefore \ AC^2 = u^2 + u^2 + 2u \cdot u \quad \text{(Fig. 154)}$$
$$= 4u^2.$$

Relative velocity, $\qquad AC = 2u$;

and the number of encounters per second of the single molecule with members of this group is $\pi\sigma^2 . 2u . \dfrac{N}{6} = \tfrac{1}{3}\pi\sigma^2 u N.$

The four groups parallel to the axes Ox and Oy are all in the same condition with respect to the single molecule, $\theta = 90°$;

$$\therefore \ AC^2 = u^2 + u^2 = 2u^2 ;$$
$$\therefore \ AC = \sqrt{2}u.$$

Number of encounters per second $= \pi\sigma^2 . \sqrt{2}u . \dfrac{N}{6}$ for each group, and for all four,

$$4\pi\sigma^2 . \sqrt{2}u . \frac{N}{6} = \frac{2\sqrt{2}}{3} \pi\sigma^2 u . N.$$

Considering now all the six groups, the total number of encounters per second made by the single molecule is

$$\tfrac{1}{3}\pi\sigma^2 u N + \frac{2\sqrt{2}}{3} \pi\sigma^2 u N = \frac{1 + 2\sqrt{2}}{3} \pi\sigma^2 u N.$$

The average time between encounters is therefore

$$\frac{3}{1+2\sqrt{2}} \cdot \frac{1}{\pi\sigma^2 uN},$$

and the mean free path is

$$\frac{3}{1+2\sqrt{2}} \cdot \frac{u}{\pi\sigma^2 uN},$$

that is,

$$\lambda = \frac{3}{1+2\sqrt{2}} \cdot \frac{1}{\pi\sigma^2 N} = \frac{1}{1\cdot276\pi\sigma^2 N}.$$

Method of Clausius.—A more general method of finding the value of λ consists in using the assumption made by Clausius (p. 220), that all the molecules have the same velocity, but are travelling in all directions. Then the number travelling in the direction AO (Fig. 152) is $N \cdot \dfrac{2\pi r \sin\theta \cdot r\,d\theta}{4\pi r^2} = \frac{1}{2}N \sin\theta \cdot d\theta$, and if a single molecule travels with velocity u along PO, its number of encounters per second with these can be calculated from their relative velocities,

$$\sqrt{u^2 + u^2 - 2 \cdot u \cdot u \cos\theta} = u\sqrt{2(1-\cos\theta)}.$$

Number of encounters per second

$$= \pi\sigma^2 u \sqrt{2(1-\cos\theta)} \cdot \tfrac{1}{2}N \sin\theta \cdot d\theta$$

$$= \pi\sigma^2 u \sqrt{4\sin^2\frac{\theta}{2}} \cdot \tfrac{1}{2}N \sin\theta \cdot d\theta.$$

For all values of θ from 0 to π, number of encounters per second

$$= \pi\sigma^2 uN \int_0^\pi \sin\frac{\theta}{2} \sin\theta \cdot d\theta$$

$$= \pi\sigma^2 uN \int_0^\pi 2 \cdot \sin\frac{\theta}{2} \cdot \sin\frac{\theta}{2} \cos\frac{\theta}{2} \cdot d\theta$$

$$= 4\pi\sigma^2 uN \int_0^1 \sin^2\frac{\theta}{2}\, d\left(\sin\frac{\theta}{2}\right) = \frac{4\pi\sigma^2 Nu}{3}.$$

The time between collisions is $\dfrac{3}{4\pi\sigma^2 Nu}$;

$$\therefore \lambda = \frac{3u}{4\pi\sigma^2 Nu}$$

$$= \frac{3}{4\pi\sigma^2 N}.$$

Mean free path and pressure.—The more complete consideration due to Maxwell (p. 221) gives $\lambda = \dfrac{1}{\sqrt{2}\pi\sigma^2 N}$, and the successive degrees of approximation give therefore $\lambda = \dfrac{1}{1\cdot276\pi\sigma^2 N}$ for the simple theory (p. 225), $\dfrac{1}{1\cdot333\pi\sigma^2 N}$ for Clausius' theory, and $\dfrac{1}{1\cdot414\pi\sigma^2 N}$ for Maxwell's. The form of the expression is the same, the result of the closer and closer approximation to the truth being represented by the numbers 1·276, 1·333 and 1·414. They agree in giving $\lambda \propto \dfrac{1}{N}$. Now the pressure of the gas is proportional to N (p. 216), the number of molecules in unit volume, thus **the mean free path varies inversely as the pressure of the gas.** At the atmospheric pressure the values of λ are, for hydrogen $1\cdot83 \times 10^{-5}$ cm.; nitrogen $0\cdot944 \times 10^{-5}$ cm., and oxygen $0\cdot995 \times 10^{-5}$ cm.

Viscosity of gases.—The viscosity of a gas is a purely mechanical property, defined by the relation $f = \eta\dfrac{dv}{dx}$ (p. 191), where $\dfrac{dv}{dx}$ is the velocity gradient in the gas, η the coefficient of viscosity, and f the force over unit area retarding the more quickly-moving layer and accelerating the more slowly-moving layer. It should therefore be possible to account for this viscosity on the kinetic theory.

The molecular velocities, taking place in all directions indiscriminately, do not involve any motion of translation of the gas. When there is a flow of the gas in any direction, there must be a common velocity of the molecules in that direction, superimposed upon the velocity u, which produces pressure, diffusion, etc. If one layer of a gas moves over another, its velocity $\mathbf{v} + d\mathbf{v}$ is greater than the velocity $\mathbf{v}$ of an adjacent layer, so that its molecules have momentum $m(\mathbf{v} + d\mathbf{v})$, whereas those of the more slowly-moving layer have momentum $m\mathbf{v}$ in the direction of flow. The molecular velocities u cause a continual interchange of molecules between the two layers. It follows that the more rapidly-moving layer loses molecules having momentum $m(\mathbf{v} + d\mathbf{v})$ in the direction of flow, and this loss has the effect of a force tending to retard the layer. Similarly the more slowly-moving layer gains in the same time molecules with a greater momentum than its own, and so experiences a force tending to accelerate it.

In order to calculate these stresses, consider a plane CD (Fig. 156) in the gas, where the velocity in the direction of the plane is **v**. Draw planes AB and EF parallel to CD, and at distance equal to the mean free path λ from it. Then on the average the molecules travelling normally towards AB will cross CD without further collision. Similarly, those passing through EF towards CD will cross CD

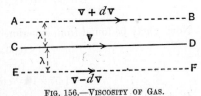

FIG. 156.—VISCOSITY OF GAS.

without further collision. The number crossing unit area per second is in each case $\frac{N}{6}\,\bar{u}$ (p. 216). The momentum in the direction of flow carried through unit area of CD by the molecules from AB is

$$m\,\frac{N}{6}\,\bar{u}(\mathbf{v}+d\mathbf{v})$$

per sec., and this is acquired on account of collisions by the gas in the layer CDFE. Similarly the momentum per second gained by gas in the layer ABDC is $m\,\frac{N}{6}\,\bar{u}(\mathbf{v}-d\mathbf{v})$. This layer therefore loses momentum

$$m\,\frac{N}{6}\,\bar{u}\{(\mathbf{v}+d\mathbf{v})-(\mathbf{v}-d\mathbf{v})\}=m\,\frac{N}{3}\,\bar{u}\,d\mathbf{v}$$

per second through unit area of AB, and the gas in CDFE gains an equal amount. This is equivalent to a force $m\,\frac{N}{3}\,u\,d\mathbf{v}$ dynes, tending to produce retardation in the upper layer and acceleration in the lower layer. But the velocity gradient is $\frac{d\mathbf{v}}{\lambda}$, and since

$$f=\eta\,\frac{d\mathbf{v}}{dx}=\eta\,\frac{d\mathbf{v}}{\lambda},$$

$$m\,\frac{N}{3}\,\bar{u}\,d\mathbf{v}=\eta\,\frac{d\mathbf{v}}{\lambda},$$

$$\eta=\frac{Nm\bar{u}\lambda}{3}=\frac{\rho\bar{u}\lambda}{3}.$$

In the case where the velocities of the molecules are all of equal value, $\bar{u}$ may be taken as the root mean square velocity $\sqrt{\bar{u}^2}$, which in turn is known from the pressure and density of the gas. Thus for hydrogen at normal temperature and pressure,

$$\eta = \frac{0 \cdot 0896 \times 10^{-3} \times 1 \cdot 84 \times 10^5 \lambda}{3}.$$

Now η may be found from experiment, and is $0 \cdot 86 \times 10^{-4}$;

$$\therefore \quad \lambda = \frac{3 \times 0 \cdot 86 \times 10^{-4}}{0 \cdot 0896 \times 10^{-3} \times 1 \cdot 84 \times 10^5}$$

$$= 1 \cdot 57 \times 10^{-5} \text{ cm.}$$

It should also be noticed that in the equation $\eta = \dfrac{\rho \bar{u} \lambda}{3}$, ρ varies directly as the pressure of the gas and λ varies inversely as the pressure (p. 226), and hence η should be independent of the pressure, the temperature remaining constant.

The fact that the coefficient of viscosity is independent of pressure is supported by experimental measurements on many gases, and affords additional evidence in favour of the kinetic theory of gases.

The equation indicates that the coefficient of viscosity is proportional to $\bar{u}$, and therefore to the square root of the absolute temperature. This is only approximately true. This result is, however, not so closely verified as in the case of the independence of pressure.

EXERCISES ON CHAPTER X

1. Give a brief account of the kinetic theory of gases, and show that on certain assumptions (which should be specified) the theory leads to Boyle's law.   C.H.S.C.

2. How is the pressure of a gas explained on the kinetic theory ?

Deduce an expression for the pressure of a gas in terms of its density and the mean square of the velocity of its molecules. Calculate the square root of the mean square of the velocity of the molecules of hydrogen at 0° C.   C.H.S.C.

3. Show that Avogadro's law follows from the simple kinetic theory of gases.

4. If the density of nitrogen is $1 \cdot 25$ gm. per litre at normal temperature and pressure, calculate the root mean square velocity of its molecules.

5. Using the expression on p. 221, find the density of the gas at normal temperature and pressure if $0 \cdot 154$ gm. escape per second through a hole 1 sq. mm. in area in a thin plate, when the pressure is atmospheric on one side of the plate and zero on the other side.

6. Prove that the simple kinetic theory leads to Graham's law of diffusion of gases.

7. Calculate the number of molecules per c.c. of a gas, taking the mean free path as $1 \cdot 83 \times 10^{-5}$ cm. and the molecular diameter σ, $2 \cdot 3 \times 10^{-8}$, using Maxwell's expression (p. 226).

CHAPTER XI

DIFFUSION AND OSMOSIS

Diffusion of liquids.—If two liquids can mix, then on placing them in contact in a vessel and leaving them undisturbed, each liquid will penetrate into the other until both liquids are uniformly distributed throughout the space occupied by the mixture. This may be observed by placing a coloured liquid such as a solution of copper sulphate at the bottom of a glass jar and pouring water upon the solution carefully, so that the separation between the solution and the pure water can be seen. On observing the jar from day to day, it will be found that the characteristic colour of the copper sulphate ascends, and will in time fill the whole space occupied by the liquid. The solute, in this case copper sulphate, has been distributed through the solution by the process called **diffusion**.

The laws which govern the diffusion of liquids were first investigated by Graham. He placed a wide-necked bottle A (Fig. 157), containing the solution to be investigated, in a larger vessel of water B. The neck of A was covered with a glass plate before immersion in B, so that the solution did not escape when A was placed in B. When the liquids had come to rest, the glass plate was carefully slid from its position and removed, so that the liquids were disturbed as little as possible. After noted intervals of time, samples of the water in B were withdrawn with a

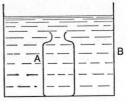

FIG. 157.—GRAHAM'S APPARATUS FOR MEASURING THE DIFFUSION OF A SOLUTE.

pipette, and the amount of solute which had diffused from A thus determined. In this way Graham established several important facts. For any one substance the amount of solute diffusing out of A is proportional to its concentration in A and increases with rise of temperature. The rate of diffusion is independent of the presence of a different solute in B, but is lowered if the same solute is in B as in A. Different substances diffuse at different rates, and if present together may be partially separated by diffusion. The substances to which he gave the name of colloids diffuse much more slowly than the crystallisable substances, which he named **crystalloids**.

Fick's law.—Graham was not able to establish any exact law for the rate of diffusion in any case. At a later time Fick considered the analogy between the process of diffusion of a solute and the flow of heat in a solid, and succeeded in establishing the law that the rate of diffusion in any direction is proportional to the gradient of concentration of the solute in that direction. This is known as **Fick's law**. It means

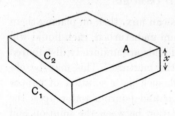

FIG. 158.—GRADIENT OF CONCENTRATION.

that if a slab of the solution of area A (Fig. 158) and thickness x is considered, and the concentration of the solute all over the lower face is c_1 and that over the upper face is c_2, then the amount of solute passing into the lower face and out at the upper face, that is, passing any cross-section, in a given time is proportional to the gradient of concentration $\dfrac{c_1 - c_2}{x}$.

More exactly, the quantity diffusing may be written $kA \cdot \dfrac{dc}{dx}$. If A is unit area, the amount of solute passing in unit time is $k \dfrac{dc}{dx}$. The quantity k is called the **coefficient of diffusion**.

If dm is the mass passing in time dt,

$$\frac{dm}{dt} = kA \frac{dc}{dx}.$$

The dimensions of k may be found by remembering that c, the concentration, is a mass per unit volume and has the dimensions $[ML^{-3}]$.

Then
$$[MT^{-1}] = [k][L^2 \cdot ML^{-3} \cdot L^{-1}] ;$$
$$\therefore \ [k] = [L^2 T^{-1}].$$

Time of diffusion and length of column.—It follows from Fick's law that the time required to pass from one distribution of concentration to another in any column of solution is proportional to the square of the length of the column. Consider two columns of lengths l_1 and l_2 (Fig. 159) respectively, which have exactly similar distributions of a solute, c_1, c_2, c_3, c_4, at a given time. The intervals t_1 and t_2 that must elapse before the similar concentrations are at c_2', c_3', c_4', are proportional to the distances travelled by each portion of the solute, and inversely proportional to the absolute velocity of the solute at each layer.

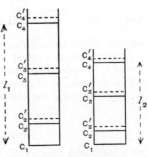

FIG. 159.—DIFFUSION IN COLUMN OF LIQUID.

The distances are proportional to the lengths of column, so that if the velocities at corresponding layers were the same, we should have $\dfrac{t_1}{t_2} = \dfrac{l_1}{l_2}$. But the velocity at each layer being v, the amount dm crossing any section in time dt is cAv, or

$$dm = cAv\, dt,$$

$$\frac{dm}{dt} = cAv;$$

$$\therefore\ cAv = kA\frac{dc}{dx};$$

$$\therefore\ v = \frac{k}{c}\cdot\frac{dc}{dx}.$$

If the distributions of the concentrations are similar in the two columns, $\dfrac{dc}{dx}$ is inversely proportional to the length of column;

$$\therefore\ \frac{v_1}{v_2} = \frac{l_2}{l_1},$$

and

$$\frac{t_1}{t_2} = \frac{l_1}{l_2}\cdot\frac{v_2}{v_1}$$

$$= \frac{l_1^2}{l_2^2}.$$

That is, the time for passing from one distribution of concentration to another is proportional to the square of the length of column.

A column of copper sulphate, 100 cm. high, of which the lower half is saturated and the upper half pure water, takes several years to acquire uniform distribution. Therefore a similar column $\frac{100}{\sqrt{12}} = 28\cdot87$ cm. high would require the same number of months, and a column $\frac{28\cdot87}{\sqrt{30}} = 5\cdot27$ cm. would require the same number of days to diffuse to uniformity.

It is therefore evident that stirring promotes diffusion to uniformity, because then layers of very small thickness may have considerable gradient of concentration. Thus the uniformity acquired in, say, 10 years for the 100 cm. column, would be acquired in

$$\frac{10 \times 365 \times 24 \times 60 \times 60}{(100)^2 \times (1000)^2} = 0\cdot03 \text{ sec.}$$

for a layer 0·01 mm. thick, such as might be produced by stirring.

Determination of coefficient of diffusion.—It is possible to calculate the coefficient of diffusion from Fick's law if the concentration at various points of a vertical column can be measured at known intervals of time. The calculation presents difficulties which are beyond the scope of this work. The experimental difficulties arise from the fact that samples of the solution may not be removed, as this would cause disturbance of the distribution of concentration. Lord Kelvin made measurements by placing floats of various densities in the column. Knowing then the concentration of the solute for each density of the solution, it is possible, by noting the position in which the floats remain at rest, to determine the distribution of concentration. The weakness of the method lies in the fact that air bubbles collect on the floats and change their mean density.

Later determinations have been made by measuring the optical properties of the column, and so following the change in concentration. It is easy to measure the refractive index at various concentrations. The refractive index can then be made to provide a measure of the concentrations at various levels of the diffusing column. Probably the best measurement is due to Clack, who measured the concentration gradient by using the movement of the interference fringes due to the passage of two thin beams of light through the solution at slightly different levels.

Osmosis.—It is a common experience that various membranes will allow certain substances to pass through them, but will not allow others. If dried fruit is placed in water, the skin of the fruit will allow water to pass through it, but will not transmit the organic contents. The result is that water passes into the fruit, which will swell to its size in the natural undried condition. Another familiar example is the crinkling of the skin of the fingers when immersed for some time in a strong solution of soap or soda. The skin allows the transmission of water, but not of the substance in solution, and the water passes from beneath the skin to the outside.

A simple experiment may be made by closing the lower end of a wide tube with a sheet of parchment paper, the upper end of the tube having been drawn out previously into a narrow tube. On filling the wide tube with a sugar solution and immersing it in pure water, the solution will be seen to rise in the narrow tube. The water has passed through the parchment paper, which is impermeable to the sugar.

This process of the passage of a solvent into a strong solution is called osmosis, and the condition necessary for it is the existence of a semi-permeable membrane, that is, one which will transmit one substance, but will prevent the passage of another. In the experiment, the parchment paper is the semi-permeable membrane, as the water passes through it, although the sugar cannot. The walls of all vegetable cells are semi-permeable, but their selective properties differ from plant to plant, enabling each plant to absorb the salts in solution necessary for its life, and to reject others.

Graham made use of the semi-permeable properties of bladder to separate crystalloids from colloids (p. 230). The membrane of bladder transmits crystalloids in solution in water, but rejects colloids. If then a mixture exists on one side of the membrane and pure water on the other, the crystalloid is transmitted and may be removed. This process he called dialysis.

Osmotic pressure.—The rise of liquid in the narrow tube described above shows that the pressure in the solution soon rises above the pressure of the pure water outside the tube. The flow of water through the parchment continues until the pressure inside the tube exceeds that outside by a certain amount, which is called the osmotic pressure of the solution.

It may seem strange that the water passes through the membrane from places of lower pressure outside to places of higher pressure inside. But it must be remembered that before the tube is immersed in the pure water, the pressures of both are the same, that is, atmospheric pressure at the surface, in addition to any hydrostatic pressure

$h\delta g$ due to depth (p. 156). But the hydrostatic pressure inside is due to water and the sugar in solution, and that outside to water alone. Thus the pressure due to water is less inside than outside, and the water passes in until the water pressure is the same inside and outside. Equilibrium is then reached when the excess pressure inside is equal to that exerted by the sugar in solution, and is due to the fact that the sugar is confined by the semi-permeable membrane to the space occupied by the solution.

This mechanical account may not be the complete explanation. For example, a wet piece of paper is semi-permeable in some cases. If ammonia gas is on one side of it and air on the other, the ammonia passes through, but the air does not. The process in this case is one of solution, as the ammonia is dissolved, diffuses through the membrane and evaporates on the other side ; while the air is only dissolved to a very minute extent. A similar process occurs with hydrogen and a sheet of palladium. The hydrogen is occluded by the palladium, diffuses through it and is given off on the other side, while other gases cannot pass through. For a similar reason, an india-rubber balloon blown up with hydrogen soon collapses, while one blown up with air lasts much longer.

Laws of osmotic pressure.—In order to find the laws connecting osmotic pressure and concentration of solute, Pfeffer employed as

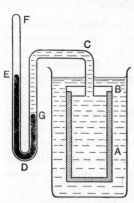

FIG. 160.—PFEFFER'S CELL.

the semi-permeable membrane freshly-formed cupric ferro-cyanide. This substance is permeable to water, but not to many substances, such as sugar. Owing to the mechanical weakness of the material, it is formed in the walls of a porous pot, the porcelain acting as a mechanical support. The porous pot is filled with a solution of copper sulphate and immersed in a dilute solution of potassium ferro-cyanide. The two substances diffuse into the walls of the pot, and where they meet cupric ferro-cyanide is formed. The porous pot A (Fig. 160) is then washed, and filled with the solution under investigation. It is then closed with the stopper B, through which passes the tube C leading to the mercury manometer GDE. In order to avoid a large travel of the mercury, the end F of the tube may be closed. If the volume of air in EF and the height of mercury column EG are known when the pressure is atmospheric, similar readings when the cell A is placed in pure water give the osmotic pressure of the solution. In this manner Pfeffer found that the osmotic pressure for any one solute is proportional to the concentration of the solute in A, provided that the solution is not an electrolyte. In the case of an electrolyte, dissociation has occurred, so that effective concentration can no longer be calculated from the mass of solute in the solution.

From Pfeffer's results van't Hoff showed that the osmotic pressure is also proportional to the absolute temperature. Hence, if c is the concentration of sugar in the solution, P the osmotic pressure and T the absolute temperature,

$$P = kcT,$$

where k is some constant.

If the concentration c is measured in gram-molecules per cubic centimetre, $\dfrac{1}{c} = V$, where V is the volume of the solution containing one gram-molecule of solute ;

$$\therefore \ PV = kT.$$

The constant k is found, at low concentration, to be identical with the gas constant R (p. 176), so that the equation may then be written

$$PV = RT,$$

which is the characteristic equation of a perfect gas. This means that if the solute could exist in the form of a gas, that is, without the water present, and occupy the space actually occupied by the solution, the gas pressure would be identical with the actual osmotic pressure.

It follows that Avogadro's law (p. 218) holds for dilute solutions. That is, in equal volumes of solution at the same temperature, the osmotic pressure will be the same when equal numbers of molecules of solute are present. It is therefore reasonable to consider, as in the case of a gas (p. 216), that the pressure is due to the bombardment of the molecules of solute on the containing walls, that is, on the semi-permeable membrane and on the free surface of the solution.

Vapour pressure of a solution.—Every liquid in an enclosed space will evaporate until the vapour exerts a definite pressure upon the walls of the space. This pressure, attained when evaporation ceases, is called the **maximum vapour pressure** of the substance. The value of the maximum vapour pressure depends upon the temperature; it always increases with rising temperature. It is shown in works on Heat that when the maximum vapour pressure is equal to the atmospheric pressure, the liquid boils. Thus **the boiling point of a liquid is the temperature at which the maximum vapour pressure is equal to the atmospheric pressure.**

When it is said that evaporation ceases, it means that there is a balance between evaporation and condensation. At the surface of the liquid, evaporation always occurs, but at the same time vapour is passing back into the liquid. The latter process increases as the pressure, and therefore density, of the vapour rises, until the condensation goes on at the same rate as the evaporation, and the vapour pressure has reached a maximum. A rise of temperature increases the rate of evaporation, so that a new condition of equilibrium will be reached. It is usual to omit the word " maximum "; thus vapour pressure is taken to mean the maximum unless otherwise stated.

The vapour pressure of a solution is always less than that of the pure solvent, and, moreover, there is a definite relation between the osmotic pressure of the solution and the change of vapour pressure when solution takes place.

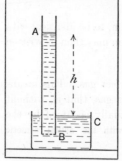

FIG. 161.—VAPOUR PRESSURE AND OSMOTIC PRESSURE.

If a tube AB (Fig. 161), containing a solution, is closed at B by a membrane, which is permeable for the solvent, but not for the solute, and the lower end dips into a vessel containing the solvent, the osmotic pressure will cause the liquid to rise to A in the tube. Imagine the whole to be enclosed in a chamber which does not conduct heat. It will then come to some steady temperature, and since no energy can enter the chamber, the liquid will come to rest, as is proved in works on Thermodynamics. The vapour at A is in contact with the solution, and its maximum pressure is, say, p_1. At C the vapour is in contact with the pure solvent, and its pressure may be taken as p_2. Then, since the system is at rest,

$$p_2 - p_1 = \text{pressure due to column AC of vapour}$$
$$= h\sigma g,$$

where σ is the density of the vapour of the solvent.

But if P is the osmotic pressure,

$$P = h(\rho - \sigma)g,$$

where ρ is the density of the solution ;

$$\therefore \ p_2 - p_1 = \frac{P}{(\rho - \sigma)g} \cdot \sigma g$$

$$= P \cdot \frac{\sigma}{\rho - \sigma} \cdot$$

The lowering of the vapour pressure, $(p_2 - p_1)$, of the solvent is therefore proportional to the osmotic pressure, P. It was seen on p. 235 that this is proportional to the concentration of the solute, whatever the chemical nature of the solute may be. This is another way of stating Raoult's law : that **the depression of the vapour pressure is proportional to the number of molecules of solute per unit volume of the solution for all solutes.**

The density σ of the vapour is the mass in grams contained in one cubic centimetre, and if v is the volume of 1 gm., $\sigma = \dfrac{1}{v}$,

then

$$p_2 - p_1 = \frac{P}{v\rho},$$

σ being very small in comparison with ρ. v is the specific volume of the vapour at pressure p_2, and treating it as a gas,

$$p_2 \cdot v = P_0 v_0, \quad \text{or} \quad p_2 \sigma_0 = P_0 \sigma,$$

where P_0 is the normal atmospheric pressure, and v_0 the corresponding specific volume ;

$$\therefore \ p_2 - p_1 = \frac{P p_2}{P_0 v_0 \rho} = \frac{P p_2 \sigma_0}{P_0 \rho},$$

$$\frac{p_2 - p_1}{p_2} = \frac{P \sigma_0}{P_0 \rho} \cdot$$

It has been assumed that the column h in Fig. 161 is not long enough for any appreciable change in σ to occur between the top and the bottom. This is no longer justified if the concentration, and therefore the osmotic pressure, is considerable. For an infinitesimal height dh,

$$dp = -g\sigma \, dh,$$

the negative sign being taken because the vapour pressure decreases as h increases;

$$\therefore \ dp = -g\frac{p\sigma_0}{P_0}dh,$$

$$dh = -\frac{P_0}{g\sigma_0}\frac{dp}{p},$$

$$h = -\frac{P_0}{g\sigma_0}\int_{p_2}^{p_1}\frac{dp}{p}$$

$$= -\frac{P_0}{g\sigma_0}[\log p_1 - \log p_2] = \frac{P_0}{g\sigma_0}\log\frac{p_2}{p_1},$$

or
$$\log\frac{p_2}{p_1} = \frac{g\sigma_0 h}{P_0}.$$

But
$$g\rho h = P ;$$

$$\therefore \ \log\frac{p_2}{p_1} = \frac{P\sigma_0}{P_0\rho}.$$

Effect of external pressure upon vapour pressure of solution.—In the case of a pure solvent, it is well known that the presence of a gas which has no chemical effect upon the solvent does not change the vapour pressure. Thus the maximum vapour pressure of water depends only upon the temperature, and is the same in the absence or presence of air. This condition no longer holds when any material is dissolved in the water. The equation for the lowering of the vapour pressure on p. 237 was obtained by considering the vapour only to be present in the closed chamber (Fig. 161).

The effect of admitting a gas such as air, which does not react chemically with the solvent, may be found by an argument somewhat similar to the last. Consider a tube ABCD (Fig. 162), with solution in AB, pure solvent in BC, and semi-permeable membrane at B. Under these conditions the solvent would pass through B, and the level rise at A and fall at C until the condition of Fig. 161 is attained, that is,

$$p_2 - p_1 = \frac{P\sigma}{\rho - \sigma}.$$

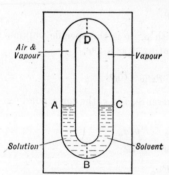

FIG. 162.—EFFECT OF GAS ON VAPOUR PRESSURE.

Now imagine a membrane to be situated at D, which is permeable to the vapour but not to air, and let air be forced into AD, driving the liquid down at A and up at C until the columns AB and BC exert equal pressures. The vapour pressures are now equal in AD and DC, but in AD there is in addition the air pressure. Thus the air pressure exactly balances the osmotic pressure, that is,

$$\text{air pressure} = P,$$

and   vapour pressure in AD $= p_2$;

∴ air pressure has changed the vapour pressure over the solution from p_1 to p_2, just as the osmotic pressure was accompanied by a change from p_2 to p_1.

Boiling point.—From the definition of boiling point given on p. 236, it will be seen that as the pressure of the atmosphere above a liquid rises, so does the boiling point.

If the curve AB in Fig. 163 represents the relation between vapour pressure and temperature for a solvent, then if AD is the atmospheric pressure, D indicates the boiling point.

If the pressure rises to EB, then E is the boiling point. If now a substance is dissolved in the solvent, every vapour pressure is lowered by the amount

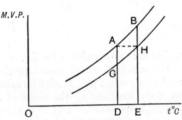

FIG. 163.—RELATION BETWEEN VAPOUR PRESSURE AND BOILING POINT.

$p_2 \dfrac{P\sigma_0}{P_0\rho}$, and the new vapour pressure curve GH will lie below AB. If AH is horizontal, then at the atmospheric pressure AD or EH, the new boiling point is E; that is, the boiling point is raised by the act of solution.

In order to calculate the change in boiling point, it is necessary to imagine a reversible cycle of change. Let the arrangement to Fig. 162 be imagined with the limb DAB maintained at a temperature $T + \delta T$ on the absolute scale, while DCB is maintained at temperature T. If 1 gm. of the solvent is forced into AB through the semi-permeable membrane B, the work done is pressure × volume $= \dfrac{P}{\rho}$, the work being performed in opposition to the osmotic pressure P, and the volume of 1 gm. of solvent being $\dfrac{1}{\rho}$. Now let this 1 gm.

evaporate at A. The heat required is L_A heat units where L_A is the latent heat at temperature $T + \delta T$. This vapour will equalise the pressure in the limbs by passing through D without work being performed, and will condense at C, giving up heat L_C, where L_C is the latent heat of the solvent at temperature T. The difference of temperature δT may be as small as we please, and the process may go on slowly. Under these conditions it is proved in works on Thermodynamics that, for the whole cycle of change,

$$\frac{\text{work performed}}{\text{heat given up}} = \frac{\delta T}{T},$$

in fact, the temperature T is defined so that this relation shall be true;

$$\therefore \frac{\frac{P}{\rho}}{L_C} = \frac{\delta T}{T},$$

or

$$P = \frac{\rho L \delta T}{T},$$

where L is now written for L_C.

For a solute which would produce an osmotic pressure equal to that of a perfect gas, P may be calculated from the relation $PV = RT$ (p. 235), first finding the value of R from the case of oxygen. At atmospheric pressure and 0° C. the density of oxygen is 1·429 gm. per litre, or $1·429 \times 10^{-3}$ gm. per c.c., and $T = 273·1$. Then since

$$P = 1·013 \times 10^6 \text{ dynes per sq. cm.,}$$

$$\frac{1·013 \times 10^6}{1·429 \times 10^{-3}} = R \times 273·1$$

$$R = \frac{1·013 \times 10^9}{1·429 \times 273·1}$$

$$= 2·596 \times 10^6 \text{ cm.}^2 \text{ sec.}^{-2}.$$

If then the concentration of oxygen is 1 gram-molecule (32 gm.) per 100 c.c., and the temperature is the boiling point, 373·1,

$$P \times \tfrac{100}{32} = 2·596 \times 10^6 \times 373·1,$$

$$P = 2·596 \times 10^4 \times 373·1 \times 32$$

$$= 3·098 \times 10^8 \text{ dynes per sq. cm.}$$

Then,
$$\delta T = \frac{PT}{\rho L},$$

and for water at the boiling point $\rho = 0.9584$, $L = 540$ calories per gram, or $540 \times 4.182 \times 10^7$ ergs per gram.

$$\delta T = \frac{3.098 \times 10^8 \times 373.1}{0.9584 \times 540 \times 4.182 \times 10^7}$$

$$= 5.340 \text{ centigrade degrees.}$$

This is known as the **molecular elevation of the boiling point**, and is the rise in the boiling point of water produced by one gram-molecule of any substance when dissolved in 100 grams of water, provided that the solute exists in the form of molecules in the solution. Solutes such as sugar fulfil this relation accurately and the observed rise in the boiling point for a given concentration enables the molecular weight to be determined with considerable precision. When the molecules dissociate, as in the case of an electrolyte, the rise in the boiling point is greater than would be indicated by the above reasoning. If, however, a solution of potassium chloride in water is made, of x gm.-mol. per 100 gm. of water, and the rise in boiling point determined, the rise, which would be $x \times 5.34$ degrees if there were no dissociation, will be found to be considerably greater than this. If the **degree of dissociation** is α, that is, the fraction of the total number of molecules which have dissociated is α, then αx gm.-mol. is the amount dissociated. Since each molecule forms two ions on dissociation, the concentration, counting molecules and ions, will change from x to $2\alpha x + (1 - \alpha)x = (1 + \alpha)x$, and the observed elevation of the boiling point will be

$$(1 + \alpha)x \times 5.34 \text{ deg.}$$

On observing the rise in the boiling point it is possible from this to calculate α. The result agrees very well, in the case of weak solutions, with that obtained from measurements of the electrical conductivity of the solution.

In the case of colloids (p. 230) the reverse of the above will be found. The substance in solution forms aggregations of molecules varying in size, in different cases, from a cluster of a few molecules up to particles that are visible in the microscope. In such cases the osmotic pressure is small, and the raising of the boiling point is much less than in the normal case, such as sugar, where the solute exists in the form of single molecules, so that the above theory applies very closely.

Freezing point.—A calculation in all ways similar to that on p. 240 leads to the conclusion that the freezing point of a solution is lower than that of a pure solvent. The depression of the freezing point δT is given by $\delta T = \dfrac{PT}{\rho L}$.

For water $T = 273 \cdot 1$, $L = 80$ and $\rho = 1$. Then, as before, for 1 gm.-mol. per 100 c.c.,

$$P \times \tfrac{100}{32} = 2 \cdot 596 \times 10^6 \times 273 \cdot 1,$$

$$P = 32 \times 2 \cdot 596 \times 273 \cdot 1 \times 10^4,$$

and

$$\delta T = \frac{32 \times 2 \cdot 596 \times 273 \cdot 1^2 \times 10^4}{80 \times 4 \cdot 182 \times 10^7}$$

$$= 18 \cdot 5 \text{ centigrade degrees.}$$

This is the value of the molecular depression of the freezing point. On making a solution of x gm.-mol. per 100 c.c. the depression is $x \times 18 \cdot 53$ deg. If the depression δT be observed when the solution consists of y gm. of substance in 100 c.c. of water, the number of gm.-mol. in solution is $\dfrac{\delta T}{18 \cdot 5}$, and if this weighs y gm., the molecular weight is

$$y \Big/ \frac{\delta T}{18 \cdot 5} = \frac{18 \cdot 5 y}{\delta T}.$$

The same limitations with regard to dissociation and aggregation apply to the depression of the freezing point as to the elevation of the boiling point.

Diffusion of gases.—It has been seen that a gas does not possess a free surface, and will therefore expand indefinitely unless confined to a given space by the walls of an enclosure. If the enclosure be suddenly enlarged, the gas expands with great rapidity to fill the increased space. This would be expected from the kinetic theory of gases, because on removing a boundary surface the molecules are no longer reflected (p. 215), but pass outwards. If, however, the increased space is occupied by another gas, the process of expansion goes on much more slowly. The two gases now diffuse through each other until both fill the space uniformly. Graham filled the lower part of a gas jar about half a metre high with carbon dioxide and the upper part with air, and noted the time that must elapse before the distribution became uniform. With a tenth of the jar occupied by carbon dioxide, the time for complete diffusion was about two hours.

The rate of diffusion obeys a law similar to Fick's law for liquids, but the coefficient of diffusion, k, while varying for different gases, is not a constant in any case. It varies somewhat with the concentration.

If CD (Fig. 164) is a plane in the mixture of two gases, and AB and EF planes parallel to CD and at distance λ from it, where λ is the mean free path of the molecules in the mixture, then $\frac{c_1\bar{u}}{6}$ molecules of gas will travel through each square centimetre of CD in the direction from AB to CD (see p. 227). $\bar{u}$ is the mean velocity of the molecules of the gas in the upper part of the vessel, and c_1 is the number of molecules per c.c. of the gas at AB. Similarly $\frac{c_2\bar{u}}{6}$ is the number passing upwards through unit area of CD in a second.

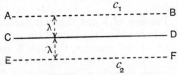

FIG. 164.—DIFFUSION OF GASES.

The resultant is $\frac{c_1 - c_2}{6}\bar{u}$. If m is the mass of a molecule, $\frac{m(c_1 - c_2)}{6}\bar{u}$ is the resultant mass diffusing downwards per sec. The concentration gradient is $\frac{m(c_1 - c_2)}{2\lambda}$.

$\therefore$ Rate of diffusion $= k \times$ concentration gradient (p. 230);

$$\therefore k = \frac{m(c_1 - c_2)\bar{u}}{6} \cdot \frac{2\lambda}{m(c_1 - c_2)} = \tfrac{1}{3}\bar{u}\lambda.$$

It is thus proportional to the velocity of the molecules, as would be expected on the kinetic theory, and to the length of mean free path.

Effusion of gases.—When a gas escapes from a vessel into a vacuum by passing through a small hole in a thin plate, the process is called effusion. The mass of gas escaping per second was found on p. 220 to be proportional to $\sqrt{\rho_1} \cdot p$, where p is the pressure and ρ_1 the density of the gas when its pressure is unity. In the case of a gas obeying Boyle's law, the actual density ρ is therefore $p \cdot \rho_1$.

The mass of gas escaping per second is therefore proportional to

$$\sqrt{\frac{\rho}{p}}\,p = \sqrt{\rho}\,p.$$ But the density of the gas being proportional to the pressure, the rate of escape is proportional to $\sqrt{p^2} = p$.

In the case of a mixture of two gases, each has its partial pressure p_1 or p_2, and the total pressure is $p = p_1 + p_2$. But the rate of effusion of each is proportional to its partial pressure, so that the rate of escape of each constituent is proportional to the amount present in the mixture.

Hence there is no separation of the constituents on effusion, and the proportion in the mixture is the same after emergence as it was before.

Passage of a gas through narrow tubes.—If the plate in the last case is not thin, the flow of the gas through it is governed by the same laws as the passage through a narrow tube. The rate of flow is determined by the viscosity of the gas (p. 199). In the case of a mixture there is no separation of the constituents.

Diffusion of gases through porous substances.—When the channels through which a gas passes are extremely narrow, as in the case of un-glazed porcelain, meerschaum, etc., real diffusion takes place (p. 242). Graham investigated the laws of diffusion of gases through porous substances. He found that the rate of diffusion of any gas through a porous partition was directly proportional to the difference of pressure of the gas on the two sides of the porous partition and inversely proportional to the square root of the density of the gas, and is independent of the passage of any other gas at the same time. He illustrated this by

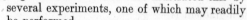

several experiments, one of which may readily be performed.

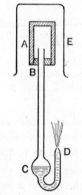

FIG. 165.—GRAHAM'S DIFFUSION EXPERIMENT.

A porous pot A (Fig. 165) is fitted with a stopper B, through which the tube BCD is introduced. The lower part CD contains water, while A contains air. On bringing an inverted beaker E, which contains hydrogen, over A, the water is, for a short time, driven in a jet from D. The reason is that the hydrogen being of about 1/16 the density of air, its rate of diffusion through the pores of A into the pot is about 4 times as rapid as the rate of diffusion of the air outwards. The pressure in A is therefore greater than the atmospheric pressure, and the jet is produced at D. After a time the pressures inside and outside A become the same, and the jet ceases. On removing E the hydrogen diffuses out of A more rapidly than the air diffuses in, giving a reduced pressure in A, and the water rises in the tube BC. After a time the hydrogen diffuses away, and the water at C returns to its original level.

Another of Graham's experiments was to pass air through a tube AB (Fig. 166), which consists of the stem of a clay tobacco pipe. AB is cemented into a wider tube CD, which is first exhausted by an air pump. The densities of oxygen and nitrogen being in the ratio of 16 to 14, the nitrogen diffuses more rapidly than the oxygen through the porous pipe. The result is that the air emerging at B is richer in oxygen than the air which enters at A. By taking the air from

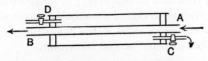

FIG. 166.—TUBE FOR ATMOLYSIS.

B through a similar tube and continuing the process, a gas could be obtained which exhibited the usual characteristics of oxygen. This process of separation of gases is called **atmolysis**.

EXAMPLE.—Describe what happens if a jar of hydrogen is put, mouth downward, on an equal jar of carbon dioxide, (a) when the mouths are open, (b) when the gases are separated by a partition of unglazed earthenware.

A mixture of argon and nitrogen is passed slowly through a series of clay tobacco pipes surrounded by a vacuum; show that the percentage composition of the mixture will be altered during the passage; the densities of argon and nitrogen are in the ratio of 20 to 14.   C.H.S.C.

(a) The pressure remains atmospheric throughout, but the carbon dioxide diffuses upwards and the hydrogen downwards until the composition of the mixture becomes uniform.

(b) Owing to the more rapid diffusion of the hydrogen through the partition, the pressure in the lower part rises above the atmospheric pressure, and that in the upper part falls, the rate of diffusion being at first in the ratio $\sqrt{44/2}$. As the concentrations of hydrogen in the lower jar and CO_2 in the upper jar increase, the difference of pressure will fall until the pressure is atmospheric throughout, and both jars contain the same amount of hydrogen and carbon dioxide.

The rates of diffusion of the argon and nitrogen through the pipes are as $\sqrt{14} : \sqrt{20}$. If the vacuum outside be maintained, the mixture inside the pipe becomes richer and richer in argon, and if the process is continued, the limiting condition of pure argon will be approached.

Brownian movement.—In 1827 Brown, a botanist, observed that small pollen grains in water, seen under the microscope, were in constant irregular motion. This he attributed to the fact that they were living organisms. It is now known that any particles suspended in water exhibit the same motion. Such aggregates of molecules have been noted under the name of colloids (p. 241) and there is no reason to suppose that they are any exception to the law of equipartition of energy, that is, that their kinetic energy of a particle is the same, at any given temperature, as that of a molecule of gas or liquid. In fact, Perrin has determined the value N, the number of molecules per c.c. of a gas from their distribution and movement.

Any colloidal suspension, gum mastic, gamboge or pollen grains, etc., provided that the grains are not too small, will serve to demonstrate the Brownian motion. If the grains are very small the ultramicroscope must be used. A thin layer of the suspension is illuminated laterally. The light diffused from the grains enters the microscope and the particles are seen as bright points of light, or sometimes as diffraction rings, the grains being too small to form an optical image. The irregular motion due to the bombardment of the grains by the molecules of the liquid can then be seen.

Perrin considered that the ultimate distribution of the grains is the same as that in a column of gas. In the case of the gas, the difference in pressure dp at levels differing by an amount dx is given by

$$dp = \rho g \, dx,$$

where ρ is the density of the gas.

For the colloidal particles p is osmotic pressure (p. 233), and the force due to gravity on one particle is $v(\sigma - \delta)g$, where v is the volume of the particle, σ its density and δ the density of the suspending liquid ;

$$\therefore \ dp = N_0 v (\sigma - \delta) g \, . \, dx,$$

where N_0 is the number of particles in 1 c.c.

From the gas equation (p. 176)

$$PV = RT,$$

or

$$P = \frac{RT}{V} = \tfrac{1}{3} m N \overline{u^2}, \quad \text{(p. 216).}$$

Thus the osmotic pressure for the grains is $p = \tfrac{1}{3} \, . \, m \overline{u^2} \, . \, N_0$, since $\tfrac{1}{3} m \overline{u^2}$ is the same for the grains as for the gas molecules, at the same temperature ;

$$\therefore \ p = \frac{N_0}{N} P = \frac{RT}{V} \, . \, \frac{N_0}{N},$$

and

$$dp = \frac{RT}{V} \frac{dN_0}{N} = N_0 v (\sigma - \delta) g \, . \, dx,$$

which corresponds to the above equation for dp in the case of a gas ;

$$\therefore \quad \frac{dN_0}{N_0} = \frac{N}{RT} v(\sigma - \delta)g\, dx.$$

Integrating,

$$\left[\log N_0\right]_1^2 = \frac{N}{RT} v(\sigma - \delta)g\left[x\right]_1^2,$$

or

$$\log \frac{N_2}{N_1} = \frac{N}{RT} v(\sigma - \delta)g(x_2 - x_1).$$

A layer $0 \cdot 1$ mm. deep was examined, the microscope being focussed in turn on layers at different depths. The relative values of N_1 and N_2 were obtained by counting the number of particles in view and taking the mean of a great number of observations. The value of v was found by evaporating the liquid and determining the mass of the residue, also by assuming the particles to be spherical and applying Stokes' law (p. 199) for the rate of fall. The distribution of particles was found to agree with the gas distribution law, and the value of N was found to be $3 \cdot 2 \times 10^{19}$.

Perrin also employed a method in which the rotational motion of the particles is observed, and another in which an equation due to Einstein is employed. This is an expression for the average distance travelled by a particle in any direction in a given time. The discussion of these methods is beyond the scope of this book.

Mercury diffusion pumps.—The process of interdiffusion of one gas into another has been utilised in a modern form of pump for evacuating vessels rapidly. A stream of mercury vapour is caused to flow past the end of a tube connected with the vessel to be evacuated. Gas in the tube diffuses into the mercury vapour at a rate which depends upon the concentration of the gas in the tube, and not upon the pressure of the mercury vapour. Such an arrangement is illustrated diagrammatically in Fig. 167. The bulb C undergoes a first stage of evacuation by means of an oil pump through the tube D. Mercury is then

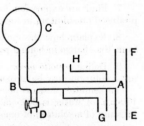

FIG. 167.—MERCURY DIFFUSION PUMP.

boiled in a vessel, not shown, and is taken through the tube EF, past the end of AB. It is at A that the diffusion of gas from C occurs, and this gas is carried away by the stream of mercury vapour in EF. A cold water condenser GH condenses the mercury vapour, preventing it from entering the tubes BC. The condensed mercury is conveyed back to the boiler.

Such pumps may be used in series, each one carrying the evacuation a stage higher than the last. Pressures of a millionth of a millimetre of mercury may be attained rapidly by such pumps.

EXERCISES ON CHAPTER XI

1. Give an account of the important facts associated with the phenomenon of diffusion.

What do you understand by osmotic pressure, and how may it be explained ?   C.W.B.H.S.C.

2. State Fick's law, and deduce from it the fact that the time taken to equalise the distribution of a solute is proportional to the square of the length of column of the solution.

3. Define coefficient of diffusion, and give its dimensions.

4. What do you understand by osmotic pressure ? Describe an experiment by which you could estimate the osmotic pressure of a given sugar solution.

How would you expect your results to vary with (a) the concentration of the solution, (b) the temperature ?   O.H.S.C.

5. Explain the process of effusion of a gas, and account for the fact that the composition of a mixture of two gases is not changed when effusion occurs, while it is changed on diffusion through a porous substance.

6. A mass of 5 grams of a substance is dissolved in 600 c.c. of water. If the molecular weight of the substance is 270, calculate the osmotic pressure.

7. Find an expression for the change in maximum vapour pressure produced on solution, in terms of the osmotic pressure.

8. Explain how the molecular weight of a solute may be determined from the change in boiling point it produces.

9. Define *osmotic pressure*, and describe how the osmotic pressure of a sugar solution may be measured.

The osmotic pressure of a solution containing 6 gm. of cane sugar in 100 c.c. of water is 307 cm. of mercury at 13° C. What is the osmotic pressure of a solution of one-sixth this concentration at 50° C. ?

Lond. Int. Sci.

10. Define *molecular elevation of the boiling point*, and calculate its value in the case of a solvent whose boiling point is 35° C., and whose latent heat of evaporation at that temperature is 81 cal. per gm. and density 0·7 gm. cm.$^{-3}$.

CHAPTER XII

SURFACE TENSION

General description of surface tension.—It is common experience that a very small quantity of a liquid, not subject to outside disturbance, will assume the form of a spherical drop. The fact that falling rain-drops are spheres is proved by the symmetrical form of the rainbow. Now a sphere is a geometrical shape which has the smallest area of surface for a given volume. It thus appears that a drop tends to form itself into the shape with minimum area of surface.

Many other simple phenomena illustrate this tendency to make the area of surface of a liquid as small as possible. For example, if a small paint brush be dipped into water, the hairs of the brush are seen to stand apart, but on raising the brush out of the water, the hairs cling together, owing to the water surface tending to shrink. If a wire ring be dipped into a soap solution and removed, a film may be produced. If two threads AB and CD (Fig. 168) have been previously tied to the ring, the threads being slack, they will not interfere with the film, but will merely slide about in it. On piercing the film between CD and the ring, this part

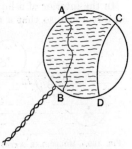

FIG. 168.—DEMONSTRATION OF SURFACE TENSION.

of the film disappears, but the rest remains, and it will be seen that the thread CD is now drawn tightly into a circular form. This clearly indicates that the film tends to shrink, that is, a tension exists in it. The thread AB remains loose, because this tension or pull exists equally on both sides of it.

The existence of this pull in the surfaces of the liquid explains all the above phenomena. The surface behaves like a stretched skin, but with this difference, that for the skin the tension is greater the more the skin is stretched, but the tension in the surface of a liquid is independent of the area of the surface. It is called the **surface tension** of the liquid. It is the force per unit length of a line drawn in the surface and acts at right angles to the line, tending to pull the surface apart along the line. The dimensions of surface tension are given by $\dfrac{\text{force}}{\text{length}}$ or $[MLT^{-2} . L^{-1}] = [MT^{-2}]$.

The simple kinetic theory of gases (Chap. X), when extended to the case of liquids, affords an explanation of surface tension. In that theory the molecules of a gas are supposed to be so far apart that any attraction between them is infinitesimal. It is well known that on compressing a gas, Boyle's law ceases to be true when the density becomes considerable. This is largely due to the fact that the molecules are so close to each other that the effect of their attraction for each other becomes appreciable. On continuing the compression, a stage will be reached at which the effect of the attraction predominates over the tendency of the molecules to fly apart with their indiscriminate velocities. It should be remembered that a liquid can have a free surface, but a gas cannot (p. 154). The reason for this is now seen.

In the interior of a liquid the molecular attractions act equally in all directions, so that a molecule is not urged in one direction more than another; it merely possesses its temperature velocity, although collisions with other molecules are much more frequent than in the gaseous state. Near the surface of the liquid the symmetry of the attracting forces no longer exists. Suppose that the attraction between two molecules ceases to be appreciable when the distance between their centres is c. With the molecule A (Fig. 169) as centre, draw a sphere of radius c. Molecules outside this sphere will not affect A, and those inside it are symmetrically situated, so that the resultant force on A is zero. But at B the sphere of influence lies partly outside the liquid, and this part will only contain the comparatively few molecules of the gas or vapour above the liquid. Hence there is a resultant downward force on B, which reaches its maximum value when B is in the surface of the liquid. If the molecule can pass through the surface, as at C, the downward force becomes less and less until the sphere

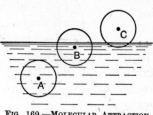

FIG. 169.—MOLECULAR ATTRACTION IN A LIQUID.

of influence leaves the liquid, when the molecule is free to wander as a molecule of the gas or vapour.

All over the surface of a liquid there is thus a pull, due to the attraction between the molecules, tending to prevent their escape. This inward pull near the surface is greater when the surface is convex than when it is plane. For at A (Fig. 170) the lower half EBF of the sphere of influence is intact, and the downward pull due to it is the same as though the surface of the liquid were plane. But the upper part is reduced from the slice CDFE for the plane surface to the piece GHFE for the spherical surface.

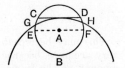

FIG. 170.—ATTRACTION FOR MOLECULES AT A CURVED SURFACE.

The upward pull is therefore reduced by the curvature of the surface of the liquid, and the resultant inward pull is increased. Thus the inward pull on molecules near the surface is greater where the surface is most curved and the liquid tends towards the form of uniform curvature, that is a sphere. This is exactly the effect that a tension in the surface would produce, and this explanation indicates that surface tension is a molecular phenomenon.

In order to extend a surface, molecules must be brought from the interior to the surface. This requires work to be performed. In a similar way, energy is liberated if a surface contracts. This fact shows that every surface has a tendency to contract, and explains the so-called surface tension.

Determination of surface tension by the balance.—The balance affords a direct method of measuring surface tension. Make a wire framework ABCD (Fig. 171) and suspend it from one arm of a balance as on p. 163. Let it dip into a vessel of water as shown, and add weights to the other pan until the frame immersed to EF is counterbalanced. Now dip the frame until AB is immersed, and raise it until AB is just above the surface of the water. The part ABFE will be occupied by a film. On counterbalancing by adding weights until the balance is again in equilibrium, it will be found that the additional weight m is required. The film therefore pulls the frame downwards with a force mg dynes. If the length of EF is l cm. and T is the surface tension of the

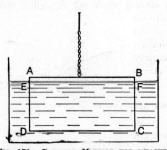

FIG. 171.—BALANCE METHOD FOR MEASURING SURFACE TENSION.

water, the total pull is $2lT$, for the film has two surfaces, each having surface tension T;

$$\therefore\; 2lT = mg,$$

$$T = \frac{mg}{2l}.$$

This may be repeated with the other liquids. The result is not very accurate, because of the difficulty of making sure that the same amount of the frame is immersed each time. Also if the frame is raised too far, the film will break.

Work done in producing surface.—If a film is produced in a frame ABCD (Fig. 172), of which the side AD can slide, the force $F = 2lT$ is

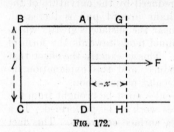

FIG. 172.

required to maintain AD at rest. If now AD is moved to GH, the work done in opposition to F is Fx ergs, that is, $2lTx$ ergs, where x cm. is the distance AD moves. The area of film created in this movement is lx and the new area of surface is $2lx$, for the film has two sides. Thus the work done per unit area of surface in opposition to the force due to surface

tension is $\dfrac{2lTx}{2lx} = T$ ergs per sq. cm. On this account surface tension is sometimes, but wrongly, called the surface energy. If no heat is supplied to the film, it is cooled when AD is pulled outwards. If heat is supplied to restore its temperature, this heat is also part of the surface energy. The term " free surface energy " is often used for the quantity of energy that is numerically equal to the surface tension.

Angle of contact.—If two liquids are brought into contact as at P (Fig. 173), both being in contact with air, there are three surface tensions to consider, namely, T_1, that of the surface between air and

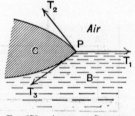

FIG. 173.—ANGLE OF CONTACT.

liquid B; T_2, that between air and liquid C; and T_3, that between liquid B and liquid C. If the figure is a section at right angles to the line of contact, a fine wire along the line of contact at P would have three forces acting upon it, T_1, T_2 and T_3 dynes per unit length. If a triangle of forces can be constructed, its sides will give the directions of T_1, T_2 and T_3 for equilibrium. This triangle of forces is known as **Neumann's triangle.** There are no two pure liquids known for which it is possible to construct the triangle of forces. One of the three surface tensions is always greater than the other two, so that there is no equilibrium like that shown in the diagram. The lighter liquid thus spreads over the surface of the liquid on which it rests. Thus a drop of pure water placed on the surface of pure mercury spreads over it, forming a uniform thin layer, the surface tension of mercury being about 550 dyne cm.$^{-1}$, and of water 75 dyne cm.$^{-1}$. If, however, the surface of the mercury is contaminated with grease, it is possible for drops of water to stand upon it; the surface tension of the mercury is lowered and it is possible to construct Neumann's triangle.

A more important case is that of a liquid in contact with a solid. There is no reason to suppose that the act of solidification destroys surface tension, and the arguments used in the explanation of the surface tension of liquids (p. 250) are just as valid for the case of a solid, although the result of it may not be seen, on account of the rigidity of the solid. If a drop of molten glass is allowed to solidify, it undoubtedly has surface tension before solidification, because it assumes a spherical shape. As surface tension always decreases with rise of temperature, or increases with fall of temperature, it is natural to suppose that the surface tension of the solid may be even greater than that of the molten glass.

In Fig. 174 let T_2, T_3 and T_1 be the surface tensions for air-solid, air-liquid and liquid-solid respectively. Then if $T_2 > T_1 + T_3$, there cannot be equilibrium and the liquid spreads over the solid. If, how-

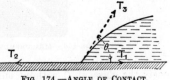

FIG. 174.—ANGLE OF CONTACT.

ever, there is equilibrium, $T_2 = T_1 + T_3 \cos \theta$, where θ is the **angle of contact** of the liquid with the solid,

$$\cos \theta = \frac{T_2 - T_1}{T_3}.$$

If $T_2 > T_1$, $\cos \theta$ is positive and θ is less than 90°. If $T_1 > T_2$, $\cos \theta$ is negative and θ lies between 90° and 180°. This is the case with mercury on glass, where θ is about 140°. For water and many liquids that wet glass, the angle of contact is 0°.

Measurement of angle of contact.—In the case of mercury and glass the angle of contact may be found by sloping the glass in such

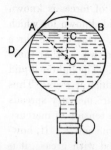

a way that the surface of the mercury is plane, right up to the glass. A spherical bulb (Fig. 175) is nearly filled with clean mercury, and the level of mercury adjusted until there is no meniscus or curved portion where the mercury meets the glass. This may be tested by observing the image of a bright light produced by the surface of the mercury. A bright band near the point of contact indicates that the surface is still curved. If the diameter of the circle AB is measured with a pair of calipers, and also the diameter of the bulb, $AC = \frac{1}{2}AB$ and $OA = \frac{1}{2}$ (diameter of bulb). If the bulb consists of a thin layer of blown

FIG. 175.—MEASUREMENT OF ANGLE OF CONTACT.

glass, the error in taking outside measurements is not great. Then $\cos OAC = \dfrac{AC}{OA}$, from which angle OAC may be found, and the angle of contact DAC is $(90° + \widehat{OAC})$.

An alternative method consists of dipping a strip of plane glass into mercury, as shown in section in Fig. 176, until the mercury

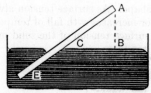

FIG. 176.—MEASUREMENT OF ANGLE OF CONTACT.

meets the glass at C without curvature. Then if a plumb line AB is dropped from A, AB and BC may be measured. Then

$$\tan ACB = \frac{AB}{BC},$$

and the angle of contact ECB is $(\pi - \widehat{ACB})$.

Pressure, curvature and surface tension.—Whenever the surface of a liquid is curved, there results from surface tension an inward pressure, which, if the surface is at rest, must be balanced by an equal

pressure acting outwards. Let ABCD (Fig. 177) be a surface, curved
in one direction only, that is, part of a cylindrical surface. The
surface tension is a force acting across every unit length of the
boundary. The forces over AD and BC are equal and opposite, and
therefore have zero resultant. The forces over AB and DC, however,
are not opposite, but have a resultant perpendicular to the surface.
In order to find this resultant, consider a small piece of the surface,

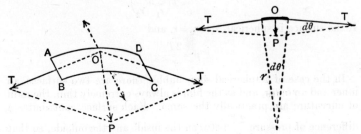

FIG. 177.—CYLINDRICAL SURFACE.   FIG. 178.—PRESSURE DUE TO CURVATURE.

of unit length in the direction AB. The force at each end is T dynes.
If these forces meet at O (Fig. 178), the resultant OP is $T\,d\theta$. Now
the area of the element of surface is $1 \times r\,d\theta$, and a resultant pressure
p on this area gives rise to a force $pr\,d\theta$ directed outwards. If then

$$pr\,d\theta = T\,d\theta,$$

the element is at rest under the action of
these two forces;

$$\therefore\; p = \frac{T}{r}\ \text{dyne cm.}^{-2}.$$

This resultant pressure is the difference
of pressure on the two sides of the surface
that is required to balance the effect of
surface tension. The pressure must be
greater on the concave side of the surface
than on the convex side, for the resultant
to be directed outwards and so balance
the force due to surface tension.

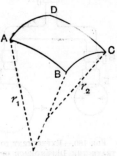

FIG. 179.—SURFACE CURVED
IN TWO DIRECTIONS.

In the same manner, it may be found, if the film is curved at right
angles to the first direction, that there is a similar pressure due to
this second curvature. If then the film is curved in two directions
at right angles to each other, as in Fig. 179, the pressure due to the

curvature of AB and DC is $\dfrac{T}{r_1}$, and that due to the curvature of AD and BC is $\dfrac{T}{r_2}$, so that the total difference of pressure p between the two sides of the film is given by

$$p = \frac{T}{r_1} + \frac{T}{r_2}$$

$$= T\left(\frac{1}{r_1} + \frac{1}{r_2}\right).$$

If the surface is spherical, $r_1 = r_2 = r$, and

$$p = \frac{2T}{r}.$$

In the case of a spherical soap bubble there are two surfaces, an inner and an outer, and as the film is always extremely thin, the radii of curvature are practically the same. Each surface contributes a difference of pressure $\dfrac{2T}{r}$ between the inside and the outside, so that in this case $p = \dfrac{4T}{r}$. In the case of a drop of liquid there is difficulty in measuring the pressure inside, but for a bubble there is no difficulty, as the inside is occupied by a gas or air.

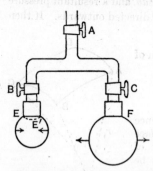

FIG. 180.—EXPERIMENT TO ILLUS-
TRATE THE DEPENDENCE OF PRES-
SURE UPON RADIUS OF A SOAP
BUBBLE.

It will be noticed that the smaller the radius of the bubble, the greater is the pressure inside required to maintain it in equilibrium. This may be illustrated by a simple experiment. Two tubes with equal circular apertures E and F (Fig. 180) are dipped into a soap solution so that films are formed at E and F. On closing tap C and opening taps A and B, a bubble may be blown on E. Now closing B and opening C, a bubble is blown on F, as nearly equal in size to the bubble on E as the eye can judge. On closing A and opening B and C, the two bubbles are put into internal communication. Although they are apparently of the same size and the pressure in them would be expected to be the same, this apparent equilibrium is unstable. Whichever bubble has the smaller radius has the greater pressure, so that air will pass through B and C from the smaller to the larger bubble. Thus the smaller bubble shrinks and the larger one is blown out. But at a certain stage the bubble, say E, becomes a hemisphere, and any further shrinkage means an increase of radius of curvature. Stable equilibrium is reached when the curvature at E′ is the same as the curvature of the bubble at F.

Measurement of surface tension of bubble.—If a bubble be blown at the end of a tube, the excess pressure can be measured by means of a manometer. The bubble D (Fig. 181) is blown with the tap A open. A is then closed and the diameter of the bubble is measured by means of a travelling microscope. The same microscope may be placed so that it can be used to measure the difference of level of the limbs B and C of the manometer. If h is this difference of level, and r the radius of the bubble, $h\rho g = \dfrac{4T}{r}$, where ρ is the density of the liquid of the manometer. The success of the measurement depends upon having a small bubble, and therefore a small diameter of the tube at D, so that the difference of level between B and C may be considerable.

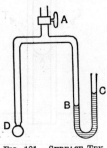

FIG. 181.—SURFACE TEN-
SION OF BUBBLE.

Rise of liquid in a capillary tube.—One of the most important and striking effects of surface tension is the rise of liquid in a capillary tube. A capillary tube is one having a fine bore, and is so named from the Latin word *capillus*, a hair. On this account surface tension is sometimes called **capillarity.**

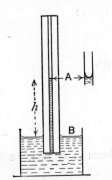

FIG. 182.—MEASUREMENT OF
SURFACE TENSION BY MEANS OF
CAPILLARY TUBE.

When the lower end of a capillary tube is dipped into a liquid such as water, there is an immediate rise of liquid in the tube. If the liquid wets the tube, its angle of contact can be taken to be zero, and in the case of a very fine tube the shape of the meniscus at A (Fig. 182) may be taken to be spherical. If r is the radius of the tube at A and T the surface tension of the liquid, then the difference of pressure on the two sides of the surface is

$\frac{2T}{r}$. But the pressure of the air at A and in the liquid at level B is atmospheric. Therefore, for equilibrium, the pressure $\frac{2T}{r}$ is equal to that of the column of liquid of height h;

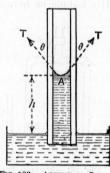

FIG. 183.—ASCENT OF LIQUID IN MODERATELY WIDE TUBE.

$$\therefore \ \frac{2T}{r} = h\rho g,$$

$$T = \frac{h\rho g r}{2}.$$

If the tube is not very narrow and the angle of contact is not zero, the direction of the surface tension makes an angle θ (Fig. 183) with the wall of the tube. The vertical component of this is $T \cos \theta$, and the total upward force due to it is $T \cos \theta \cdot 2\pi r$. This force supports the column h of liquid, where h is measured from the horizontal surface of liquid outside the tube to the bottom of the meniscus at A. There is also a small volume v to be taken into account, which is the volume of liquid in the meniscus itself.

$$\therefore \ \text{Total volume raised} = \pi r^2 h + v,$$

$$\text{total weight raised} = (\pi r^2 h + v)\rho g \ \text{dynes};$$

$$\therefore \ T \cos \theta \cdot 2\pi r = (\pi r^2 h + v)\rho g,$$

$$T = \left(\frac{\pi r^2 h + v}{\cos \theta \cdot 2\pi r}\right)\rho g.$$

If v is negligible in comparison with $\pi r^2 h$,

$$T = \frac{r h \rho g}{2 \cos \theta}.$$

Or, as a next approximation, if the meniscus is assumed to be spherical,

$$v = \pi r^2 \cdot r - \tfrac{2}{3}\pi r^3$$

$$= \pi r^3 - \tfrac{2}{3}\pi r^3 = \tfrac{1}{3}\pi r^3,$$

and $$\pi r^2 h + v = \pi r^2 h + \tfrac{1}{3}\pi r^3$$

$$= \pi r^2 (h + \tfrac{1}{3}r).$$

That is, the effective height is $h + \frac{1}{3}r$.

$$T = \frac{\pi r^2 \left(h + \frac{1}{3}r\right)}{\cos\theta \cdot 2\pi r}\, \rho g$$

$$= \frac{r\left(h + \frac{1}{3}r\right)\rho g}{2\cos\theta}.$$

If in addition $\theta = 0$, as it is for most liquids examined,

$$T = \frac{r\left(h + \frac{1}{3}r\right)\rho g}{2} \text{ dynes cm.}^{-1}.$$

Measurement of surface tension by capillary tube.—In making a measurement by means of a capillary tube, the radius of the tube should be measured by placing a thread of mercury in it and measuring its length in various parts of the tube. If the length varies much, the tube should be rejected, but if the measurements agree fairly well, the mean should be taken. The weight of the mercury is found, and from this in turn the volume, the area of cross-section and the radius. Immediately before the surface tension measurements are made, the tube should be cleaned with strong soda, followed by concentrated nitric acid, and finally washed with distilled water. If it is to be used with water, it may now be placed in position, but if with any other liquid, it must be dried.

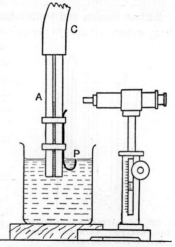

FIG. 184.—APPARATUS FOR MEASURING SURFACE TENSION BY CAPILLARY TUBE.

In order to find the capillary rise it is advisable to attach a bent pin to the tube by rubber bands so that the point of the pin may be adjusted to touch the liquid surface at P (Fig. 184). After focussing the vernier microscope on the meniscus of the liquid in the tube at A, the beaker of liquid can be taken away and the microscope lowered and focussed on P. The difference in the vernier readings gives the required height h for calculating the surface tension. The density of the liquid must be found by a separate experiment.

In measuring h a difficulty arises through the unavoidable minute contamination of the tube and the liquid, particularly in the case of water. If the india-rubber tube C, which is open at the top, be pinched with the fingers in an appropriate manner, the liquid can be drawn up above A in the capillary tube. On releasing C, the liquid drops suddenly and stops in a definite position. It is this position that should be used in the measurement of surface tension. If the surface be watched, it will, in the case of water, be seen to creep to a position considerably below the first. This is due to contamination mentioned above causing the angle of contact to depart from zero, and the surface tension to drop. In the case of ether, benzene or petroleum, there is no such creep. The meniscus drops to a certain position and will stay there indefinitely. The reason for this seems to be that the liquid dissolves any greasy contamination from the surface of the glass.

Surface tension and temperature.—Surface tension depends upon temperature; it always decreases with rise of temperature, with the

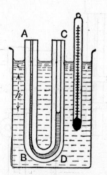

FIG. 185.—APPARATUS FOR FINDING THE RELATION BETWEEN SURFACE TENSION AND TEMPERATURE.

two exceptions of molten cadmium and copper. The critical temperature of a substance is the temperature at which its surface tension disappears. It is therefore important to record the temperature when making a determination of surface tension.

The apparatus of Fig. 184 is only applicable for a small range of temperature, but the method may be modified to give readings over a larger range. A fine bore tube AB (Fig. 185) is joined to a tube CD, whose bore is not so fine as that of AB. If r_1 is the radius of bore of AB and r_2 that of CD, the pressure just under the surface of liquid in AB is $\dfrac{2T}{r_1}$ below the atmospheric pressure. In CD it is $\dfrac{2T}{r_2}$. Therefore the difference of pressure in AB and CD is $2T\left(\dfrac{1}{r_1}-\dfrac{1}{r_2}\right)$;

$$\therefore\ 2T\left(\frac{1}{r_1}-\frac{1}{r_2}\right)=h\rho g,$$

or

$$T=\frac{h\rho g}{2\left(\dfrac{1}{r_1}-\dfrac{1}{r_2}\right)}.$$

The value of T should be found for many temperatures and the values plotted against $t°$.

The method of the double tube may be used to measure the surface tension of mercury, but in this case the depression is in the smaller tube, because the meniscus of mercury is convex upwards.

Then
$$\frac{2T \cos \theta}{r_1} - \frac{2T \cos \theta}{r_2} = h\rho g,$$

$$T = \frac{h\rho g}{2\left(\dfrac{1}{r_1} - \dfrac{1}{r_2}\right) \cos \theta},$$

where θ is the angle the surface of the liquid makes with the glass or the supplement of the angle of contact (p. 254).

EXAMPLE.—Find an expression for the difference of pressure between the inside and the outside of a spherical air bubble of radius r in a liquid of surface tension T.

A U-tube, whose ends are open and whose limbs are vertical, contains oil of a specific gravity 0·85 and surface tension 28 dynes per cm. If one limb has a diameter of 2·2 mm. and the other a diameter of 0·8 mm., what is the difference in level of the oil in the two limbs ? (Assume that the angle of contact between the oil and the glass is zero.)   C.H S.C.

For the first part, see p. 256.
For the second part, refer to Fig. 185.
Difference of pressure under liquid surface in the two limbs is
$$\frac{2T}{r_1} - \frac{2T}{r_2} = \frac{2 \times 28}{0·04} - \frac{2 \times 28}{0·11}$$
$$= 1400 - 509 = 891 \text{ dynes };$$
$$\therefore \ h\rho g = 891 \text{ dynes.}$$
$$h(0·85)981 = 891,$$
$$h = 1·07 \text{ cm.}$$

Ferguson's method of measuring surface tension.—An important modification of the capillary tube method was made by Ferguson. One of the chief objections to the original method is that a considerable quantity of the liquid is required. In this method a small quantity of the liquid is introduced into the capillary tube AB (Fig. 186). If the liquid wets the capillary tube, the upper and lower surfaces A and B would be curved in a concave manner. Air is forced in through E until the lower surface at B is accurately plane. An electric lamp is placed obliquely at a distance of 30 or 40 cm and illuminates the surface at B. This is examined through a lens L, aided by an inclined mirror, and appears uniformly illuminated when the surface is accurately plane. Otherwise an image of the lamp is seen, which broadens out into a pool of light as the plane condition is attained. The method is very sensitive, and enables the balance to be made very accurately. Since the liquid surface at B is plane, surface tension does not produce any difference of pressure

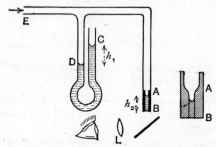

Fig. 186.—Surface Tension by Ferguson's Method.

on its two sides. Since the pressure at C is atmospheric (P), that of the air inside the tubes is $P + h_1\rho_1 g$, where ρ_1 is the density of liquid in the gauge CD. If R is the maximum radius of curvature of the meniscus at A, $\dfrac{2T}{R}$ is a step down in pressure in passing through the liquid surface. There is an increase in pressure due to the column of liquid h_2 in AB equal to $h_2\rho_2 g$ when the atmospheric pressure is again reached;

$$\therefore \ h_1\rho_1 g - \frac{2T}{R} + h_2\rho_2 g = 0;$$

$$\therefore \ T = \frac{Rg}{2}(h_1\rho_1 + h_2\rho_2).$$

If the radius of the tube is small and the angle of contact is zero, $R = r$, where r is the radius of the tube ;

$$\therefore \ T = \frac{rg}{2}(h_1\rho_1 + h_2\rho_2).$$

If the last conditions are not fulfilled, it is still possible to make a correction for them.

The method was later modified in such a manner that it is not necessary to know the density ρ_2 of the liquid under test. This was done by placing the tube AB horizontally, as in Fig. 187. Since the column AB does not in this case exert any hydrostatic pressure, the equation of pressure becomes

$$h_1 \rho_1 g = \frac{2T}{R} \, ,$$

or with the same approximations as before,

$$T = \frac{h_1 \rho_1 r g}{2} \, .$$

Precautions were taken to see that the film at B is not, when in the vertical position, distorted by gravitational effects, and it was

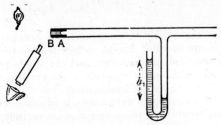

FIG. 187.—FERGUSON'S METHOD WITH HORIZONTAL TUBE.

found that with tubes less than 1 mm. in bore this distortion effect is negligible.

Jaeger's method.—It was seen on p. 256 that the pressure inside a spherical bubble in a liquid exceeds the pressure outside by the quantity $\frac{2T}{r}$. If a tube has a small aperture A (Fig. 188) at a depth

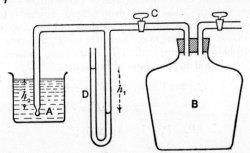

FIG. 188.—JAEGER'S METHOD OF MEASURING SURFACE TENSION.

h_2 below the surface of a liquid of density ρ_2, and an air bubble is formed at A, the air pressure inside the bubble must be in excess of the atmospheric pressure by an amount $h_2\rho_2 g + \dfrac{2T}{r}$ for the bubble to grow. This excess pressure may be applied by an air reservoir B and measured by the manometer D. On opening the tap C slightly, the pressure in the tube grows slowly, and when the liquid is forced down to A, a bubble will begin to form. At first the radius of curvature diminishes, but reaches a minimum when the bubble is hemispherical (p. 257), its radius then being equal to the radius of the tube r.

Then
$$h_2\rho_2 g + \frac{2T}{r} = h_1\rho_1 g,$$

$$T = \frac{rg}{2}(h_1\rho_1 - h_2\rho_2).$$

At this point the bubble becomes unstable, because any growth causes the pressure inside it due to surface tension to become less. It therefore grows and breaks away, and the whole process begins again. The value of h_1 in the equation is the greatest value, and is reached just before the bubble breaks away.

The method does not give very accurate absolute values for the surface tension, because the phenomenon is not entirely statical, and there is an uncertainty in the exact value of the radius of the bubble when it breaks away. It is, however, useful for the comparison of surface tensions, particularly for a liquid at various temperatures, for it is easy to measure the temperature of the bath.

Drop-weight method.—When a drop of liquid is on the point of becoming detached from the bottom of a vertical circular tube, a simple consideration shows that until instability is passed, the vertical forces on the drop must balance. These forces are mg downwards, where m is the mass of the drop ; $2\pi r T$ upwards, where T is the surface tension and r the radius of the cylindrical part which is supposed to be at the aperture of the tube ; $\pi r^2 P_1$ upwards, where P_1 is the atmospheric pressure and $\pi r^2 P_2$ downwards, where P_2 is the pressure of the liquid in the plane of the orifice.

$$\therefore \ 2\pi r T = mg + \pi r^2 P_2 - \pi r^2 P_1$$
$$= mg + \pi r^2 (P_2 - P_1).$$

Now
$$P_2 - P_1 = \frac{T}{r} \quad \text{(p. 255)} ;$$

$$\therefore \ 2\pi r T = mg + \pi r T,$$

$$T = \frac{mg}{\pi r}.$$

An examination of Fig. 198 will show that no such simple relation is valid, for the radius of the neck when the drop falls, and the amount of the drop detached, are both uncertain quantities.

By using liquids of known surface tension, Harkins and Brown have shown that the relation $T = \dfrac{mg}{r} F$ holds good, where F is related to V/r^3, V being the volume of the drop and r the radius of the tube. The relation between F and V/r^3 is given by means of a table.

V/r^3	F	V/r^3	F
0·8	0·255	4·0	0·256
1·0	0·261	5·0	0·253
2·0	0·264	6·0	0·249
3·0	0·260	10·0	0·261

Outside these limits the relation is complicated. In making measurements, the drops must be allowed to form very slowly, when an accuracy of 0·2 per cent. may be attained.

EXAMPLE.—Describe the most accurate method you know of measuring the surface tension of water.

Water from a depth of 4 cm. drips into the carbide chamber of a bicycle lamp through a nozzle 0·5 mm. in diameter. Show that the lamp can produce intermittently a gas pressure equal to a 10 cm. head of water without blowing back. The surface tension of water is 75 dynes per cm.

C.W.B.H.S.C.

If the water drips from the nozzle of 0·5 mm. diameter, the gas pressure below the nozzle must be less than a certain amount. If this gas pressure rises, the water will be driven back to the top of the nozzle, where it forms a hemispherical bubble of radius 0·25 mm. = 0·025 cm. Any greater pressure than this will cause the bubble to grow and blow back.

$$\text{Downward pressure in bubble} = \frac{2T}{r} = \frac{2 \times 75}{0·025}$$

$$= 6000 \text{ dyne cm.}^{-2}$$

$$= \frac{6000}{981} \text{ cm. of water column}$$

$$= \underline{6·1 \text{ cm. of water column.}}$$

Therefore together with a head of 4 cm. of water, the downward pressure is equivalent to a head of 10·1 cm. of water. As the gas pressure in the lamp never exceeds a head of 10 cm. of water, it will not blow back.

Large drop on horizontal plate.—When a quantity of liquid rests upon a horizontal solid plate, which it does not wet, the shape of the drop is determined by surface tension and gravity. For extremely small drops the surface tension effects are great and the gravitational effects small, so that the former determine the shape of the drop. It is therefore spherical, as may be seen by placing minute drops of mercury upon a glass plate or water upon paraffin wax.

On increasing the size of the drop, the effect of gravitation becomes greater and that of surface tension less. Now the effect of gravita-

FIG. 189.—LARGE DROP OF MERCURY ON GLASS.

tion alone would be to make the drop spread out until its surface is horizontal (p. 156). Therefore as the drop grows it becomes flattened. There is a limit to this process, which is reached when the upper surface becomes horizontal. Taking this fact in conjunction with our knowledge of the angle of contact of mercury with glass (p. 254), it follows that the shape of a very large drop of mercury upon glass is as shown in Fig. 189. The angle θ is about 40°, and the central part AB of the upper surface is plane. The shape at the edges of the drop will not concern us here, except to notice that at some level such as C the surface is vertical.

Consider the forces acting over the boundaries of a thin slice of the drop such as ABHG (Fig. 190), of horizontal width dl and having parallel vertical faces. The forces over the side ABHG and the back face are, from symmetry, equal and opposite. Now consider the

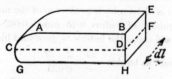

FIG. 190.—FORCES ON LARGE DROP.

part of the drop that lies above the horizontal plane CDF, which passes through the point C where the surface of the drop is vertical. Taking the horizontal forces in the direction AB or CD, the force due to surface tension at C is vertical, and consequently has no horizontal component. At the end BD, the only horizontal forces are the hydrostatic pressure over the face BDFE due to the liquid in the neighbouring part, and the surface tension pull over BE. The hydrostatic thrust over BDFE is

$$BD \times BE \times \rho g \times (\tfrac{1}{2}BD) \text{ dynes} = h \,.\, dl \,.\, \rho g \,.\, \frac{h}{2} . \quad \text{(p. 159)}.$$

$$= \frac{h^2 \rho g \, dl}{2},$$

where h is the depth BD or EF and ρ is the density of the mercury. The surface tension pull over BE is $T \, dl$;

$$\therefore \; T \, dl = \frac{h^2 \rho g \, dl}{2},$$

$$T = \frac{h^2 \rho g}{2}.$$

If the whole thickness of the bubble had been taken into account instead of the upper part alone, the hydrostatic thrust over the end EH is $\dfrac{g \rho h_1^2 dl}{2}$, where h_1 is BH the total thickness of the drop; the surface tension pull on BE is $T \, dl$ as before, and the horizontal pull at G is $T \, dl \cos \theta$, where θ is the supplement of the angle of contact, about $140°$ for mercury on glass.

$$\frac{g \rho h_1^2 \, dl}{2} = T \, dl - T \, dl \cos \theta,$$

$$= T \, dl \, (1 - \cos \delta),$$

$$\text{or} \qquad T = \frac{g \rho h_1^2}{2 \, (1 - \cos \theta)}.$$

This affords an alternative method of finding T when the angle of contact θ is known. Or, if T is determined by the first part, θ may be calculated from the second.

The thickness of the whole drop may be measured by means of the vernier micro-

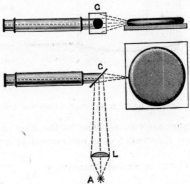

FIG. 191.—EDSER'S METHOD FOR MERCURY DROP.

scope, but there is some difficulty in finding the thickness BD of the upper part, because of the uncertainty in finding the location of C, the place where the surface is vertical.

This difficulty was got over by Edser as follows. The objective of the vernier microscope is provided with a piece of plain glass G (Fig. 191), and light from an incandescent lamp A is focussed by the lens L and the plain glass G acting as a mirror upon the edge of the drop. The light is reflected and, the plain glass being unsilvered, part passes through it and enters the microscope. On focussing the microscope, a thin bright horizontal line is seen at C where the surface is vertical. The microscope is raised or lowered until this line coincides with the cross wire in the field of vision, and the vernier reading is noted. The microscope is then raised by its screw and moved forwards until the image of the flat top of the bubble is on the cross wire. This is facilitated by scattering some fine dust such as lycopodium powder on the flat top of the bubble. The vertical travel of the microscope is the height BD or h. The whole height h_1 may be found, either by means of a spherometer, or by the vernier microscope, focussing first on the top and then on the bottom of the drop.

Cylindrical film.—On blowing a spherical soap bubble and placing it on a wire ring, and bringing another ring in contact with it, a

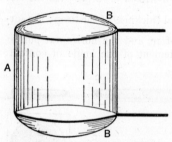

FIG. 192.—CYLINDRICAL SOAP BUBBLE.

cylindrical soap film may be formed. The film may have a variety of shapes, according to the distance apart of the rings. A distance may be found for which the film A between the rings is cylindrical, as in Fig. 192; the film B on each ring is, of course, part of a sphere. The air pressure inside the bubble is the same at every point, so that if p is the excess pressure of air inside over air outside and r is the radius of each wire ring, then for the cylindrical film, $p = \dfrac{2T}{r}$, since there are two surfaces to the film, and a cylinder is only curved in one direction; it is not curved in a plane which contains the axis.

For the spherical portion B, $p = \dfrac{4T}{r_1}$;

$$\therefore \quad \frac{2T}{r} = \frac{4T}{r_1},$$

or $$r_1 = 2r.$$

Thus for the same excess pressure, the spherical film must have twice the radius of curvature of the cylindrical film.

If the rings are drawn apart, the value of p is reduced. Thus the radius r_1 is increased, and the films B flatten. This reduced pressure means that the cylinder is drawn in, so that r becomes r_2 (Fig. 193).

This in itself would mean an increased pressure inside, but the surface is now curved longitudinally with the centre of curvature *outside* the film. Thus the two radii of curvature r_2 and r_3 are oppositely directed, and $p = \dfrac{2T}{r_2} - \dfrac{2T}{r_3}$. A surface having curvatures in opposite directions is called an anti-clastic surface.

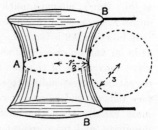

If the separation of the rings is continued until the portions B are plane, the pressure inside is the same as that outside, that is,

$$p = 0 \quad \text{and} \quad \frac{2T}{r_2} - \frac{2T}{r_3} = 0 \, ;$$

$$\therefore \quad r_2 = r_3.$$

FIG. 193.—FILM WITH OPPOSITELY DIRECTED CURVATURES.

Thus it is possible to have a curved film with the gas pressure the same on both sides of it, and if the plane films B are destroyed, the film A will not be affected. On moving the rings still further apart without destroying B, the pressure may be lowered below that of the atmosphere, but as the neck at A gets narrow, the film becomes unstable, as will be seen later, and it breaks into two separate bubbles.

Stability of cylindrical film.—By means of two rings A and B (Fig. 194) a cylindrical soap film may be formed. By means of the tap

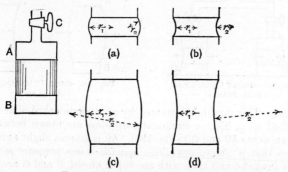

FIG. 194.—STABILITY OF SOAP BUBBLE.

C the interior of the film may be cut off from the atmosphere, or air may be blown in or drawn out, so that the relation between the pressure and the dimensions of the film may be studied.

If the cylinder is short, as at (a), an increase of pressure p blows it out, and both r_1 and r_2 are directed inwards. If the tap C is opened so that $p = 0$, the film moves inwards, and r_2 is directed outwards as at (b). But r_2 changes much more rapidly than r_1, so that the condition $r_2 = r_1$ is soon reached, and the film is in stable equilibrium.

If, however, AB is large $(r_2 > r_1)$, an increase in p produces a bulging as in (c), and on opening C as in (d), r_2 becomes negative. But for a given movement of the film r_1 changes more rapidly than r_2. The curvature corresponding to r_1 produces an inward force due to surface tension and r_2 an outward force, and as the former increases more rapidly than the latter, the inward force will always predominate, and by a greater and greater amount as the film moves in, so that there is instability and the film collapses.

There is consequently some limiting length of cylinder, which separates the unstable from the stable film. This limiting length is πr, or a length equal to half the circumference of the

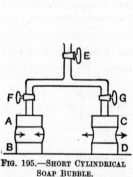

FIG. 195.—SHORT CYLINDRICAL
SOAP BUBBLE.

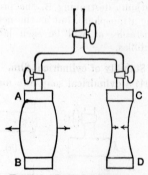

FIG. 196.—LONG CYLINDRICAL
SOAP BUBBLE.

cylinder. This may be illustrated by an experiment similar to that described on p. 256. Cylindrical soap films are blown between circular supports AB and CD (Fig. 195). AB is given a slight extra pressure so that it bulges outwards, and CD a less pressure so that it bulges inwards, and then with the tap E closed, F and G are opened so that the air inside the films can come to the same pressure. Provided that AB is less than half the circumference of the ring A, air will pass from AB to CD until the two bubbles come to the same shape. But if AB is greater than half the circumference of ring A (Fig. 196), a similar experiment will have a different result. The air pressure in CD is greater than in AB, and on putting the two in communication, air will pass from CD to AB. CD will therefore shrink and AB will grow, until the walls of CD meet and the bubble breaks up.

If we imagine the bubbles AB and CD joined end to end to form one long cylindrical bubble, the state of affairs in the last experiment is repeated. AB and CD (Fig. 197) are the two halves of the bubble, whose length AD is greater than the circumference of the cylinder. The bubble is unstable, because any slight disturbance which makes, say, CD shrink brings into play pressures which will cause CD to shrink further, by forcing air

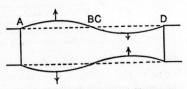

FIG. 197.—INSTABILITY OF LONG CYLINDRICAL BUBBLE.

from CD to AB. This ends with CD collapsing and forming a large spherical bubble at A and a small one at D.

This instability of a cylindrical film may be seen if it is attempted to wet a small wire throughout its length. The water will gather into globules at regular intervals.

As a rule the breaking up of a cylinder of liquid is too rapid to follow by eye, but if the process is made to go slower by using a viscous liquid, it may be watched. A fine thread of treacle will remain for some time owing to its great viscosity, but it will be seen that it breaks up eventually into drops.

If a tube A (Fig. 198) contains carbon disulphide, and this be allowed to flow very slowly into a beaker of water, the formation of the drop may be watched. The stages B, C, D, E and F can be seen. At E a very narrow neck is developed, and as this elongates it becomes unstable as described

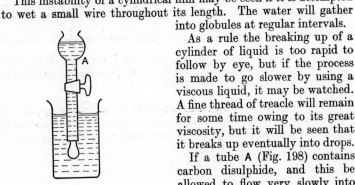

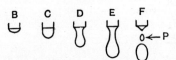

FIG. 198.—FORMATION OF DROPS.

above, and breaks up, leaving a very small drop P, known as Plateau's spherule.

Drop between plates.—If two clean pieces of plate glass are put face to face, there is no difficulty in separating them. But if there is a small drop of water between them, which is squeezed into a thin layer, it requires a considerable force to pull the plates apart. The reason is that the surface tension at the outer edge of the film of water causes a difference of pressure $\frac{2T}{d}$ between the water and the outer air, where d is the distance between the plates (Fig. 199). If

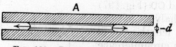

A

FIG. 199.—DROP BETWEEN PLATES.

A is the area of the film, the total force pushing the plates together is due to the excess of atmospheric pressure outside the plates over the liquid pressure between them, acting over the area A. Thus,

$$\text{force} = \frac{2TA}{d}.$$

This force presses the plates together, making d small and A large. The curvature of the water surface parallel to the plane of the plates is so slight that its effect may be neglected in comparison with the very great curvature $\frac{2}{d}$ at right angles to them. Also, if the glass surfaces are not quite plane, they may touch at some places before d becomes very small. The force urging the plates together will then not be very great.

EXAMPLE.—Two glass plates are separated by water. If the area of each plate wetted is 8 sq. cm. and the distance between the plates is 0·0012 mm., what is the force urging the plates together ? ($T = 75$ dyne cm.$^{-1}$.)

$$\text{Force} = \frac{2TA}{d}$$

$$= \frac{2 \times 75 \times 8}{0 \cdot 00012} \text{ dynes}$$

$$= 10^7 \text{ dynes.}$$

That is, nearly 10 kilograms wt.

Force between bodies partly immersed in a liquid.—It is well known that light bodies such as pieces of cork, floating on water, will adhere together and collect into groups. This may be explained by the capillary rise which occurs when the space between the bodies is small.

If two glass plates are wetted by the water in which they are partially immersed (Fig. 200 (a)), they are pushed together. The reason is similar to that described on p. 272. On the outside, over AB and CD, the pressure is atmospheric, but inside the column of liquid the pressure is less than atmospheric. Hence over AB and CD there is a resultant force pushing the plates together.

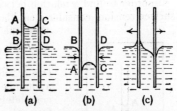

FIG. 200.—BODIES PARTLY IMMERSED.

If the liquid does not wet the plates, as in the case of glass plates partially immersed in mercury (Fig. 200 (b)), there is still an apparent attraction between them. Owing to the depression of the liquid between the plates, the pressure of the liquid at each point outside at AB or CD is greater than the atmospheric pressure which exists on the inside between AB and CD. Hence there is a resultant force pushing the plates together.

If, however, one plate is wetted by the liquid and the other is not (Fig. 200 (c)), as, for example, with a clean glass plate and one with a thin coating of paraffin wax, the plates when close together will appear to repel each other. The hydrostatic pressures will not explain this effect, and the pulls due to surface tension must be examined. In the first two cases the horizontal forces due to surface tension were the same on both sides of each plate, because there is a horizontal part of the surface of the liquid between the plates as well as outside. But in (c), when the plates are close together, there is no horizontal surface of liquid between them, so that the horizontal component of the surface tension between the plates is less than that outside. Hence there is a resultant force on each plate pulling them apart.

Vapour pressure and surface tension.—It was seen on p. 250 that the process of evaporation, or the escape of molecules through a liquid surface, is connected with the attraction between the molecules, as was the surface tension of the liquid. It seems reasonable then that there should be some relation between vapour pressure and surface tension. The escape of molecules from the liquid is hindered by the attraction of those beneath the surface, but the reverse process is not hindered. Every molecule in the vapour which strikes the liquid surface, enters it, so that condensation goes on at a rate which is proportional to the pressure of the vapour above the liquid. When the vapour in an enclosed space has risen to such a value that the processes of evaporation and condensation go on at equal rates, the maximum vapour pressure is reached.

In order to find a relation between maximum vapour pressure and surface tension, consider a capillary tube AB dipping into a liquid so

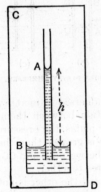

FIG. 201.—CAPILLARY TUBE IN ENCLOSURE.

that the capillary rise AB is given by $T = \dfrac{h\rho gr}{2}$, where ρ is the density of the liquid (see p. 258). If the system is enclosed within a chamber CD (Fig. 201) which cuts it off completely, thermally as well as otherwise, from the exterior, it will settle down to a steady state. There is then a difference of vapour pressure $h\sigma g$, between the levels A and B, where σ is the density of the vapour. If p is the maximum vapour pressure at B, then that at A is $(p - h\sigma g)$, and this must be the maximum vapour pressure in contact with the curved surface of the liquid at A. If it were not, then there would be either condensation or evaporation at A and a circulation would be set up. As such a circulation would mean perpetual motion without the supply of energy from outside, and as this is contrary to experience, we must conclude that the vapour pressure $(p - h\sigma\rho)$ is the maximum for contact with the curved surface at A, where p is that for the vapour in contact with a plane surface such as B. If $h\sigma g = dp$, then since

$$T = \frac{h\rho gr}{2}, \quad h = \frac{2T}{\rho gr};$$

$$\therefore \; dp = \frac{2T\sigma g}{\rho gr} = \frac{2T\sigma}{\rho r},$$

It does not matter whether air is present or not, except for the small effect of the pressure of a column of air and vapour in supporting the column of liquid. But as the density of the liquid is always many times that of the gas and vapour, this small correction has been omitted.

If the vapour is treated as a gas and subject to the equation $pv = R\theta$, since $v = \dfrac{1}{\sigma}$, $\sigma = \dfrac{p}{R\theta}$;

$$\therefore \; dp = \frac{2Tp}{R\theta\rho r}.$$

Note that the absolute temperature has here been written θ, to prevent confusion with the surface tension T.

The quantity $\dfrac{dp}{p}$ is the relative lowering of the maximum vapour pressure.

Effect on evaporation and condensation.—It will be seen from above that when the liquid surface is concave (Fig. 201), the maximum vapour pressure is below that for a plane surface. A similar argument would show that when the meniscus is convex, the column is depressed and the maximum vapour pressure is greater than that over a plane surface.

Hence if a drop of water is in a space in which the vapour pressure is the maximum for a plane surface, the vapour pressure existing is less than that for the drop. The drop will therefore evaporate. The effect is very small for large drops, for, taking $T = 75$ dyne cm.$^{-1}$, $\theta = 273°$, $\rho = 1$ and $\sigma = 0.61 \times 10^{-3}$ gm. per c.c.,

$$dp = \frac{2T\sigma}{\rho r} = \frac{2 \times 75 \times 0.61 \times 10^{-3}}{1 \times 0.05} \text{ dyne cm.}^{-2}$$

for a drop of 1 mm. diameter,

or $\qquad dp = \dfrac{2 \times 75 \times 0.61 \times 10^{-3}}{1 \times 0.05 \times 981 \times 13.6}$ cm. of mercury column

$$= 0.000137 \text{ cm. of mercury column.}$$

This is such a small amount that its effect is unimportant. But if the diameter of the drop is one-thousandth of a millimetre,

$$dp = 0.137,$$

and in the incipient stage of drop formation the diameter of the drop is nearer a millionth of a millimetre ;

$$\therefore \ dp = 137.$$

Of course, this result must not be taken literally, as the surface tension would certainly not remain constant for such small drops. It does show, however, that the rate of evaporation for very small drops is considerable. In fact, it seems likely that the direct formation of drops from vapour is impossible. A collection of a few molecules would exert such a small attraction on others that the collection would never grow into a drop. The fact that dust-free vapour does not form drops at a temperature far below the normal temperature of condensation is well known. A dust particle is a comparatively large body, so that condensation in a supersaturated vapour would immediately occur on the comparatively large particle, and once started, every drop so formed would grow. This accounts for the fact that in a dust-laden atmosphere, a fall in temperature which produces supersaturation immediately causes a cloud or fog, which in a dust-free atmosphere would not be formed.

The opposite phenomenon occurs in the process of boiling, for a concave surface produces a lowering of the maximum vapour pressure. Hence it favours condensation. A liquid may be heated above the normal boiling point if free from bubbles of air, because of the difficulty in starting the bubble. But if once started, the evaporation goes on to form the bubble with explosive violence. Hence the term " bumpy " boiling for air-free water. But any porous body in the liquid, which contains minute air-bubbles, provides a bubble of suitable size, so that evaporation goes on easily and the boiling is no longer bumpy.

Surface energy and temperature coefficient of surface tension.—It is possible to find a relation between the change of surface tension with temperature and the total energy required to produce unit area of surface. For this purpose, imagine a film to be used as a reversible engine (p. 239). The efficiency of such an engine is known in terms of the absolute temperatures of the heater and cooler. The relation is

$$\frac{\text{heat converted into work in a cycle}}{\text{heat drawn from heater}} = \text{efficiency}$$

$$= \frac{\text{difference in temperatures of heater and cooler}}{\text{temperature of heater}}.$$

Consider a film to be stretched isothermally at absolute temperature θ. Mechanical work AT is required (p. 252) to perform the stretching, where A is the area of film produced, and T the surface tension. At the same time heat is supplied by the heater at temperature θ, in order to maintain the temperature of the film constant. If h is the amount of heat supplied for the formation of unit area of surface, hA is the heat given by the heater to the film to produce unit area isothermally.

When the stretching A is complete, let a very small adiabatic expansion be produced. As no heat is supplied, the temperature falls, by the small amount $d\theta$. The surface tension is now $T - \dfrac{dT}{d\theta} d\theta$, where $\dfrac{dT}{d\theta}$ is the coefficient of increase of surface tension with temperature. Let the film now contract by the amount A. Mechanical work

$$A\left(T - \frac{dT}{d\theta} d\theta\right)$$

is performed by it. A further small adiabatic contraction brings the film back to its original condition. The adiabatic changes may be made as small as we please, and the two amounts of work during them are in opposite directions, and so may be considered not to add to the total work performed. Thus the balance of work performed by the film upon external bodies is

$$A\left(T - \frac{dT}{d\theta}d\theta\right) - A\,d\theta = -A\,\frac{dT}{d\theta}\,d\theta.$$

The heat drawn from the source is Ah, and if this is expressed in ergs, the above efficiency equation becomes

$$\frac{-A\,\dfrac{dT}{d\theta}d\theta}{Ah} = \frac{d\theta}{\theta}\,;$$

$$\therefore\ h = -\theta\,\frac{dT}{d\theta}.$$

The negative sign occurs because $\frac{dT}{d\theta}$ is negative for all liquids.

The total energy (E) supplied to produce unit area of film is therefore $T + h$,

or
$$E = T + h,$$

$$E = T - \theta\,\frac{dT}{d\theta}\,.$$

E is known as the **total surface energy**, and its value has been calculated, in the case of many substances, from the measured values of T and $\frac{dT}{d\theta}$.

Taking the surface tension of water at 15° C., or 288° A. as 74 dynes per cm. and $\frac{dT}{d\theta}$ as -0.148,

$$E = 74 + (288 \times 0.148)$$

$$= 74 + 43 = 117\ \text{ergs per sq. cm.}$$

The total surface energy is thus much greater than the energy due to surface tension. The latter is sometimes called **free surface energy**, and is numerically equal to T (p. 252).

Internal or intrinsic pressure.—It has been seen how Laplace accounted for surface tension (p. 250) by suggesting that the molecules of a liquid attract each other. In the interior of the liquid the forces of attraction due to surrounding molecules are arranged symmetrically in all directions, while at or near the surface, the resultant of all the attractions is directed inwards. The law of force between the molecules is not known with any certainty. It is not the ordinary law of gravitational attraction, that the force varies inversely as the square of the distance apart. It is more likely that instead of the square, it is the eighth power of the distance that determines the force, and there is a large amount of evidence that the forces are of the kind concerned with chemical combination.

Owing to these attractions, there must be a pressure in the interior of a liquid. This has been named **internal or intrinsic pressure**, and is the cause of cohesion. In liquids, the cohesive force is considerable when the liquid is in the pure state and free from minute air-bubbles, while in a gas it is exceedingly small. This pressure is the term a/v^2 (see Edser's *Heat*), which is added to the external pressure p in order to give the whole pressure in van der Waals' modification of the gas equation,

$$\left(p + \frac{a}{v^2}\right)(v - b) = RT.$$

Let us consider the attraction between a thin plane of the liquid and a small particle of mass m situated at distance r from the plane to be $mm'\psi(r)$, where m' is the mass per square centimetre of the liquid in the plane. Then, if the thickness of the plane is dr and the density of the liquid ρ,

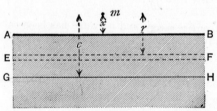

FIG. 202.—ATTRACTION OF LIQUID FOR EXTERNAL PARTICLE.

$$m' = \rho \, dr,$$

and the attraction between the mass m and the plane is $m\rho\psi(r)\,dr$.

To fix our ideas, consider the mass m to be situated above the free surface of the liquid, as in Fig. 202. Then if EF is the layer of the liquid, the attraction of EF for m is $m\rho\psi(r)\,dr$. This, of course, becomes zero when the distance r is equal to the limit at which the attraction between molecules produces any effect, that is, when r equals c the range of molecular attraction (p. 250). c is very small on account of the rapid falling off of the force between molecules corresponding to the eighth power of the distance, although, on the other hand, the force between molecules is probably very great when they are close together, if the forces are connected with chemical affinities. It must be remembered that chemical affinity is due to electric charges possessed by atoms, and these have electric and magnetic fields, to which chemical combination is due. These fields surround the molecule to some distance, and it is to these stray fields that the attraction between molecules is due. It is therefore not surprising that the attraction should fall off according to a high power law, when it is remembered that the force between two magnets, which have strong fields surrounding them, falls off inversely as the fourth power of the distance. Neither is it surprising that the effective range c should not be a constant and definite quantity for all substances.

Returning to Fig. 202, the force exerted on m by the whole liquid is the sum of the forces due to all the layers of liquid between AB and GH, where GH is at a distance c from m.

That is,
$$\text{total force} = \int_x^c m\rho\psi(r)\,dr$$
$$= m\rho\int_x^c \psi(r)\,dr.$$

The integration cannot be performed, because the form $\psi(r)$ is unknown. But if it could be performed and the limits c and x substituted for r, the result would be a function of x, c being considered constant for the given liquid. It is convenient to write

$$\int_x^c \psi(r)\,dr$$

as a function of x only; thus

$$\int_x^c \psi(r)\,dr = \phi(x).$$

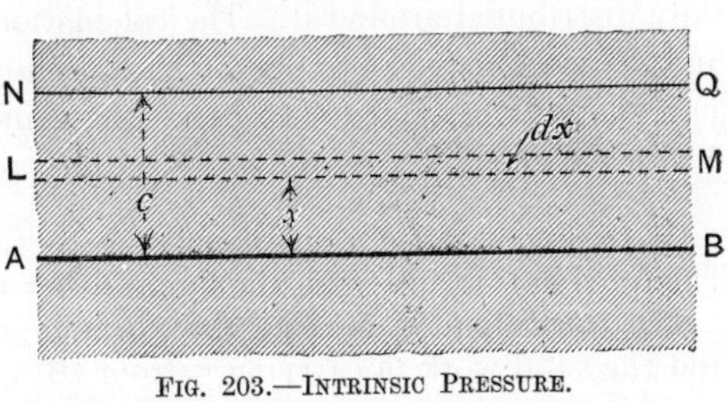

This means that the attraction of the whole liquid for a point mass

FIG. 203.—INTRINSIC PRESSURE.

m situated at distance x from its plane surface is $m\rho\phi(x)$.

It is now possible to calculate the force acting across unit area of a plane in the liquid, due to molecular attractions. For, consider AB (Fig. 203) to be any plane drawn in the interior of the liquid, and let LM be a layer of liquid of thickness dx, parallel to AB. Unit area of LM contains a mass $m = \rho\,dx$ of liquid, and the attraction upon this due to all the liquid below AB is $m\rho\phi(x) = \rho^2\phi(x)\,dx$. Only that liquid within distance c of AB experiences any sensible force due to the liquid below AB.

∴ whole force across unit area on the liquid above AB due to the liquid below AB is $\int_0^c \rho^2 \phi(x)\,dx$. This is the intrinsic pressure in the liquid, which causes cohesion. Calling it K,

$$K = \rho^2 \int_0^c \phi(x)\,dx.$$

Estimation of intrinsic pressure.—The quantity a/v^2 in van der Waals' equation affords a means of estimating intrinsic pressure, but for this the student is referred to works on Heat. A more direct method is to calculate the work done on a small quantity of the liquid in carrying it from the interior, into the free space above the liquid, where it becomes vapour. This work, together with the work done in driving back any gas or vapour present (p. 135), is the mechanical equivalent of the heat required to produce evaporation at constant temperature. This quantity is very well known, and it remains to apply our method of molecular attraction to the calculation of the amount of work required to carry a small quantity of the liquid from the interior to the free space above the surface. No work is done while the element of liquid is at a greater depth than c below the surface, as the forces due to the rest of the liquid are symmetrically distributed around it. The calculation is in two parts : (a) to find the work required to carry a small volume v of liquid from depth c to the surface, and (b) to carry the same from the surface to a distance c above it. As (b) is the simpler, it will be taken first.

(b) In Fig. 203 let a small mass m be situated in the layer LM. The force in this due to all the liquid below the surface AB is $m\rho\phi(x)$.

The work done in moving this through distance dx is $m\rho\phi(x)\,dx$, and the total work in carrying it from AB to NQ is

$$\int_0^c m\rho\phi(x)\,dx = m\rho \int_0^c \phi(x)\,dx.$$

If v is volume of the mass m of liquid,

$$m = \rho v\,;$$

$$\therefore \text{ work} = v\rho^2 \int_0^c \phi(x)\,dx = vK \text{ (see above)}.$$

∴ work done in removing unit volume of the liquid from the surface to distance c is K. The liquid, in evaporating at the surface, does not, of course, move away in layers; it escapes molecule by molecule. But the total mechanical work done in removing a given quantity of the liquid is independent of the rate at which this takes place.

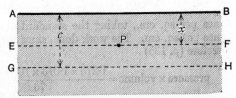

FIG. 204.—INTERIOR OF LIQUID.

(a) In order to find the work done in carrying the mass m from GH (Fig. 204) to the surface AB, the resultant force at each point must be found. The downward force is known: it is

$$m\rho \int_0^c \psi(r)\,dr,$$

where r is measured downwards from P (p. 278). There is also an upward force $m\rho \int_0^x \psi(r)\,dr$ due to the liquid between AB and EF. Hence the resultant downward force on m is

$$m\rho \int_0^c \psi(r)\,dr - m\rho \int_0^x \psi(r)\,dr = m\rho \int_x^c \psi(r)\,dr$$

$$= m\rho\phi(x). \quad \text{(p. 279)}.$$

Work done in moving over distance $dx = m\rho\phi(x)\,dx$.

And total work done in moving from GH to AB or AB to GH is

$$\int_0^c m\rho\phi(x)\,dx = m\rho \int_0^c \phi(x)\,dx$$

$$= v\rho^2 \int_0^c \phi(x)\,dx,$$

or for unit volume,   work $= \rho^2 \int_0^c \phi(x)\,dx = K$.

It follows that in order to remove unit volume from the interior of the liquid to the free space above it, the total work is $2K$, that is, it is numerically equal to twice the intrinsic pressure.

If the case of water at 15° C. is taken, $\rho = 0\cdot999$, and may be taken as unity. The latent heat of evaporation at 15° C. is 586 calories per gm. If the water vapour at 15° C. obeys the gas laws, its volume per gram calculated from a vapour pressure of 1·278 cm. of mercury is 78,030 c.c. The evaporation of this volume of vapour pushes back the vapour already present, whose pressure is $\dfrac{1·278}{76} \times 1·013 \times 10^6$ dynes per sq. cm., taking the standard atmosphere as $1·013 \times 10^6$ dynes per sq. cm. The work done, since the pressure is constant, is therefore (p. 135)

$$\text{pressure} \times \text{volume} = \frac{1·278 \times 1·013 \times 10^6 \times 78030}{76} \text{ ergs}$$

$$= \frac{1·278 \times 1·013 \times 10^6 \times 78030}{4·182 \times 10^7 \times 76} \text{ calories}$$

$$= 31·76 \text{ calories.}$$

$$\therefore \text{ Internal heat} = 586·5 - 31·76$$

$$= 554·7 \text{ calories per gm.}$$

$$\therefore 2K = 554·7 \times 4·182 \times 10^7,$$

$$K = 554·7 \times 2·091 \times 10^7 = 1·160 \times 10^{10} \text{ dynes per sq. cm.}$$

$$= \frac{554·7 \times 2·091 \times 10^7}{1·013 \times 10^6} \text{ atmospheres}$$

$$= \underline{11450 \text{ atmospheres.}}$$

This is of the same order of magnitude as the result obtained by considering van der Waals' equation (p. 278), and is the value of the intrinsic pressure in the liquid. From its magnitude it is seen that cohesion must be very great. The difficulty of observing the cohesive force directly arises from the fact that impurities such as dissolved gases are present, and produce a discontinuity at which the liquid breaks on applying a tensile stress to a column of the liquid.

Estimate of range of molecular attraction.—If a liquid can be divided along a plane and the two parts pulled apart perpendicularly to this plane, two new surfaces are created. The energy required to produce unit area of new surface is equal to the surface tension T, apart from the heat required to maintain constant temperature (p. 277). As the separation produces two new surfaces, the total work done is equal to $2T$.

The work done in raising one part of fluid from the other so that AB (Fig. 203) is the plane of separation may be found by noting that the force on mass m in the layer LM is $\rho m \phi(x)$, and the work done in moving it from distance x to distance c is

$$\int_x^c \rho m \phi(x)\, dx \quad \text{or} \quad \rho m \int_x^c \phi(x)\, dx.$$

For a moment, write p for $\int_x^c \phi(x)\, dx$. Then, work done in moving mass m from LM to NQ is $\rho m p$. Now if m is the mass of unit area of the layer, $m = \rho\, dx$, and work $= \rho^2 p\,.\,dx$. For all the layers from AB to NQ

$$\text{total work} = \int_0^c \rho^2 p\, dx = \rho^2 \int_0^c p\,.\,dx.$$

If $\int p\, dx$ is integrated by parts, it is

$$px - \int x\,.\,\frac{dp}{dx}\, dx.$$

Now $\qquad\qquad p = \int_x^c \phi(x)\, dx\,; \quad \therefore \ \frac{dp}{dx} = -\phi(x),$

and $\qquad\qquad \rho^2 \int_0^c p\, dx = \left[\rho^2 p\,.\,x\right]_0^c - \rho^2 \int_0^c x\phi(x)\, dx.$

Since $\rho^2 p = \rho^2 \int_x^c \phi(x)\, dx$, this is zero when $x = c$, and $(\rho^2 p\,.\,x)$ it is zero when $x = 0$;

$$\therefore \ \left[\rho^2 p x\right]_0^c = 0.$$

Without knowing the form of the function ϕ it is impossible to integrate $\int_0^c x\phi(x)\, dx$, but since both force and work become zero when x exceeds c, c is the greatest value of x entering into the expression for the work, so that the greatest value the expression can have is

$$\rho^2 c \int_0^c \phi(x)\, dx = cK. \dots\dots\dots\dots\dots\dots\text{(p. 280)}$$

Now, putting $\rho^2 \int_0^c x\phi(x)\, dx = 2T$, then $\rho^2 c \int_0^c \phi(x)\, dx$, or cK must be greater than $\rho^2 \int_0^c x\phi(x)\, dx$, or $2T$,

$$cK > 2T \quad \text{or} \quad c > \frac{2T}{K}\,.$$

Taking the values $T = 74$ dynes per cm. and $K = 1{\cdot}16 \times 10^{10}$ (p. 282),

$$c > \frac{2 \times 74}{1{\cdot}16 \times 10^{10}}$$

$$> 1{\cdot}27 \times 10^{-8} \text{ cm.,}$$

$$> 0{\cdot}127 \ \mu\mu \text{ (micro-millimetres).}$$

This gives the smallest value that c can have. It is in fair agreement with molecular distances as obtained from other experiments, which shows that the attraction between molecules does not extend to much more than the distance between adjacent molecules.

Solutions and stability of thin films.—When a substance is dissolved in a liquid, the surface tension may be increased or decreased, according to the nature of the substance. Many organic substances lower the surface tension when dissolved in water. For example, the surface tension of methyl alcohol is 23 dyne cm.$^{-1}$, and the surface tension of various solutions of alcohol and water lies between 23 and 74 dyne cm.$^{-1}$. On the other hand, some substances such as the inorganic salts increase the surface tension. A solution of 5 gm. mol. per litre of sodium chloride has a surface tension of 82 dyne cm.$^{-1}$.

In the case of a pure liquid there is no possibility of varying the composition of the surface layer. It follows that large films of pure liquid cannot be produced. For if a vertical film of pure water exists, the weight of the film requires that the surface tension at the upper part should be greater than at the lower part, since the surface tension at the upper part has the weight of the film to carry. As this is impossible, the film breaks. It is common experience that only small films and bubbles can be produced with pure water. But with some solutions, the case is different. If the solute lowers the surface tension, the stretching in the upper part of the vertical film causes a weakening of the concentration of the solute in the upper part of the film with a corresponding increase in the surface tension. This occurs to a marked degree with soap solutions, so that the surface tension is adjusted to compensate for the increased pull in the upper part of the film. Soap solutions are able to produce films and bubbles of great durability.

The surface layer differs in several ways from the bulk of the liquid. If the liquid is pure, the only change possible is a difference in density between the surface layer and the interior of the solution. But in the case of a solution there is a further possibility ; the concentration of the solute may vary. Accepting the principle that the potential energy of a system tends towards a minimum, and that the surface tension is a measure of the energy associated with the surface layer, it follows that the solute will move towards that condition which will make the surface tension a minimum. If the solute causes a lowering of the surface tension, it will be found to be more concentrated in the surface layer than in the interior of the liquid. On the other hand, if the solute causes an increase in surface tension, it will be less concentrated in the surface layer than in the interior. This can be established by thermodynamical reasoning, and is completely borne out by experiment. The proof is beyond the scope of this book, and the student is referred to more advanced works on the physics and chemistry of surface layers.*

This is in accord with the fact that highly soluble substances would be more concentrated in the interior of the solution than at the surface, owing to the great attraction between the water molecules and the molecules of the solute. The solute molecules are pulled into the interior, with increase in surface tension (p. 250). The opposite effect occurs in the case of slightly soluble substances.

The amount of substance transferred in this way from the interior of the liquid to the surface layer is called the **adsorption** per unit area of surface. Adsorption may therefore be either positive or negative. It is positive when the solute lowers the surface tension and enters the layer, and negative when it raises the surface tension and so leaves the surface layer. The latter case occurs with many inorganic salts.

The term adsorption is most commonly applied to the case of gases deposited or clinging to solid surfaces. Perhaps the most important case is that of charcoal, which can adsorb large quantities of many gases. It is used in producing high vacua. A vessel containing charcoal is in communication with the vacuum vessel. When a low pressure has been reached by pumping (p. 247), the vessel containing the charcoal is surrounded by liquid air. At this low temperature the charcoal adsorbs large quantities of the remaining gas, and so produces a great lowering of the pressure in the vacuum vessel. In some cases the gas adsorbed forms a solution in the solid, and diffuses into the interior. The name **sorption** has been given to the whole process.

The remarkable stability of soap films has received a great deal of investigation. It is now considered that the stability is due to a monomolecular layer at the surface (p. 286). The soap consists of long chain molecules having an extremely soluble group, such as

* E. K. Rideal, *An Introduction to Surface Chemistry.* N. K. Adam, *The Physics and Chemistry of Surfaces.*

COONa, at one end. This group forms a strong anchorage in the water, and the lateral attraction between the long molecules maintains a stable layer with sufficient mobility to increase the surface tension wherever the film is stretched. A freshly-formed soap film rapidly thins, and soon the characteristic interference colours are seen. These change as the film gets thinner, until eventually the film becomes so thin that it cannot produce interference, and it is then black. There is little doubt that the black film consists of two monomolecular layers of soap molecules with a small amount of water between them. The black film may also consist of two such double layers in contact. Any change from this to the thinner film is abrupt, and the thinner presents a sharp, though irregular boundary.

Thickness of surface film.—An estimate of the thickness of the surface film indicates that it is about molecular dimensions. The late Lord Rayleigh examined the thickness of an oil film on water by placing a very small amount of oil on the surface of clean water in a dish. By means of a movable barrier, the area of surface of the oil film could be varied as desired. On increasing the area and so diminishing the thickness of the oil layer, it was found that the surface tension remained constant until the thickness was reduced to about 5 $\mu\mu$ (micro-millimetres). At 1·6 $\mu\mu$ the surface tension increased rapidly, and at 1 $\mu\mu$ the surface tension was sensibly that of pure water. This layer is of the order of one molecule in thickness, and it may be concluded that when the layer of oil is so spread that the spacing of its molecules is such that they do not cover the water surface, the surface tension is that of pure water. Later experiments bear out this conclusion (p. 287).

Monomolecular layers.—The existence of surface layers one molecule in thickness has been proved definitely by Langmuir. Certain oils and fats are very slightly soluble. By taking a small quantity of a solution in benzene and dropping it on the surface of the water, the benzene evaporates and a layer of oil is obtained. From the area of the layer and the quantity of oil used, it was found that the layer was one molecule thick.

The experiment is carried out in a shallow trough of water. A light rod placed across the trough separates pure water at one end from the water whose surface is contaminated with the oil or fatty acid on the other. The rod is attached to a lever so that it can move horizontally along the surface. Weights added to the lever determine the force on the rod required to keep it in equilibrium. This force is a measure of the difference of surface tension between the pure water and the oily water. A movable barrier enables the layer of oil to be pushed towards the counterpoised rod. By this means it was found that when the layer has such a great area that there are spaces between the oil molecules, that is, the layer does not cover the water, the surface tension does not differ appreciably from that of pure water. As the layer is diminished in area by pushing along the barrier, the surface tension slowly falls and the force trying to cause spreading increases. At this stage the molecules in the layer are mobile, as may be shown by placing dust particles on the surface. They can be blown about quite easily.

On further contraction of the layer, a stage is reached at which the force on the rod increases more rapidly and in a linear manner. The film has lost its mobility, as shown by dust particles being fixed. The behaviour of the film is analogous to that of a solid undergoing an elastic strain (p. 127). At the close of this stage a further squeezing causes the film to crumple visibly, and the spreading force remains nearly constant.

It was shown that such monomolecular layers act like two dimensional solids or liquids. In the mobile stage, the spreading force F, or difference between surface tensions of the clean and the contaminated surface, obeys a law similar to the gas law $pv = kT$, where k is the gas constant for one molecule. In this case, $Fa = kT$, where k is the same constant as before and a is the area of the monomolecular layer.

The explanation of these molecular layers given by Langmuir is that one end of the molecule has a considerable affinity for water, while the other has none. The molecules of the oils and fatty acids which produce monomolecular layers on water consist of chains, each link in the chain being CH_2, one end of the chain being CH_3 and the other $-OH$ or $-COOH$. The hydrocarbon group CH_3 has no affinity for water, while the $-OH$ or $-COOH$ has. This active end is held beneath the water surface, while the inactive CH_3 end projects above it. The mobile or expanded layer corresponds to the fluid state, and the melting point is the temperature at which the transition from the immobile to the mobile state takes place.

Adam classifies such films, or layers, formed by insoluble substances, under four heads.

(i) *Condensed films*, or those in which the molecules in the monomolecular layer are so closely packed that they are immobile and are steeply inclined to the surface.

(ii) *Gaseous films*, in which the molecules are so far separated that they have independent movement in the surface and exert a pressure on the linear boundary, analogous to a gas pressure. Such an ideal case is never realised in practice, because the molecules, if large, will either dissolve or disappear by evaporation.

(iii) *Liquid expanded films*, in which the molecules adhere strongly to each other, but are not so closely packed together as in (i).

(iv) *Vapour expanded films* are those in which there is still adhesive force between the molecules, but not of sufficient magnitude to keep the molecules together in islands as in (i) and (iii). This class of film shades off into (ii).

Calming of sea waves by oil.—Several explanations have been given of the fact that oil poured upon the sea renders the waves less dangerous. All agree that the oil has no effect upon the height of large waves, but is active in suppressing the ripples produced by the wind. These ripples may, by the action of the wind, give rise to large waves. They may also give rise to dangerous breaking of the large waves. The late Lord Rayleigh explained the effect of the oil by saying that the wind, pushing the oil along the surface, increased the contamination, and so lowered the surface tension in advance of the ripple and left a cleaner surface with higher surface tension behind. The surface tension thus produces forces which oppose the motion of the surface produced by the wind, and so tends to prevent the formation of ripples.

The above explanation is not complete, because the surface tension is not lowered until the whole surface is covered by oil. It has, however, been shown that a film of oil which does not cover more than a small fraction of the surface is effective in damping ripples. It is more probable that the viscous resistance to displacement of the oil on the water plays the most important part in the damping of the ripples. Adam states that good spreading power on the surface of the water is important. Mineral oils are not effective, but in emergency they may be improved by melting stearine candles and mixing with the oil. The carboxyl group in the stearine molecules gives a good anchorage in the water.

EXERCISES ON CHAPTER XII

1. Write an essay on *surface tension*.   C.H.S.C.

2. What is meant by the *surface tension* of a liquid ?
Describe and explain a method of measuring the surface tension of water.   C.H.S.C.

3. What do you understand by " surface tension " ?
Describe some natural phenomena depending upon surface tension. Explain fully a method of measuring the surface tension of water.
                                                                 Lond. H.S.C.

4. Give a brief outline of a method of measuring the surface tension of a liquid.

A glass plate, of length 10·0 cm., breadth 1·54 cm., and thickness 0·20 cm., weighs 8·2 gm. in air. If it is held vertically, with its long side horizontal, and its lower half immersed in water, what will be its apparent weight? (Surface tension of water = 73 dynes per cm.) C.H.S.C.

5. Describe experiments to illustrate the phenomenon of surface tension.

A glass tube of 1 mm. internal diameter is held vertically with one end below the surface of some water, and the water level inside the tube rises 2·4 cm. above that outside. Deduce from first principles a value for the surface tension of water. What is the probable cause of the erroneous value obtained? C.H.S.C.

6. Describe the capillary tube method of measuring the surface tension of a liquid. Why is it unsuitable for measurements of surface tension at temperatures other than that of the surroundings? Design a piece of apparatus with which this difficulty might be overcome by measuring the pressure necessary to force the meniscus back to the level of the surrounding liquid. O. & C.H.S.C.

7. Describe a method of measuring the surface tension of water by means of a capillary tube.

The stem of a common hydrometer is a circular cylinder of diameter 2 mm. It floats, with its stem wetted, in alcohol, whose specific gravity is 0·796, and surface tension 25·5 dynes per cm. Calculate how much deeper it floats than if the alcohol had had zero surface tension. C.H.S.C.

8. How is the difference in the curvatures of a water meniscus and a mercury meniscus explained?

Water rises to a height of 5·0 cm. in a certain capillary tube. In the same tube the level of a mercury surface is depressed by 1·54 cm. Compare the surface tensions of water and mercury. (The specific gravity of mercury is 13·6, the angle of contact for water is 0° and for mercury 130°.) Lond. Int. Sci.

9. Describe the capillary tube method of measuring the surface tension of a liquid, proving the expression for the rise of liquid in the tube.

A capillary tube of internal diameter 1 mm. and external diameter 5 mm. hangs vertically from the arm of a balance, the lower end of the tube being in a liquid of surface tension 40 dyne cm. Assuming that the liquid wets the tube, what is the change in the apparent weight of the tube due to surface tension? (g = 980 cm. sec.$^{-2}$.) L.H.S.C.

10. Explain *surface tension, angle of contact*. Show how the existence of an acute angle of contact and of a pressure difference due to curvature accounts for the rise of a liquid in a capillary tube.

A tube of 1 mm. bore is dipped into a vessel containing a liquid of density 0·8 gm. cm.$^{-3}$, surface tension 30 dyne cm.$^{-1}$ and contact angle zero. Calculate the length which the liquid will occupy in the tube when the tube is (*a*) held vertical, (*b*) inclined to the vertical at an angle of 30°. Lond. Int. Arts.

11. Obtain an expression for the rise (or fall) of a liquid in a vertical capillary tube dipped into a wide vessel containing the liquid. What determines whether the liquid rises or falls ?

A U-tube is made up of two capillaries of bore 1 mm. and 2 mm. respectively. The tube is held vertically and partially filled with a liquid of surface tension 49 dyne cm.$^{-1}$ and zero contact angle. Calculate the density of the liquid if the difference in the levels of the menisci is 1·25 cm.

Lond. Int. Sci.

12. A capillary tube of 0·5 mm. bore stands vertically in a wide vessel containing a liquid of surface tension 30 dyne cm.$^{-1}$, density 0·8 gm. cm.$^{-3}$ and zero contact angle. Calculate the height (h) to which the liquid will rise in the tube. Establish any formula which you employ.

What will happen if the length of the capillary projecting from the surface of the liquid is less than h ?

Lond. Int. Sci.

13. Describe a method for the determination of the surface tension of a soap solution, and prove any formula required for the reduction of the observations.

Find the difference of the levels of the mercury in the two limbs of a U-tube if the diameter of the bore of one limb is 1 mm. and of the other 8 mm. The surface tension of mercury is 440 c.g.s. units, its density 13·6 gm. per c.c., and the angle of contact with the walls of the tube 140°.

J.M.B.H.S.C.

14. Find an expression for the difference of pressure between the inside and outside of a soap-bubble.

Two bubbles, of the same radius, are blown on one end of each of two open tubes. Describe and explain what happens when the tubes are connected together at their free ends.

O. & C.H.S.C.

15. Describe in detail how you would determine the surface tension of water by capillary elevation. Why does the water in a glass capillary tube rise above the level of that outside, while in a tube of paraffin wax it sinks below ? Is it necessary to take into account the material of the tube in working out the surface tension of the liquid ?

What would be the pressure inside a small air-bubble of 0·1 mm. radius, situated just below the surface of water ? (Take the surface tension of water as 70 dynes per cm. and atmospheric pressure as $1·013 \times 10^6$ dynes/sq. cm.)

O.H.S.C.

16. Define *surface tension* (T), and show that the pressure inside a spherical soap-bubble of radius r exceeds that outside by $4T/r$. If this pressure is balanced by that due to a column of oil (sp. gr. 0·80) 1·4 mm. high when $r = 1$ cm., find the surface tension of the solution. State the unit in which your result is expressed.

Lond. Int. Sci.

CHAPTER XIII

WAVES

Wave motion.—A disturbance of any kind which travels may be called a wave. The term, however, is generally reserved for a disturbance which travels without change of form.

As a simple example, think of a rope, one end of which is held in the hand. On giving the hand a sharp jerk to one side, a pulse is seen to travel along the rope, provided that the rope is not stretched tight. If the rope is tight there will still be a pulse produced on giving the jerk, but this pulse may travel so quickly that the eye cannot follow it. In any case, if the rope is sufficiently long, the pulse is very nearly a true wave. It travels along the rope, and keeps its shape while travelling.

Other types of wave are very well known: for example, ripples spread outwards along the surface of a pond when a stone is thrown into it. These ripples become feebler through attenuation as the circles become bigger. The larger waves seen on the sea are not of the same character as the ripples, but may be looked upon as true waves when they travel with constant shape.

Then again the waves in the air which produce the sensation of sound are of a still different type, and are invisible. They will be studied later (p. 300). Electromagnetic waves, ranging from those used in wireless transmission, through light waves, to the shortest known waves, such as gamma rays and cosmic rays, are further examples. They will not be studied here, as our attention is confined to waves of a mechanical type, but many of the wave equations apply to waves in general, whatever the particular type may be.

General equation of wave motion.—The disturbance which travels may have a variety of forms. In the rope or the ripple it is a displacement which takes place at right angles to the direction in which the wave is travelling. Let Ox (Fig. 205) represent the rope or the surface of the water, and take the axis Oy in the direction of the displacement. If a displacement be given at O, at a certain time, the pulse may have travelled to the position ABC at a later time. The curve ABC may have a variety of shapes, but some equation can be found to represent it. The commonest type is represented by a sine or cosine curve, but for the moment we will write it $y = f(x)$, where the function f is quite general.

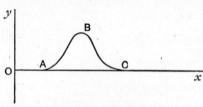

FIG. 205.—WAVE FORM.

Since the pulse ABC travels along Ox it must have a velocity (v), and after t seconds it will have travelled a distance vt. The complete equation for the wave motion must then be $y = f(x - vt)$, because this represents a displacement which travels along Ox with velocity v and with shape unchanged. After a lapse of t sec. the wave has travelled a distance vt. Moving the origin to the right by this distance and calling x' the new abscissa, $x = x' + vt$, and on substituting for x, $y = f(x' + vt - vt)$ or $y = f(x')$. That is, the curve has the same equation referred to the new origin as it had t sec. earlier with respect to the old origin. Hence the wave $y = f(x - vt)$ travels with velocity v and shape unchanged.

In a similar manner the equation $y = f(x + vt)$ represents a wave travelling in the direction xO, because the origin must now be moved in the negative direction, that is, to the left, in order to preserve the equation. For $x = x' - vt$ or $y = f(x' - vt + vt) = f(x')$.

Simple harmonic wave.—In Nature the waves which occur most frequently are produced by vibrating bodies, that is, bodies which possess simple harmonic motion, or motion represented by the equation $y = a \sin \omega t$ (p. 90). If the hand which holds the end of the rope (p. 291) executes this motion, the end of the rope will do likewise, and the equation of its motion is $y = a \sin \omega t$. As in Chapter IV, a is the amplitude and $\omega = 2\pi n$, where n is the frequency of the vibration ;

$$\therefore \quad y = a \sin 2\pi n t$$

$$= a \sin 2\pi \frac{t}{T},$$

where T is the periodic time of vibration, that is, $\frac{1}{n}$.

The distance travelled by the wave while the end makes one complete vibration is called the wave-length, λ (Fig. 206), and therefore in one second the wave travels a distance $n\lambda$,

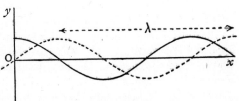

or $v = n\lambda = \dfrac{\lambda}{T}.$

FIG. 206.—SINE WAVE.

Now the equation of the wave must be of the form $y = f(x - vt)$, and this is consistent with the equation

$$y = a \sin 2\pi \left(\frac{x}{\lambda} - \frac{t}{T} \right)$$

$$= a \sin \frac{2\pi}{\lambda} \left(x - \frac{\lambda}{T} t \right)$$

$$= a \sin \frac{2\pi}{\lambda} (x - vt).$$

It is also consistent with the motion of the end at the origin O, for when $x = 0$,

$$y = -a \sin 2\pi \frac{t}{T}.$$

The negative sign arises because, when $t = 0$, $y = a \sin \frac{2\pi}{\lambda} x$. This is the equation of the curve shown in dotted line in Fig. 206, and as this curve moves forwards, the end of the rope at O moves downwards, so that the equation of its motion is $y = -a \sin 2\pi \frac{t}{T}$.

Again, if t in the equation $y = a \sin 2\pi \left(\frac{x}{\lambda} - \frac{t}{T} \right)$ be increased by the amount T,

$$y = a \sin 2\pi \left(\frac{x}{\lambda} - \frac{t + T}{T} \right)$$

$$= a \sin \left\{ 2\pi \left(\frac{x}{\lambda} - \frac{t}{T} \right) - 2\pi \right\}.$$

The angle is decreased by 2π, and its sine therefore has the same value as at the beginning of the interval T. Similarly if x is increased by the amount λ,

$$y = a \sin \left\{ 2\pi \left(\frac{x}{\lambda} - \frac{t}{T} \right) + 2\pi \right\},$$

and at any instant y has the same value at points separated by distance λ.

Transverse and longitudinal waves.—The rope has been chosen as an illustration, but it must be understood that the above equation applies to all waves in which the particles of the medium execute simple harmonic motion. As any other periodic motion may be resolved into a series of sines and cosines, all waves may be represented by such a series, but only simple sine waves will be considered here. There is one characteristic common to waves in a rope, or stretched string and to ripples, which is that the motion of the particles is at right angles to the direction in which the waves travel. Such are called **transverse waves**.

In sound waves the motion of the particles is in the same direction as that in which the waves are travelling. These are called **longitudinal waves**. These longitudinal motions of the particles cause compressions and rarefactions, as will be seen later (p. 298). Solids, owing to the possession of compressibility, as well as rigidity and tensile elasticity, can transmit both longitudinal and transverse waves, but gases, having compressibility only, can only transmit longitudinal waves. Liquids can transmit longitudinal waves, and at their surface, on account of surface tension, can transmit ripples, which are transverse waves.

Particle velocity and acceleration.—Each particle of the medium transmitting a wave moves in a line, its amplitude of vibration being a. Its velocity must not be confused with the velocity, v, of the wave. If the displacement at a point in the medium is y, the velocity of the particle at any instant is the quantity $\dfrac{dy}{dt}$, and may be obtained from the wave equation $y = a \sin 2\pi \left(\dfrac{x}{\lambda} - \dfrac{t}{T} \right)$.

$$\frac{dy}{dt} = -\frac{2\pi a}{T} \cos 2\pi \left(\frac{x}{\lambda} - \frac{t}{T} \right)$$

$$= \frac{2\pi a}{T} \sin \left\{ 2\pi \left(\frac{x}{\lambda} - \frac{t}{T} \right) - \frac{\pi}{2} \right\}$$

$$= \frac{2\pi a}{T} \sin 2\pi \left(\frac{x - \dfrac{\lambda}{4}}{\lambda} - \frac{t}{T} \right).$$

This may also be represented by a sine curve. Its amplitude is $\frac{2\pi a}{T}$, and it is situated a **quarter of a wave-length** from the displacement curve. If the full-line curve in Fig. 207 is the curve of displacement,

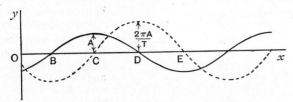

FIG. 207.—PARTICLE VELOCITY AND ACCELERATION.

the velocity curve is the dotted line. At B and D the particle has greatest velocity $\left(\frac{2\pi a}{T}\right)$, and it is negative at B and positive at D. At C and E the particle velocity is zero.

In a similar way the acceleration of a particle is

$$\frac{d^2y}{dt^2} = -\frac{4\pi^2 a}{T^2} \cos 2\pi \left(\frac{x - \frac{\lambda}{4}}{\lambda} - \frac{t}{T}\right)$$

$$= \frac{4\pi^2 a}{T^2} \sin \left\{ 2\pi \left(\frac{x - \frac{\lambda}{4}}{\lambda} - \frac{t}{T}\right) - \frac{\pi}{2} \right\}$$

$$= \frac{4\pi^2 a}{T^2} \sin 2\pi \left(\frac{x - \frac{\lambda}{2}}{\lambda} - \frac{t}{T}\right).$$

That is, the particle acceleration varies harmonically between $+\frac{4\pi^2 a}{T^2}$ and $-\frac{4\pi^2 a}{T^2}$, and may be represented by a sine curve half a wave-length from the displacement curve.

Also, the wave velocity is $\frac{dx}{dt}$;

$$\therefore \frac{\text{particle velocity}}{\text{wave velocity}} = \frac{\frac{dy}{dt}}{\frac{dx}{dt}} = \frac{dy}{dx},$$

and is thus the slope, at any point, of the displacement curve.

Velocity of transverse wave in stretched string.—If the string is so thin that any bending moment (p. 145) may be neglected, and any part of the string is displaced laterally from its equilibrium position, the only restoring force is due to the tension in the string. If f is the total stretching force in the string, that is (tension × cross-section), and AB (Fig. 208) is a very short length dx of the string displaced from the line EF, the restoring force is represented by GH,

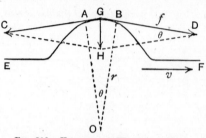

FIG. 208.—VELOCITY OF WAVE IN STRING.

and is the resultant of the two forces GC and GD, each equal to f. The displacements are greatly exaggerated in the figure. From the diagram it is seen that if AB is very small, GHD and ABO are similar triangles, where O is the centre of curvature of the element of string AB;

$$\therefore \ \frac{GH}{GD} = \frac{dx}{AO} = \frac{dx}{r};$$

$$\therefore \ GH = \frac{GD \cdot dx}{r} = \frac{f \, dx}{r}.$$

If the string has mass m per unit length, the mass of AB is $m \, dx$, and its acceleration is

$$\frac{\text{force}}{\text{mass}} = \frac{f \, dx}{r m \, dx} = \frac{f}{r m}.$$

Now, to express the acceleration in terms of the velocity v of the wave travelling from E to F, remember that the string at the point B has particle velocity $v \cdot \left(\dfrac{dy}{dx}\right)_B$ (p. 293), and the particle velocity of the string at A is $v \left(\dfrac{dy}{dx}\right)_A$. As the wave travels over the distance AB, the velocity of an element of string B changes from $v \left(\dfrac{dy}{dx}\right)_B$ to $v \left(\dfrac{dy}{dx}\right)_A$, since the condition of the string shown at A has now reached B. The acceleration of a point on the string is therefore

$$\frac{v \left(\dfrac{dy}{dx}\right)_B - v \left(\dfrac{dy}{dx}\right)_A}{dt},$$

where dt is the time taken for the wave to travel the distance AB or dx. $\left(\dfrac{dy}{dx}\right)_B$ is the slope of the displacement curve at B and $\left(\dfrac{dy}{dx}\right)_A$ that at A, so that when both of these are small,

$$\left(\frac{dy}{dx}\right)_B - \left(\frac{dy}{dx}\right)_A = \theta = \frac{dx}{r}.$$

The particle acceleration is thus $\dfrac{v\,dx}{r\,dt} = \dfrac{v^2}{r}$, since $\dfrac{dx}{dt} = v$. But it has been shown above that the acceleration is $\dfrac{f}{rm}$;

$$\therefore \frac{v^2}{r} = \frac{f}{rm},$$

$$v = \sqrt{\frac{f}{m}} = \sqrt{\frac{\text{stretching force}}{\text{mass per unit length}}}.$$

This expression is not valid if the displacements are very large, but holds in the ordinary case of the stretched string used in musical instruments.

Longitudinal wave.—The representation on a diagram of a longitudinal wave is not so easy as that of a transverse wave, because the displacement is in the direction of the wave. In the transverse wave the diagram may be an actual picture of the string. If particles of the medium transmitting a longitudinal wave are at A, B, C, D and E (Fig. 209) when normally at rest at these points, then

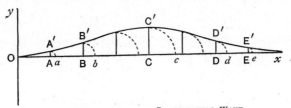

FIG. 209.—REPRESENTATION OF LONGITUDINAL WAVE.

when the wave passes they may, at some particular moment, be at a, b, c, d and e. On describing arcs of circles aA′, bB′ and cC′, etc., the points A′, B′ and C′, etc., are obtained, and the curve A′B′C′D′E′ represents to scale the state of the medium at that moment. Whether the medium is air, or a solid rod, the points A, B and C represent layers at right angles to the direction of propagation of the wave. Each layer is moved forwards or backwards by the amount Aa, Bb,

Cc, etc. Displacements forwards are plotted upwards and those backwards are plotted downwards, as in Fig. 210. If AB′CD′E is a sine curve, the medium is evidently compressed in the neighbour-

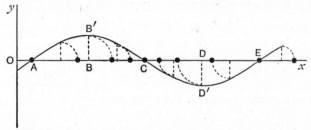

FIG. 210.—LONGITUDINAL WAVE REPRESENTED BY A SINE CURVE.

hood of points represented by C and rarefied at points such as A and E. As the wave travels forwards, these compressions and rarefactions move onwards.

Referring again to Fig. 209 ; if the displacement Aa, Bb, etc., is represented by y, Bb – Aa is δy, the change in displacement over the distance AB or δx. The quantity $-\dfrac{\delta y}{\delta x}$, or in the limit when AB is very small, $-\dfrac{dy}{dx}$, is the compression of the layer AB. The negative sign is taken, because y must decrease with increasing x for the medium to be compressed, as it is in Fig. 210, from B to D. Thus when the curve AB′CD′E has a negative slope $\dfrac{dy}{dx}$ is negative, and the medium is in compression. Where the slope, that is, $\dfrac{dy}{dx}$, is positive, the medium is rarefied.

Velocity of compression wave.—Imagine two parallel planes drawn in the medium at right angles to Ox (Fig. 211), one through A and

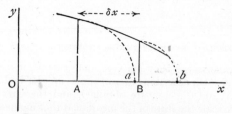

FIG. 211.—VELOCITY OF COMPRESSION WAVE.

the other through B. Draw an area s round A and B in these planes, forming a prism of volume $s\,dx$ in the medium, with sides parallel to

Ox. If ρ is the density, $\rho s\, dx$ is the mass of medium in this prism. The compression at A is $\left(\dfrac{dy}{dx}\right)_A$, and if k is the bulk elasticity of the medium the pressure at A due to the compression is $k\left(\dfrac{dy}{dx}\right)_A$ (p. 128). This gives a force $sk\left(\dfrac{dy}{dx}\right)_A$ on the base of the prism at A. There is a similar force of $sk\left(\dfrac{dy}{dx}\right)_B$ over the base at B, so that there is a resultant force $sk\left\{\left(\dfrac{dy}{dx}\right)_A-\left(\dfrac{dy}{dx}\right)_B\right\}$ on the prism due to the difference in compression at A and B. The acceleration of the medium in the prism is therefore

$$\frac{\text{force}}{\text{mass}}=\frac{sk\left\{\left(\dfrac{dy}{dx}\right)_A-\left(\dfrac{dy}{dx}\right)_B\right\}}{\rho s\,\delta x}=\frac{k\left\{\left(\dfrac{dy}{dx}\right)_A-\left(\dfrac{dy}{dx}\right)_B\right\}}{\rho\,\delta x}.$$

The particle velocity at A is $v\left(\dfrac{dy}{dx}\right)_A$ (p. 295) and at B is $v\left(\dfrac{dy}{dx}\right)_B$, so that the ratio of the change in velocity of a layer as the wave passes over the distance dx to the time taken, δt, is

$$\frac{v\left\{\left(\dfrac{dy}{dx}\right)_A-\left(\dfrac{dy}{dx}\right)_B\right\}}{\delta t},$$

and this also is the acceleration;

$$\therefore\quad\frac{v\left\{\left(\dfrac{dy}{dx}\right)_A-\left(\dfrac{dy}{dx}\right)_B\right\}}{\delta t}=\frac{k\left\{\left(\dfrac{dy}{dx}\right)_A-\left(\dfrac{dy}{dx}\right)_B\right\}}{\rho\,\delta x},$$

$$v\,\frac{\delta x}{\delta t}=\frac{k}{\rho}.$$

Now $\dfrac{\delta x}{\delta t}$ is the velocity of the wave v;

$$\therefore\ v^2=\frac{k}{\rho}.$$

$$v=\sqrt{\frac{k}{\rho}},$$

If the wave is travelling in a solid rod, the elasticity is Young's modulus (e) (p. 127), and

$$\text{velocity}=\sqrt{\frac{e}{\rho}}.$$

If the wave is in air, the elasticity may have one of two forms, according to whether the changes occurring are considered to take place so slowly that heat diffusion causes the temperature to remain constant, or whether they occur so rapidly that there is no leak of heat from one layer to another. In the former case, the elasticity is calculated from the isothermal relation

$$pv = \text{const.},$$

that is, from Boyle's law (p. 174),

$$p = \frac{c}{v},$$

$$\frac{dp}{dv} = -\frac{c}{v^2}.$$

Now, $$\text{elasticity} = \frac{\text{stress}}{\text{strain}} \quad \text{(p. 128)}$$

$$= \frac{dp}{\frac{dv}{v}} = v\frac{dp}{dv} = -\frac{c}{v} = p.$$

The negative sign occurs because $\frac{dp}{dv}$ is essentially negative, increasing pressure causing decreasing volume. The elasticity is therefore equal to the pressure, and

$$\text{velocity of wave} = \sqrt{\frac{p}{\rho}}.$$

This result is due to Newton. On putting in the values

$$p = 76 \times 13\cdot6 \times 981 \text{ dynes per cm.}^2$$

and $$\rho = 0\cdot001293 \text{ gm. per c.c.}$$

for air at normal temperature and pressure,

$$v = \sqrt{\frac{76 \times 13\cdot6 \times 981}{0\cdot001293}}$$

$$= 28000 \text{ cm. sec.}^{-1}.$$

This is less than the observed value. It was pointed out by Laplace that the adiabatic elasticity should have been taken, as the latter of the two above alternatives is the more likely to be correct. In this case

$$pv^{\gamma} = \text{const.} \quad \text{(p. 211)}; \quad \text{and for air } \gamma = 1 \cdot 41;$$

$$\therefore \quad p = cv^{-\gamma}$$

$$-\frac{dp}{dv} = \gamma cv^{\gamma - 1};$$

$$\text{elasticity} = -v\frac{dp}{dv} = \gamma cv^{\gamma} = \gamma p;$$

$$\therefore \quad \text{velocity of wave} = \sqrt{\frac{\gamma p}{\rho}}$$

$$= \sqrt{\frac{1 \cdot 41 \times 76 \times 13 \cdot 6 \times 981}{0 \cdot 001293}}$$

$$= 33250 \text{ cm. sec.}^{-1}.$$

This is very close to the observed value of the velocity of sound in air at normal temperature and pressure, and justifies the use of the adiabatic elasticity.

Interference of waves.—Provided that the displacements are not excessive, two or more waves may travel independently through a medium at the same time. The resultant displacement at any place is then the sum of the displacements produced by the separate waves at any particular instant. In the case of two waves, the resultant displacement is the arithmetic sum of the separate displacements where these are of the same sign, and the difference where the two have opposite signs. Thus the displacement due to the first wave may be increased at some points by the presence of the second wave and diminished at other points. The waves are said to **inter-fere**, and the phenomenon is called **interference.** The name is in some ways unfortunate, since what is really meant is that each wave preserves its independent existence and does *not* interfere with the other. The resultant is the algebraic sum of the effects of the two waves at each place.

The name " interference " is, however, so long established and so well recognised that its use is not likely to be discontinued.

Interference is illustrated in Fig. 212, where the ripples on the surface of mercury are shown. They are produced by two pointed wires, attached together to the prong of a tuning fork. They have thus the same frequency, and produce two sets of ripples which

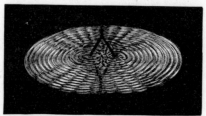

FIG 212.—INTERFERENCE OF MERCURY RIPPLES.

travel in circles from them. The surface is viewed for an instant, and the points of maximum disturbance are seen as lightly-shaded circles. These are crossed by darker rays passing through points where the two sets of waves together produce minimum disturbance.

Stationary vibration.—A very important example of interference is seen when two waves of equal frequency and amplitude travel through a medium in opposite directions. The equations for the waves are

$$y = a \sin 2\pi \left(\frac{x}{\lambda} - \frac{t}{T} \right) \quad \text{and} \quad y = a \sin 2\pi \left(\frac{x}{\lambda} + \frac{t}{T} \right) \quad \text{(p. 292).}$$

The resultant displacement is then

$$y = a \sin 2\pi \left(\frac{x}{\lambda} - \frac{t}{T} \right) + a \sin 2\pi \left(\frac{x}{\lambda} + \frac{t}{T} \right)$$

$$= 2a \sin 2\pi \frac{x}{\lambda} \cos 2\pi \frac{t}{T}.$$

The x's and the t's are thus separated, and at any given place in the medium the particle executes a vibration $\cos 2\pi \frac{t}{T}$ with amplitude $2a \sin 2\pi \frac{x}{\lambda}$. At points for which $x = 0, \frac{\lambda}{2}, \lambda, \frac{3\lambda}{2}$, etc., $\sin 2\pi \frac{x}{\lambda} = 0$ and the amplitude of vibration is zero. Such points are shown at O, A, B and C in Fig. 213. They are called nodes, for the medium is always at rest at these points. On the other hand, if $x = \frac{\lambda}{4}, \frac{3\lambda}{4}, \frac{5\lambda}{4}$, etc., the amplitude has the values $2a$, and the displacements are alternately

positive and negative. Such points are D, E and F (Fig. 213), and
are called **antinodes**.

This state of affairs is represented by a thin line curve for the wave

$$y = a \sin 2\pi \left(\frac{x}{\lambda} - \frac{t}{T} \right),$$

and a dotted line curve for

$$y = a \sin 2\pi \left(\frac{x}{\lambda} + \frac{t}{T} \right).$$

The thick line gives the curve of resultant displacement. In Fig.
213 (*a*) the constituent waves are in the same condition. In (*b*) each

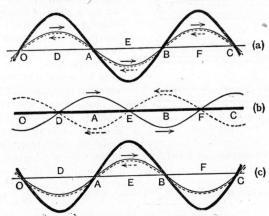

FIG. 213.—WAVES PRODUCING STEADY VIBRATION.

wave has moved forward a distance $\frac{\lambda}{4}$ in its own direction, and the
resultant displacement is for this instant everywhere zero. Another
advance of $\frac{\lambda}{4}$ and the condition (*c*) is reached. Two further advances
of $\frac{\lambda}{4}$ would produce the condition (*a*) again.

Such a motion is a **steady vibration**. It is sometimes called stationary wave motion, but it differs in an important point from a wave
motion, because each part of the medium moves backwards and
forwards without the advancing of a pulse in any direction. A wave
motion is essentially a phenomenon in which some state of disturbance travels from one place to another.

It will be noticed that the distance between consecutive nodes is $\frac{\lambda}{2}$ or half the wave-length of either constituent wave. The wave-length is thus the distance between alternate nodes or alternate antinodes.

The above applies to all simple harmonic waves, whether the transverse motion of a stretched string or the longitudinal waves in a column of air. The conditions of production, however, differ in various cases.

Vibration of stretched strings.—On plucking or striking a stretched string, a transverse wave is started, which on reaching a fixed end is reflected. The reflected wave together with the direct wave set up a state of steady vibration. As both ends of the string are fixed, reflection occurs at both ends, and a steady state of vibration of the string can only be reached if the waves reflected from one end coincide in phase with those travelling towards the other end. With a steady state of vibration the ends of the string must be nodes, because they are fixed. The simplest form of vibration is then, as in Fig. 214 (a), with an antinode in the middle of the string. The

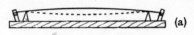

(a)

(b)

(c)

FIG. 214.—MODES OF VIBRATION OF A STRETCHED STRING.

length l of the string is then $\frac{\lambda}{2}$ (above), where $n\lambda = v = \sqrt{\dfrac{f}{m}}$ (p. 297);

$$\therefore \ n = \frac{1}{\lambda}\sqrt{\frac{f}{m}} = \frac{1}{2l}\sqrt{\frac{f}{m}} \ .$$

This is known as the **fundamental** form of vibration of the string. The next possible mode of vibration is shown in (b). There is a node in the middle and $\lambda = l$; $\therefore \ n = \frac{1}{l}\sqrt{\dfrac{f}{m}}$. Similarly in (c) there are two nodes besides those at the ends, and $\lambda = \frac{2}{3}l$, or $n = \frac{3}{2l}\sqrt{\dfrac{f}{m}}$. Thus the various possible forms of vibration have frequencies proportional to $1 : 2 : 3 : \dots$, etc.

An account of the notes emitted by the string vibrating will be found in books on Sound.

Vibration of air column.—A train of reasoning similar to the above shows that a column of air confined in a cylindrical tube may be set in steady vibration. But there are here two possibilities. At a closed end of the tube reflection occurs with a node of displacement, while an end open to the atmosphere is at or near a node of pressure, that is, an antinode of displacement. Thus with a tube open at both ends, the ends are antinodes and there is a node in the middle of the tube. The simplest form of vibration therefore has wave-length $\lambda = 2l$, and $n\lambda = v = \sqrt{\dfrac{k}{\rho}}$ (p. 299), where l is the length of the tube;

$$\therefore \quad n = \frac{1}{2l}\sqrt{\frac{k}{\rho}}.$$

The next mode of vibration has, like the string, a frequency

$$n = \frac{1}{l}\sqrt{\frac{k}{\rho}},$$

and so on.

If one end of the tube is open and the other closed, one end is an antinode and the other a node,

$$\therefore \quad \lambda = 4l \quad \text{and} \quad n = \frac{1}{4l}\sqrt{\frac{k}{\rho}}.$$

For the next form of vibration there must be an antinode and a node in the tube, because antinodes and nodes must alternate;

$$\therefore \quad l = \frac{3\lambda}{4} \quad \text{and} \quad n = \frac{3}{4l}\sqrt{\frac{k}{\rho}}.$$

For the next,

$$n = \frac{5}{4l}\sqrt{\frac{k}{\rho}},$$

and so on. For a study of the notes produced the student is referred to books on Sound.

Vibrating rod.—If a wooden rod be clamped at its middle point and stroked with a resined cloth, it may be set in longitudinal vibration; or a glass rod rubbed with a wet cloth may be used. Since the rod is free at both ends, these are antinodes, and the fundamental has frequency

$$n = \frac{1}{2l}\sqrt{\frac{e}{\rho}},$$

where e is Young's modulus.

Owing to the great value of e this fundamental frequency is very high, and the question of the higher frequencies is not of practical importance.

Waves on water.—Everyone is familiar with the waves which occur on the sea, or when a stone or heavy body is plunged into a pond. Such waves are transverse, the surface moving up and down, while the wave travels horizontally. But the water being incompressible, a transverse motion at or near the surface must be accompanied by some longitudinal motion. If this were not the case there would be a cavity under each crest and an enormous compression under a hollow. As this is not so, there must be a movement of liquid from hollow to crest to preserve the continuity of the liquid. It is possible from the equation expressing this continuity to find the velocity of such waves, but a less general and more descriptive

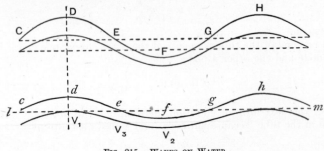

FIG. 215.—WAVES ON WATER.

method will be adopted here. If CDEFGH (Fig. 215) is a section of the actual surface of the water at a given instant, then *cdefgh* is a section of a surface in the water drawn at a depth in the water at the same instant. Each particle in a vertical line, say D*d*, executes vertical simple harmonic motion in the same phase and periodic time T, but the amplitude decreases as the depth increases. That this is so follows from the fact that at the bottom, the amplitude must be zero, but in deep water the amplitude has become zero long before the bottom is reached (see p. 312).

In order to produce such a motion, without discontinuity, the water must pass from hollows to crests. Since the crests and hollows pass any point periodically, each particle of the water has a horizontal oscillation which must have the same periodic time as the vertical oscillation. If this were not so there would not be a permanent wave transmission, the wave would continually be changing in type. If the velocity of the wave, say from left to right (Fig. 215), is v, let us imagine an equal and opposite velocity to be superimposed on the medium. This would maintain the wave at rest while the medium streamed past it with velocity v. The lines CDEFGH and *cdefgh* now become stream-lines. The crests and hollows are supposed to be in parallel lines, and if a slice of unit thickness, of which the diagram is a section, be taken, the parts CDEFGH and *cdefgh* indicate stream-tubes. From p. 205 the velocity of the medium is greatest at the narrowest parts of the stream-tubes such as f, and least at the widest parts such as d.

If V_1 is the resultant velocity of the water at d,

$$V_1 = v - \left(\frac{dx}{dt}\right)_1,$$

where x is the horizontal particle displacement due to the horizontal oscillation. Also the velocity V_2 at f is

$$V_2 = v + \left(\frac{dx}{dt}\right)_2,$$

$\left(\frac{dx}{dt}\right)_1$ and $\left(\frac{dx}{dt}\right)_2$, being the velocities due to oscillation at d and f.

Since V_1 is the minimum resultant horizontal velocity and v is constant, $\left(\frac{dx}{dt}\right)_1$ is the maximum oscillatory velocity from left to right. Similarly $\left(\frac{dx}{dt}\right)_2$ is the maximum oscillatory velocity from right to left, and there is a zero value at e, half-way between d and f.

If the vertical oscillation of any particle is given by

$$y = a \sin 2\pi \frac{t}{T},$$

and the horizontal oscillatory displacement by

$$x = b \sin \left(2\pi \frac{t}{T} + \theta\right),$$

$$\frac{dx}{dt} = \frac{2\pi}{T} \ b \cos \left(2\pi \frac{t}{T} + \theta\right)$$

$$= \frac{2\pi}{T} \ b \sin \left(2\pi \frac{t}{T} + \theta + \frac{\pi}{2}\right).$$

Now this has its maximum value at d, where y is greatest and at f where y is negative, but of maximum negative value ;

$$\therefore \ \theta + \frac{\pi}{2} = 0, \quad \text{or} \quad \theta = -\frac{\pi}{2};$$

$$\therefore \ \frac{dx}{dt} = \frac{2\pi}{T} \ b \sin 2\pi \ \frac{t}{T}$$

and
$$x = b \sin \left(2\pi \frac{t}{T} - \frac{\pi}{2} \right).$$

Thus the vertical and the horizontal oscillations have the same periodic time T and differ in phase by $\frac{\pi}{2}$. Their resultant is therefore an elliptical motion of semi-major and minor axes a and b (p. 104).

In order to find the relation between a and b, Bernouilli's theorem (p. 207) may be applied to the stream-line $cdefgh$:

$$gh + \frac{p}{\rho} + \tfrac{1}{2}V^2 = \text{const.}$$

Taking lm, the undisturbed horizontal plane, as datum level,

at d,
$$h = a, \quad p = p_1,$$

and
$$V_1 = v - \frac{2\pi}{T} \cdot b = v - \frac{2\pi}{\lambda} \ vb = v\left(1 - \frac{2\pi}{\lambda} \ b \right),$$

since the particle makes a complete oscillation in time T, while the wave travels through a wave-length λ ; or, $v = \lambda/T$.

Similarly, at f, $\quad h = -a, \quad p = p_2$ and $V_2 = v\left(1 + \frac{2\pi}{\lambda} \ b \right)$.

Bernoulli's equation then gives

$$ga + \frac{p_1}{\rho} + \tfrac{1}{2}V_1^2 = -ga + \frac{p_2}{\rho} + \tfrac{1}{2}V_2^2,$$

$$ga + \frac{p_1}{\rho} + \tfrac{1}{2}v^2 \left(1 - \frac{2\pi}{\lambda} b \right)^2 = -ga + \frac{p_2}{\rho} + \tfrac{1}{2}v^2 \left(1 + \frac{2\pi}{\lambda} b \right)^2,$$

$$2ga + \frac{p_1 - p_2}{\rho} = \frac{4\pi v^2 b}{\lambda} \ . \quad \dots\dots\dots\dots\dots\dots\dots\dots(i)$$

At e the oscillatory horizontal velocity is zero, being half-way between two points d and f of maximum velocity, and the vertical velocity is the maximum value of

$$\frac{dy}{dt} = \frac{2\pi}{T} \, a \cos 2\pi \, \frac{t}{T},$$

which is $\qquad \frac{2\pi}{T} a \quad$ or $\quad \frac{2\pi}{\lambda} va.$

If V_3 is the resultant velocity at e, then since v and $\dfrac{dy}{dt}$ are at right angles to each other,

$$V_3{}^2 = v^2 + \frac{4\pi^2 v^2}{\lambda^2} \, a^2.$$

Also $\qquad\qquad h = 0 \quad$ and $\quad p = p_3,$

so that applying Bernoulli's equation to the points d and e,

$$ga + \frac{p_1}{\rho} + \tfrac{1}{2} V_1{}^2 = 0 + \frac{p_3}{\rho} + \tfrac{1}{2} V_3{}^2,$$

$$ga + \frac{p_1}{\rho} + \tfrac{1}{2} v^2 \left(1 - \frac{2\pi}{\lambda} b\right)^2 = \frac{p_3}{\rho} + \tfrac{1}{2} v^2 + \frac{1}{2} \frac{4\pi^2 v^2 a^2}{\lambda^2},$$

$$ga + \frac{p_1 - p_3}{\rho} = \frac{2\pi v^2}{\lambda} \, b - \frac{1}{2} \frac{4\pi^2 v^2 b^2}{\lambda^2} + \frac{1}{2} \frac{4\pi^2 v^2 a^2}{\lambda^2} \ . \ \ \dots\dots\dots(ii)$$

Multiplying by 2,

$$2ga + \frac{2\,(p_1 - p_3)}{\rho} = \frac{4\pi v^2 b}{\lambda} + \frac{4\pi^2 v^2}{\lambda^2} (b^2 - a^2).$$

On subtracting this from equation (i),

$$\frac{p_1 - p_2 - 2p_1 + 2p_3}{\rho} = \frac{4\pi^2 v^2}{\lambda^2} (a^2 - b^2),$$

$$\frac{2p_3 - (p_1 + p_2)}{\rho} = \frac{4\pi^2 v^2}{\lambda^2} (a^2 - b^2).$$

The pressures p_1, p_2 and p_3 may be very small, but in any case p_3 is the mean of p_1 and p_2, so that the left-hand side of the equation is zero. Hence it follows that $a = b$, and the vertical and horizontal amplitudes of a particle are equal. This means that the particles describe circles (p. 105).

Three layers in a liquid are drawn in Fig. 216, and the positions of the particles are shown for a given instant. Since the wave travels from left to right, each circle is in an earlier phase than the one on its left. If now the circles rotate as shown until every circle has made a complete rotation, the crest at A will travel to B. It will

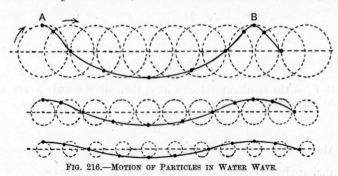

FIG. 216.—MOTION OF PARTICLES IN WATER WAVE.

be seen that the waves are not simple harmonic, although if the amplitude is small the departure from the simple harmonic form is slight.

Velocity of propagation.—In order to find the velocity of propagation v of the wave, put $b = a$ in equation (ii);

then
$$ga + \frac{p_1 - p_3}{\rho} = \frac{2\pi v^2}{\lambda} a,$$

$$v^2 = \frac{(p_1 - p_3) + \rho g a}{\rho \cdot \frac{2\pi a}{\lambda}}.$$

At the surface of the liquid, the equation is as valid as for any other part, but the difference of pressure between D and F (Fig. 215) can only be due to the surface tension of the liquid, since the liquid is in contact with the atmosphere at both places. If the waves are so large that the curvature is negligible, the surface tension may be ignored and

$$v = \sqrt{\frac{g\lambda}{2\pi}},$$

which is the velocity of deep-sea waves.

Again, the curvature at E (Fig. 215) is zero, so that $p_3 = 0$;

$$\therefore v^2 = \frac{p + \rho g a}{\rho \cdot \frac{2\pi a}{\lambda}},$$

where p is the pressure just under the surface at D, due to surface tension.

If the amplitude a is comparatively small with respect to the wave-length, the curvature at D is practically the same for all harmonic waves, and if the simple harmonic form is taken, the equation of the line CDE, etc., is $y = a \sin 2\pi \frac{x}{\lambda}$. Now

$$\frac{dy}{dx} = \frac{2\pi}{\lambda} a \cos 2\pi \frac{x}{\lambda} \quad \text{and} \quad \frac{d^2y}{dx^2} = -\left(\frac{2\pi}{\lambda}\right)^2 a \sin 2\pi \frac{x}{\lambda},$$

and the maximum value of this is $\left(\frac{2\pi}{\lambda}\right)^2 a$. On p. 146 it was seen that when the curvature is not great, its value is $\frac{d^2y}{dx^2}$, or the radius of curvature, $r = \dfrac{1}{\dfrac{d^2y}{dx^2}}$. Now the pressure due to surface tension is $\dfrac{T}{r}$ (p. 255), that is, $T \left(\frac{2\pi}{\lambda}\right)^2 a$, in which case the expression for v becomes

$$v^2 = \frac{T \left(\dfrac{2\pi}{\lambda}\right)^2 a + \rho g a}{\rho \cdot \dfrac{2\pi a}{\lambda}}$$

$$= \frac{2\pi T}{\rho \lambda} + \frac{g\lambda}{2\pi}.$$

If the waves are so small that the propagation is almost entirely due to surface tension, the term $g\lambda$ may be neglected, and

$$v = \sqrt{\frac{2\pi T}{\rho \lambda}}.$$

Relation between amplitude and depth.—In order to find how the amplitude a changes with depth below the surface, refer again to Fig. 215 and consider the stream-tube whose upper layer is $cdefgh$. If the rate of change of a with depth h is $\frac{da}{dh}$, then if the thickness of the tube in its undisplaced condition is δ, the difference of displacement between the upper and lower surfaces at d is $-\frac{da}{dh}\delta$, and $\delta - \frac{da}{dh}\delta$ the actual area of the tube, remembering that it has unit thickness perpendicular to the plane of the diagram and that $\dfrac{da}{dh}$ is negative. Also at f the area is $\delta + \dfrac{da}{dh} \delta$. Now from the principle of continuity (p. 205) the product of velocity and area is constant for any tube;

$$\therefore \; V_1\left(\delta - \frac{da}{dh}\delta\right) = V_2\left(\delta + \frac{da}{dh}\delta\right);$$

$$\therefore \; V_1 - V_2 = (V_1 + V_2)\frac{da}{dh}.$$

But $\qquad V_1 = v - \dfrac{2\pi v}{\lambda} a \quad$ and $\quad V_2 = v + \dfrac{2\pi v}{\lambda} a\,;$

$$\therefore \; V_1 - V_2 = -\frac{4\pi v}{\lambda} a \quad \text{and} \quad V_1 + V_2 = 2v.$$

Then $\qquad\qquad -\dfrac{4\pi v}{\lambda} a = 2v \dfrac{da}{dh},$

$$dh = -\frac{\lambda}{2\pi}\frac{da}{a},$$

$$h = -\frac{\lambda}{2\pi}\log a + \mathrm{C},$$

where C is any constant. Let a_0 be the amplitude at the surface, where $h = 0$. Then

$$h = -\frac{\lambda}{2\pi}\log\frac{a}{a_0},$$

$$\log\frac{a}{a_0} = -\frac{2\pi h}{\lambda},$$

$$a = a_0 \epsilon^{-2\pi h/\lambda}.$$

That is, the amplitude falls off exponentially with the depth. If $h = \lambda$, $a = a_0 \epsilon^{-2\pi} = 0 \cdot 00186 a_0$. Thus at a depth of a wave-length the amplitude has fallen to roughly $0 \cdot 2$ per cent. of the surface amplitude, and the decrease for the next wave-length in depth is at the same rate.

Minimum velocity.—It will be seen that the expression for v^2 on p. 311 will be smallest for some particular value of λ. The minimum value of v^2 may be found by differentiation with respect to λ:

$$v^2 = \frac{2\pi T}{\rho\lambda} + \frac{g\lambda}{2\pi},$$

$$\frac{dv^2}{d\lambda} = -\frac{2\pi T}{\rho\lambda^2} + \frac{g}{2\pi};$$

equating this to zero,

$$\frac{g}{2\pi} = \frac{2\pi T}{\rho \lambda^2}, \quad \text{or} \quad \frac{g\lambda}{2\pi} = \frac{2\pi T}{\rho \lambda},$$

$$\lambda^2 = \frac{4\pi^2 T}{\rho g}.$$

This value might correspond to a maximum or a minimum of v^2. In order to decide, differentiate again,

$$\frac{d^2 v^2}{d\lambda^2} = +\frac{4\pi T}{\rho \lambda^3}.$$

Since every term here is positive, $\dfrac{d^2 v^2}{d\lambda^2}$ is positive, and the value for λ found above corresponds therefore to a minimum of v^2.

In the case of water, $T = 74$ dyne cm.$^{-1}$, $\rho = 1$ gm. cm.$^{-3}$, and $g = 981$ cm. sec.$^{-2}$;

$$\therefore \quad \lambda = 2\pi\sqrt{\tfrac{74}{981}} = 1\cdot726 \text{ cm.},$$

and putting this value in the expression,

$$v^2 = \frac{2\pi T}{\rho \lambda} + \frac{g\lambda}{2\pi},$$

$$v = 23\cdot19 \text{ cm. sec.}^{-1}.$$

This is the smallest velocity that waves on the surface of water can have. For smaller wave-length, the surface tension term predominates and velocity increases with decreasing wave-length. For large wave-length, the gravitational term predominates and the velocity increases with increasing wave-length. For wave-lengths below that corresponding to minimum velocity, the disturbances are usually called ripples.

It is interesting to note that at the minimum velocity

$$\frac{2\pi T}{\rho \lambda} = \frac{g\lambda}{2\pi};$$

that is, the surface tension effect and the gravitational effect contribute equally to the value of v^2.

The late Lord Rayleigh used the measurement of the wave-length of ripples for determining the surface tension of the liquid. A glass plate dips into the liquid, and is rapidly raised and lowered by being attached to the prong of a tuning fork of known frequency. The surface of the liquid is illuminated intermittently with the same frequency as the fork. Under these conditions the ripples appear to stand still, and their wave-length can be measured.

Then
$$v^2 = \frac{2\pi T}{\lambda \rho} + \frac{g\lambda}{2\pi},$$

and $v = n\lambda$, where n is the frequency;

$$\therefore \ T = \frac{\rho n^2 \lambda^3}{2\pi} - \frac{g\rho\lambda^2}{4\pi^2}.$$

For fairly high frequencies $\dfrac{g\rho\lambda^2}{4\pi^2}$ may be neglected in comparison with the first term, so that

$$T = \frac{\rho n^2 \lambda^3}{2\pi}.$$

Ripples in front of moving body.—An interesting example of the dependence of velocity on wave-length is exhibited in the production

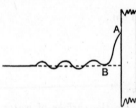

FIG. 217.—RIPPLES IN FRONT OF MOVING BODY.

of steady ripples in front of a partly sub-merged object moving through water. Such a phenomenon occurs in front of the bow of a boat or when a stream flows past a fixed post. These two cases are the same, because it is the relative velocity of the water and the obstacle that matters. The movement of the water causes a heaping up against the fixed obstacle, as at A, Fig. 217. This causes a concavity at B, which will produce lowering of the pressure under the surface, due to surface tension, and a wave is started in the opposite direction to the stream. Since the water in contact with the obstacle is at rest, the ripple moves away from it; that is, up-stream. On proceeding from the obstacle, the water gradually increases in velocity until at a distance it reaches the main-stream velocity. When a place is reached where the velocity of the stream equals the velocity of the ripple, the ripple is stationary. Thus there is a fixed wave pattern in front of the obstacle. If the water is at rest and the solid body moving, the problem may be reduced to the above by imagining a velocity equal and opposite to the body to be superimposed on both.

The greater the velocity the sharper is the heaping up of the water and the shorter the wave-length of the ripple produced. This again means a greater velocity of the ripple, so that at a greater distance a velocity equal to the water is reached. If the velocity of the water is less than 23 cm. sec.$^{-1}$ there is no possible velocity of ripple corresponding to it, and no stationary ripples will be formed.

Beats.—There are several important phenomena that may occur when two trains of harmonic waves of nearly equal frequency have the same direction. If the velocity is independent of the frequency, as in the case of sound waves, the two waves compound in a manner that gives rise to beats. For example, if two tuning forks of nearly the same frequency are sounded together, the ear will hear a regular pulsation or throbbing superimposed on the note.

If the difference in wave-length of the waves is $d\lambda$, and the difference in periodic time dT, one wave may be represented by

$$y = a \sin 2\pi \left(\frac{x}{\lambda - \frac{1}{2}d\lambda} - \frac{t}{T - \frac{1}{2}dT} \right),$$

and the other by

$$y = a \sin 2\pi \left(\frac{x}{\lambda + \frac{1}{2}d\lambda} - \frac{t}{T + \frac{1}{2}dT} \right),$$

where λ and T are the mean wave-length and periodic time.

The resultant of these two is represented by

$$y = a \sin 2\pi \left(\frac{x}{\lambda - \frac{1}{2}d\lambda} - \frac{t}{T - \frac{1}{2}dT} \right) + a \sin 2\pi \left(\frac{x}{\lambda + \frac{1}{2}d\lambda} - \frac{t}{T + \frac{1}{2}dT} \right)$$

$$= 2a \sin 2\pi \left(\frac{x\lambda}{\lambda^2 - \frac{1}{4}(d\lambda)^2} - \frac{tT}{T^2 - \frac{1}{4}(dT)^2} \right)$$

$$\times \cos 2\pi \left(\frac{1}{2} \frac{x\,d\lambda}{\lambda^2 - \frac{1}{4}(d\lambda)^2} - \frac{1}{2} \frac{t\,dT}{T^2 - \frac{1}{4}(dT)^2} \right).$$

If $d\lambda$ and dT are small, $(d\lambda)^2$ and $(dT)^2$ are of a second order of smallness and will be neglected;

$$\therefore \quad y = 2a \sin 2\pi \left(\frac{x}{\lambda} - \frac{t}{T} \right) \cos 2\pi \left(\frac{x\,d\lambda}{2\lambda^2} - \frac{t\,dT}{2T^2} \right).$$

This may be looked upon as a wave

$$\sin 2\pi \left(\frac{x}{\lambda} - \frac{t}{T} \right)$$

of mean wave-length λ, which has an amplitude

$$2a \cos 2\pi \left(\frac{x\,d\lambda}{2\lambda^2} - \frac{t\,dT}{2T^2} \right).$$

This amplitude also travels with velocity

$$\frac{\lambda^2}{d\lambda} \cdot \frac{dT}{T^2} = \frac{\lambda^2}{T^2} \cdot \frac{dT}{d\lambda}.$$

But $\lambda = vT$, or $d\lambda = v\,dT$, if v is constant, or $\dfrac{dT}{d\lambda} = \dfrac{1}{v}$;

$$\therefore \frac{\lambda^2}{T^2} \cdot \frac{dT}{d\lambda} = v^2 \cdot \frac{1}{v} = v.$$

That is, the condition of amplitude travels with the same velocity as the constituent waves.

The distribution of amplitude at any instant, say $t = 0$, is

$$2a \cos 2\pi \cdot \frac{x\,d\lambda}{2\lambda^2}.$$

If the frequency is n,

$$n = \frac{v}{\lambda} \quad \text{and} \quad \frac{dn}{d\lambda} = -\frac{v}{\lambda^2} \quad \text{or} \quad \frac{d\lambda}{\lambda^2} = -\frac{dn}{v};$$

$$\therefore 2a \cos 2\pi \frac{x\,d\lambda}{2\lambda^2} = 2a \cos 2\pi \frac{x\,dn}{2v}.$$

This is numerically equal to $2a$ when

$$\frac{2\pi x\,dn}{2v} = 0, \ \pi, \ 2\pi, \ 3\pi, \ \text{etc., or} \ x = 0, \ \frac{v}{dn}, \ \frac{2v}{dn}, \ \frac{3v}{dn}, \ \text{etc.,}$$

and equals zero when

$$\frac{2\pi x\,dn}{2v} = \frac{\pi}{2}, \ \frac{3\pi}{2}, \ \frac{5\pi}{2}, \ \text{etc.,} \quad \text{or} \quad x = \frac{v}{2\,dn}, \ \frac{3v}{2\,dn}, \ \frac{5v}{2\,dn}, \ \text{etc.;}$$

that is, points of maximum amplitude are separated by a distance $\dfrac{v}{dn}$, as are points of zero amplitude. If the difference in frequency dn of the constituent waves is unity, $x = v$, which means that in the path traversed in one second there is one maximum of amplitude. Similarly, if $dn = 2$ there are two maxima, and so on. Thus the number of beats per second is the difference in the frequencies of the two constituent waves.

In a similar manner, if a fixed point, say $x = 0$, is taken, the amplitude of the particle at this point is

$$2a \cos 2\pi \left(-\frac{t\,dT}{2T^2} \right) = 2a \cos 2\pi \frac{t\,dn}{2},$$

since

$$n = \frac{1}{T} \quad \text{and} \quad \frac{dn}{dT} = -\frac{1}{T^2}.$$

The amplitude equals $2a$ when

$$\pi t\,dn = 0, \ \pi, \ 2\pi, \ \text{etc.,} \quad \text{or} \quad t = 0, \ \frac{1}{dn}, \ \frac{2}{dn}, \ \text{etc.}$$

That is, the time between consecutive maxima is $\dfrac{1}{dn}$, and there are consequently dn maxima per second.

In Fig. 218 this effect is illustrated, but the constituent frequencies are much smaller than would be used in practice. In (a) the distance AC represents $\frac{1}{2}v$, so that in the whole distance v there would be respectively 12 and 10 wave-lengths, and in (b) the resultant at a given instant is drawn. At A and C the waves are assisting each other, and at B they are in opposite phases, giving zero resultant. If AC is half the velocity or the distance travelled in half a second,

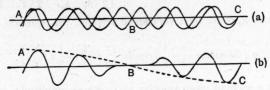

FIG. 218.—RESULTANT OF TWO WAVES OF NEARLY EQUAL WAVE-LENGTH.

then one maximum and one minimum per half second will pass any fixed point. Thus there will be two maxima and two minima passing per second, or there are two beats per second. This is in accordance with the statement that the number of beats per second is the difference in the frequencies of the constituent waves. Also the curve shown in dotted line in (b), which passes through the tips of the resultant wave-crests and hollows, is the curve

$$2a \cos 2\pi \, \frac{x \, d\lambda}{2\lambda^2},$$

obtained above (see p. 316).

Group velocity.—In the last case, the velocity has been considered to be independent of the wave-length, and the compound wave has maxima at A and C (Fig. 218 (b)), which travel with the common velocity of the constituent waves. In some cases the velocity is not independent of the wave-length, as in waves on the surface of water, and light travelling in a transparent medium other than empty space. If λ_1, λ_2 and T_1, T_2 are the respective wave-lengths and periodic times, the equation of one wave may be written

$$y_1 = a \sin 2\pi \left(\frac{x}{\lambda_1} - \frac{t}{T_1} \right),$$

and of the other

$$y_2 = a \sin 2\pi \left(\frac{x}{\lambda_2} - \frac{t}{T_2} \right).$$

The resultant is

$$y = y_1 + y_2 = a \sin 2\pi \left(\frac{x}{\lambda_1} - \frac{t}{T_1} \right) + a \sin 2\pi \left(\frac{x}{\lambda_2} - \frac{t}{T_2} \right)$$

$$= 2a \sin 2\pi \left\{ \frac{x}{2} \left(\frac{1}{\lambda_1} + \frac{1}{\lambda_2} \right) - \frac{t}{2} \left(\frac{1}{T_1} + \frac{1}{T_2} \right) \right\}$$

$$\times \cos 2\pi \left\{ \frac{x}{2} \left(\frac{1}{\lambda_1} - \frac{1}{\lambda_2} \right) - \frac{t}{2} \left(\frac{1}{T_1} - \frac{1}{T_2} \right) \right\}.$$

If λ_1 and λ_2 differ by a very small amount, the equation may be written

$$y = 2a \sin 2\pi \left(\frac{x}{\lambda} - \frac{t}{T} \right) \cos 2\pi \left\{ \frac{x}{2} d \left(\frac{1}{\lambda} \right) - \frac{t}{2} d \left(\frac{1}{T} \right) \right\}.$$

This is a wave of mean velocity $v = \dfrac{\lambda}{T}$, whose amplitude

$$2a \cos 2\pi \left\{ \frac{x}{2} d \left(\frac{1}{\lambda} \right) - \frac{t}{2} d \left(\frac{1}{T} \right) \right\}$$

has velocity $\dfrac{d\left(\frac{1}{T}\right)}{d\left(\frac{1}{\lambda}\right)}$. The quantity $\dfrac{\lambda}{t}$ is generally called the **phase**

velocity and $\dfrac{d\left(\frac{1}{T}\right)}{d\left(\frac{1}{\lambda}\right)}$ the **group velocity** (v'). In Fig. 219 (a) two consti-

tuent waves are drawn, and in (b) the resultant wave at a given instant is represented by the full line. Any given wavelet, such as EFG, travels with the phase velocity v or $\dfrac{\lambda}{T}$. The dotted-line curve ABC, which represents the amplitudes at different points, is the curve

$$2a \cos 2\pi \left\{ \frac{x}{2} d \left(\frac{1}{\lambda} \right) - \frac{t}{2} d \left(\frac{1}{T} \right) \right\},$$

whose velocity is no longer v, but is $v' = \dfrac{d\left(\frac{1}{T}\right)}{d\left(\frac{1}{\lambda}\right)}$, the group velocity.

The wavelets between two consecutive points of zero amplitude LM constitute a group. The number of groups passing any fixed

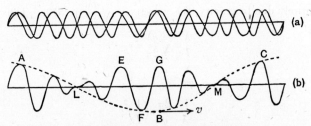

FIG. 219.—ILLUSTRATION OF GROUP VELOCITY.

point in space in a second may be found by taking a fixed point such as $x=0$ and noting that the amplitude is then given by

$$2a \cos 2\pi \left\{ -\frac{t}{2} d \left(\frac{1}{T}\right) \right\} = 2a \cos \pi t \, d \left(\frac{1}{T}\right).$$

This is zero when

$$\pi t \, d \left(\frac{1}{T}\right) = \frac{\pi}{2}, \ \frac{3\pi}{2}, \ \frac{5\pi}{2}, \ \text{etc.},$$

or when

$$t = \frac{1}{2d \left(\frac{1}{T}\right)}, \ \frac{3}{2d \left(\frac{1}{T}\right)}, \ \text{etc.}$$

The interval between points on the wave, such as L and M, passing the chosen fixed point is thus

$$\frac{1}{d \left(\frac{1}{T}\right)}, \ \text{or} \ \frac{1}{\dfrac{1}{T_1} - \dfrac{1}{T_2}}.$$

Now if n_1 and n_2 are the frequencies of the constituent waves,

$$n_1 = \frac{1}{T_1} \ \text{and} \ n_2 = \frac{1}{T_2},$$

so that the time taken for a group to pass a fixed point is

$$\frac{1}{n_1 - n_2}.$$

The number of groups passing per second is therefore $n_1 - n_2$, or the difference in the frequencies of the two waves.

Group velocity of waves on water.—For waves on deep water when surface tension effects can be neglected and the propagation is entirely due to gravity, the velocity is $\sqrt{\dfrac{g\lambda}{2\pi}}$ (p. 310). Thus

$$\frac{\lambda}{T} = \sqrt{\frac{g\lambda}{2\pi}} = v,$$

$$\frac{\lambda}{T^2} = \frac{g}{2\pi},$$

$$\frac{1}{\lambda} = \frac{2\pi}{g} \cdot \left(\frac{1}{T}\right)^2;$$

$$\therefore \frac{d\left(\dfrac{1}{\lambda}\right)}{d\left(\dfrac{1}{T}\right)} = 2 \cdot \frac{2\pi}{g} \cdot \frac{1}{T} = 2 \cdot \frac{2\pi}{g\lambda} \cdot \frac{\lambda}{T} = 2 \cdot \frac{1}{v^2} \cdot v = \frac{2}{v}.$$

$$\therefore \text{ group velocity } \frac{d\left(\dfrac{1}{T}\right)}{d\left(\dfrac{1}{\lambda}\right)} = \frac{v}{2}.$$

That is, the group velocity is half the phase velocity.

In the case of ripples of wave-length small enough for the effect of gravity to be neglected, $v = \sqrt{\dfrac{2\pi S}{\lambda\rho}}$ (p. 311), where S is the surface tension and ρ the density. The surface tension is here written S to avoid confusion with the periodic time.

Then, $\quad\quad \dfrac{\lambda^2}{T^2} = \dfrac{2\pi S}{\lambda\rho} \quad$ or $\quad \dfrac{1}{T^2} = \dfrac{2\pi S}{\rho} \cdot \left(\dfrac{1}{\lambda}\right)^3,$

that is, $\quad\quad\quad\quad \dfrac{1}{T} = \sqrt{\dfrac{2\pi S}{\rho}} \left(\dfrac{1}{\lambda}\right)^{\frac{3}{2}};$

and $\quad$ group velocity $= \dfrac{d\left(\dfrac{1}{T}\right)}{d\left(\dfrac{1}{\lambda}\right)} = \dfrac{3}{2} \sqrt{\dfrac{2\pi S}{\rho}} \cdot \left(\dfrac{1}{\lambda}\right)^{\frac{1}{2}}$

$$= \frac{3}{2} \sqrt{\frac{2\pi S}{\lambda\rho}}$$

$$= \tfrac{3}{2}v.$$

That is, the group velocity is 3/2 times the phase velocity.

Waves formed by moving body.—A solid body moving through any medium produces a disturbance which travels from it in the form of waves. If the velocity is independent of the wave-length, the group velocity is equal to the phase velocity. This is the case for air waves (p. 299). If then a bullet has such a velocity that it produces a compression in front of it, the wave group travels outwards with the common wave velocity. When the nose of the bullet is at A (Fig. 220) the compression wave starts outwards and travels as a spherical compression of velocity v. After an interval of time t let the wave have reached a sphere C whose radius is vt. The bullet

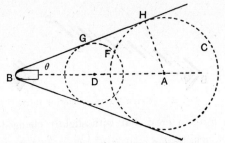

FIG. 220.—WAVES FORMED BY BULLET IN AIR.

has now reached B where AB $= Vt$, V being the velocity of the bullet. After time $\dfrac{t}{2}$ the bullet is at D, and at the end of t sec. the wave which started at time $\dfrac{t}{2}$ sec. has become the spherical wave F, where DF $= v \cdot \dfrac{t}{2}$, and BD $= V\dfrac{t}{2}$. From geometry it will be seen that a cone BGH will touch all such spheres, and this cone is the shape of the compression wave when the bullet is at B.

If θ is the angle ABH,

$$\sin \theta = \frac{AH}{AB} = \frac{v}{V}.$$

By observing such compression waves by means of the shadow they produced when illuminated for an instant, C. V. Boys measured the velocities of bullets fired from a rifle.

The long waves made by a ship moving through water are not so simple as the above. The velocity of these long waves is not independent of the wave-length, and the group velocity is $\dfrac{v}{2}$ (p. 320). As it is the group that is observable and not the constituent waves, the matter is more complicated than in the case of an air wave. As the ship passes A (Fig. 221) the water is heaped up at the bow, and if the group velocity were equal to the wave velocity v, the wave would have reached C when the bow is at B, where $\dfrac{AC}{AB} = \dfrac{v}{V}$. But as the bow passes any point, the water subsides, the crest forming a hollow,

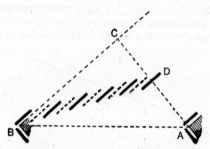

FIG. 221.—WATER WAVES AT BOW OF BOAT.

which again forms a crest, but with slightly changed period and wave-length. The group velocity is thus $\dfrac{v}{2}$, and the group has reached D when the bow reaches B, where $AD = \frac{1}{2}AC$.

The track of the group is therefore from B to D, but it is not continuous, like the track BH in Fig. 220. As the bow passes, the crest E (Fig. 222 (a)) subsides, and the crest which left at G and has

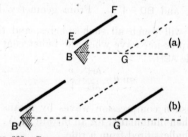

FIG. 222.—PRODUCTION OF WAVES AT BOW OF BOAT.

reached F has become a hollow at G, which travels outwards, to be in turn followed by a crest at G (Fig. 222 (b)). So long as the oscillations last, successive waves are sent out, and the result is a series of crests and hollows in the line BD (Fig. 221). Such a series of waves can always be seen when a body, large enough to produce gravitational waves, passes along the surface of water.

EXERCISES ON CHAPTER XIII

1. Define wave motion and show that it can be represented by a simple equation involving the velocity of propagation.

2. Give the equation of a simple harmonic wave in terms of wavelength and periodic time. Find an expression for the particle velocity in such a case.

3. Distinguish between a transverse wave and a longitudinal wave, giving examples of each.

4. Show how a longitudinal wave may be represented by means of a sine curve. Find the value for the compression in such a wave.

5. Find an expression for the velocity of a compression wave in air. What value of the elasticity should be used in calculating the velocity of the wave from this expression ?

6. Define the term " interference." Show that two simple harmonic waves of the same amplitude and frequency travelling in opposite directions compound into a steady state of vibration.

7. Describe the meaning of the term " beats," and show that the frequency of the beats is the difference of the frequencies of the constituent waves.

8. Explain group velocity, and calculate its value when

$$v = \sqrt{\frac{g\lambda}{2\pi}} \quad \text{and when} \quad v = \sqrt{\frac{2\pi S}{\lambda\rho}} \; .$$

8. Contrast the meaning of *longitudinal progressive wave* and *transverse stationary wave*.

Write down the equation of a simple harmonic progressive wave of amplitude 0·1 mm. and frequency 100 vibrations per sec. travelling in the positive direction of the axis of x with a velocity of 33,000 cm. per sec. Explain the equation.

Lond. Int. Sci.

	0	1	2	3	4	5	6	7	8	9	1 2 3	4 5 6	7 8 9
10	0000	0043	0086	0128	0170						4 9 13	17 21 26	30 34 38
						0212	0253	0294	0334	0374	4 8 12	16 20 24	28 32 36
11	0414	0453	0492	0531	0569						4 8 12	15 19 23	27 31 35
						0607	0645	0682	0719	0755	4 7 11	15 19 22	26 30 33
12	0792	0828	0864	0899	0934						3 7 11	14 18 21	25 28 32
						0969	1004	1038	1072	1106	3 7 10	14 17 20	24 27 31
13	1139	1173	1206	1239	1271						3 7 10	13 16 20	23 26 30
						1303	1335	1367	1399	1430	3 7 10	13 16 19	22 25 29
14	1461	1492	1523	1553	1584						3 6 9	12 15 19	22 25 28
						1614	1644	1673	1703	1732	3 6 9	12 15 17	20 23 26
15	1761	1790	1818	1847	1875						3 6 9	11 14 17	20 23 26
						1903	1931	1959	1987	2014	3 6 8	11 14 17	19 22 25
16	2041	2068	2095	2122	2148						3 5 8	11 14 16	19 22 24
						2175	2201	2227	2253	2279	3 5 8	10 13 16	18 21 23
17	2304	2330	2355	2380	2405						3 5 8	10 13 15	18 20 23
						2430	2455	2480	2504	2529	2 5 7	10 12 15	17 20 22
18	2553	2577	2601	2625	2648						2 5 7	9 12 14	16 19 21
						2672	2695	2718	2742	2765	2 5 7	9 11 14	16 18 21
19	2788	2810	2833	2856	2878						2 4 7	9 11 13	16 18 20
						2900	2923	2945	2967	2989	2 4 6	8 11 13	15 17 19
20	3010	3032	3054	3075	3096	3118	3139	3160	3181	3201	2 4 6	8 11 13	15 17 19
21	3222	3243	3263	3284	3304	3324	3345	3365	3385	3404	2 4 6	8 10 12	14 16 18
22	3424	3444	3464	3483	3502	3522	3541	3560	3579	3598	2 4 6	8 10 12	14 15 17
23	3617	3636	3655	3674	3692	3711	3729	3747	3766	3784	2 4 6	7 9 11	13 15 17
24	3802	3820	3838	3856	3874	3892	3909	3927	3945	3962	2 4 5	7 9 11	12 14 16
25	3979	3997	4014	4031	4048	4065	4082	4099	4116	4133	2 3 5	7 9 10	12 14 15
26	4150	4166	4183	4200	4216	4232	4249	4265	4281	4298	2 3 5	7 8 10	11 13 15
27	4314	4330	4346	4362	4378	4393	4409	4425	4440	4456	2 3 5	6 8 9	11 13 14
28	4472	4487	4502	4518	4533	4548	4564	4579	4594	4609	2 3 5	6 8 9	11 12 14
29	4624	4639	4654	4669	4683	4698	4713	4728	4742	4757	1 3 4	6 7 9	10 12 13
30	4771	4786	4800	4814	4829	4843	4857	4871	4886	4900	1 3 4	6 7 9	10 11 13
31	4914	4928	4942	4955	4969	4983	4997	5011	5024	5038	1 3 4	6 7 8	10 11 12
32	5051	5065	5079	5092	5105	5119	5132	5145	5159	5172	1 3 4	5 7 8	9 11 12
33	5185	5198	5211	5224	5237	5250	5263	5276	5289	5302	1 3 4	5 6 8	9 10 12
34	5315	5328	5340	5353	5366	5378	5391	5403	5416	5428	1 3 4	5 6 8	9 10 11
35	5441	5453	5465	5478	5490	5502	5514	5527	5539	5551	1 2 4	5 6 7	9 10 11
36	5563	5575	5587	5599	5611	5623	5635	5647	5658	5670	1 2 4	5 6 7	8 10 11
37	5682	5694	5705	5717	5729	5740	5752	5763	5775	5786	1 2 3	5 6 7	8 9 10
38	5798	5809	5821	5832	5843	5855	5866	5877	5888	5899	1 2 3	5 6 7	8 9 10
39	5911	5922	5933	5944	5955	5966	5977	5988	5999	6010	1 2 3	4 5 7	8 9 10
40	6021	6031	6042	6053	6064	6075	6085	6096	6107	6117	1 2 3	4 5 6	8 9 10
41	6128	6138	6149	6160	6170	6180	6191	6201	6212	6222	1 2 3	4 5 6	7 8 9
42	6232	6243	6253	6263	6274	6284	6294	6304	6314	6325	1 2 3	4 5 6	7 8 9
43	6335	6345	6355	6365	6375	6385	6395	6405	6415	6425	1 2 3	4 5 6	7 8 9
44	6435	6444	6454	6464	6474	6484	6493	6503	6513	6522	1 2 3	4 5 6	7 8 9
45	6532	6542	6551	6561	6571	6580	6590	6599	6609	6618	1 2 3	4 5 6	7 8 9
46	6628	6637	6646	6656	6665	6675	6684	6693	6702	6712	1 2 3	4 5 5	7 7 8
47	6721	6730	6739	6749	6758	6767	6776	6785	6794	6803	1 2 3	4 5 5	6 7 8
48	6812	6821	6830	6839	6848	6857	6866	6875	6884	6893	1 2 3	4 4 5	6 7 8
49	6902	6911	6920	6928	6937	6946	6955	6964	6972	6981	1 2 3	4 4 5	6 7 8

	0	1	2	3	4	5	6	7	8	9	1 2 3	4 5 6	7 8 9
50	6990	6998	7007	7016	7024	7033	7042	7050	7059	7067	1 2 3	3 4 5	6 7 8
51	7076	7084	7093	7101	7110	7118	7126	7135	7143	7152	1 2 3	3 4 5	6 7 8
52	7160	7168	7177	7185	7193	7202	7210	7218	7226	7235	1 2 2	3 4 5	6 7 7
53	7243	7251	7259	7267	7275	7284	7292	7300	7308	7316	1 2 2	3 4 5	6 6 7
54	7324	7332	7340	7348	7356	7364	7372	7380	7388	7396	1 2 2	3 4 5	6 6 7
55	7404	7412	7419	7427	7435	7443	7451	7459	7466	7474	1 2 2	3 4 5	5 6 7
56	7482	7490	7497	7505	7513	7520	7528	7536	7543	7551	1 2 2	3 4 5	5 6 7
57	7559	7566	7574	7582	7589	7597	7604	7612	7619	7627	1 2 2	3 4 5	5 6 7
58	7634	7642	7649	7657	7664	7672	7679	7686	7694	7701	1 1 2	3 4 4	5 6 7
59	7709	7716	7723	7731	7738	7745	7752	7760	7767	7774	1 1 2	3 4 4	5 6 7
60	7782	7789	7796	7803	7810	7818	7825	7832	7839	7846	1 1 2	3 4 4	5 6 6
61	7853	7860	7868	7875	7882	7889	7896	7903	7910	7917	1 1 2	3 4 4	5 6 6
62	7924	7931	7938	7945	7952	7959	7966	7973	7980	7987	1 1 2	3 3 4	5 6 6
63	7993	8000	8007	8014	8021	8028	8035	8041	8048	8055	1 1 2	3 3 4	5 5 6
64	8062	8069	8075	8082	8089	8096	8102	8109	8116	8122	1 1 2	3 3 4	5 5 6
65	8129	8136	8142	8149	8156	8162	8169	8176	8182	8189	1 1 2	3 3 4	5 5 6
66	8195	8202	8209	8215	8222	8228	8235	8241	8248	8254	1 1 2	3 3 4	5 5 6
67	8261	8267	8274	8280	8287	8293	8299	8306	8312	8319	1 1 2	3 3 4	5 5 6
68	8325	8331	8338	8344	8351	8357	8363	8370	8376	8382	1 1 2	3 3 4	4 5 6
69	8388	8395	8401	8407	8414	8420	8426	8432	8439	8445	1 1 2	2 3 4	4 5 6
70	8451	8457	8463	8470	8476	8482	8488	8494	8500	8506	1 1 2	2 3 4	4 5 6
71	8513	8519	8525	8531	8537	8543	8549	8555	8561	8567	1 1 2	2 3 4	4 5 5
72	8573	8579	8585	8591	8597	8603	8609	8615	8621	8627	1 1 2	2 3 4	4 5 5
73	8633	8639	8645	8651	8657	8663	8669	8675	8681	8686	1 1 2	2 3 4	4 5 5
74	8692	8698	8704	8710	8716	8722	8727	8733	8739	8745	1 1 2	2 3 4	4 5 5
75	8751	8756	8762	8768	8774	8779	8785	8791	8797	8802	1 1 2	2 3 3	4 5 5
76	8808	8814	8820	8825	8831	8837	8842	8848	8854	8859	1 1 2	2 3 3	4 5 5
77	8865	8871	8876	8882	8887	8893	8899	8904	8910	8915	1 1 2	2 3 3	4 4 5
78	8921	8927	8932	8938	8943	8949	8954	8960	8965	8971	1 1 2	2 3 3	4 4 5
79	8976	8982	8987	8993	8998	9004	9009	9015	9020	9025	1 1 2	2 3 3	4 4 5
80	9031	9036	9042	9047	9053	9058	9063	9069	9074	9079	1 1 2	2 3 3	4 4 5
81	9085	9090	9096	9101	9106	9112	9117	9122	9128	9133	1 1 2	2 3 3	4 4 5
82	9138	9143	9149	9154	9159	9165	9170	9175	9180	9186	1 1 2	2 3 3	4 4 5
83	9191	9196	9201	9206	9212	9217	9222	9227	9232	9238	1 1 2	2 3 3	4 4 5
84	9243	9248	9253	9258	9263	9269	9274	9279	9284	9289	1 1 2	2 3 3	4 4 5
85	9294	9299	9304	9309	9315	9320	9325	9330	9335	9340	1 1 2	2 3 3	4 4 5
86	9345	9350	9355	9360	9365	9370	9375	9380	9385	9390	1 1 2	2 3 3	4 4 5
87	9395	9400	9405	9410	9415	9420	9425	9430	9435	9440	0 1 1	2 2 3	3 4 4
88	9445	9450	9455	9460	9465	9469	9474	9479	9484	9489	0 1 1	2 2 3	3 4 4
89	9494	9499	9504	9509	9513	9518	9523	9528	9533	9538	0 1 1	2 2 3	3 4 4
90	9542	9547	9552	9557	9562	9566	9571	9576	9581	9586	0 1 1	2 2 3	3 4 4
91	9590	9595	9600	9605	9609	9614	9619	9624	9628	9633	0 1 1	2 2 3	3 4 4
92	9638	9643	9647	9652	9657	9661	9666	9671	9675	9680	0 1 1	2 2 3	3 4 4
93	9685	9689	9694	9699	9703	9708	9713	9717	9722	9727	0 1 1	2 2 3	3 4 4
94	9731	9736	9741	9745	9750	9754	9759	9763	9768	9773	0 1 1	2 2 3	3 4 4
95	9777	9782	9786	9791	9795	9800	9805	9809	9814	9818	0 1 1	2 2 3	3 4 4
96	9823	9827	9832	9836	9841	9845	9850	9854	9859	9863	0 1 1	2 2 3	3 4 4
97	9868	9872	9877	9881	9886	9890	9894	9899	9903	9908	0 1 1	2 2 3	3 4 4
98	9912	9917	9921	9926	9930	9934	9939	9943	9948	9952	0 1 1	2 2 3	3 4 4
99	9956	9961	9965	9969	9974	9978	9983	9987	9991	9996	0 1 1	2 2 3	3 3 4

	0	1	2	3	4	5	6	7	8	9	1	2	3	4	5	6	7	8	9
·00	1000	1002	1005	1007	1009	1012	1014	1016	1019	1021	0	0	1	1	1	1	2	2	2
·01	1023	1026	1028	1030	1033	1035	1038	1040	1042	1045	0	0	1	1	1	1	2	2	2
·02	1047	1050	1052	1054	1057	1059	1062	1064	1067	1069	0	0	1	1	1	1	2	2	2
·03	1072	1074	1076	1079	1081	1084	1086	1089	1091	1094	0	0	1	1	1	1	2	2	2
·04	1096	1099	1102	1104	1107	1109	1112	1114	1117	1119	0	1	1	1	1	2	2	2	2
·05	1122	1125	1127	1130	1132	1135	1138	1140	1143	1146	0	1	1	1	1	2	2	2	2
·06	1148	1151	1153	1156	1159	1161	1164	1167	1169	1172	0	1	1	1	1	2	2	2	2
·07	1175	1178	1180	1183	1186	1189	1191	1194	1197	1199	0	1	1	1	1	2	2	2	2
·08	1202	1205	1208	1211	1213	1216	1219	1222	1225	1227	0	1	1	1	1	2	2	2	3
·09	1230	1233	1236	1239	1242	1245	1247	1250	1253	1256	0	1	1	1	1	2	2	2	3
·10	1259	1262	1265	1268	1271	1274	1276	1279	1282	1285	0	1	1	1	1	2	2	2	3
·11	1288	1291	1294	1297	1300	1303	1306	1309	1312	1315	0	1	1	1	2	2	2	2	3
·12	1318	1321	1324	1327	1330	1334	1337	1340	1343	1346	0	1	1	1	2	2	2	2	3
·13	1349	1352	1355	1358	1361	1365	1368	1371	1374	1377	0	1	1	1	2	2	2	3	3
·14	1380	1384	1387	1390	1393	1396	1400	1403	1406	1409	0	1	1	1	2	2	2	3	3
·15	1413	1416	1419	1422	1426	1429	1432	1435	1439	1442	0	1	1	1	2	2	2	3	3
·16	1445	1449	1452	1455	1459	1462	1466	1469	1472	1476	0	1	1	1	2	2	2	3	3
·17	1479	1483	1486	1489	1493	1496	1500	1503	1507	1510	0	1	1	1	2	2	2	3	3
·18	1514	1517	1521	1524	1528	1531	1535	1538	1542	1545	0	1	1	1	2	2	3	3	3
·19	1549	1552	1556	1560	1563	1567	1570	1574	1578	1581	0	1	1	1	2	2	3	3	3
·20	1585	1589	1592	1596	1600	1603	1607	1611	1614	1618	0	1	1	2	2	2	3	3	3
·21	1622	1626	1629	1633	1637	1641	1644	1648	1652	1656	0	1	1	2	2	2	3	3	3
·22	1660	1663	1667	1671	1675	1679	1683	1687	1690	1694	0	1	1	2	2	2	3	3	3
·23	1698	1702	1706	1710	1714	1718	1722	1726	1730	1734	0	1	1	2	2	2	3	3	4
·24	1738	1742	1746	1750	1754	1758	1762	1766	1770	1774	0	1	1	2	2	2	3	3	4
·25	1778	1782	1786	1791	1795	1799	1803	1807	1811	1816	0	1	1	2	2	2	3	3	4
·26	1820	1824	1828	1832	1837	1841	1845	1849	1854	1858	0	1	1	2	2	3	3	3	4
·27	1862	1866	1871	1875	1879	1884	1888	1892	1897	1901	0	1	1	2	2	3	3	3	4
·28	1905	1910	1914	1919	1923	1928	1932	1936	1941	1945	0	1	1	2	2	3	3	4	4
·29	1950	1954	1959	1963	1968	1972	1977	1982	1986	1991	0	1	1	2	2	3	3	4	4
·30	1995	2000	2004	2009	2014	2018	2023	2028	2032	2037	0	1	1	2	2	3	3	4	4
·31	2042	2046	2051	2056	2061	2065	2070	2075	2080	2084	0	1	1	2	2	3	3	4	4
·32	2089	2094	2099	2104	2109	2113	2118	2123	2128	2133	0	1	1	2	2	3	3	4	4
·33	2138	2143	2148	2153	2158	2163	2168	2173	2178	2183	0	1	1	2	2	3	3	4	4
·34	2188	2193	2198	2203	2208	2213	2218	2223	2228	2234	1	1	2	2	3	3	4	4	5
·35	2239	2244	2249	2254	2259	2265	2270	2275	2280	2286	1	1	2	2	3	3	4	4	5
·36	2291	2296	2301	2307	2312	2317	2323	2328	2333	2339	1	1	2	2	3	3	4	4	5
·37	2344	2350	2355	2360	2366	2371	2377	2382	2388	2393	1	1	2	2	3	3	4	4	5
·38	2399	2404	2410	2415	2421	2427	2432	2438	2443	2449	1	1	2	2	3	3	4	4	5
·39	2455	2460	2466	2472	2477	2483	2489	2495	2500	2506	1	1	2	2	3	3	4	5	5
·40	2512	2518	2523	2529	2535	2541	2547	2553	2559	2564	1	1	2	2	3	4	4	5	5
·41	2570	2576	2582	2588	2594	2600	2606	2612	2618	2624	1	1	2	2	3	4	4	5	5
·42	2630	2636	2642	2649	2655	2661	2667	2673	2679	2685	1	1	2	2	3	4	4	5	6
·43	2692	2698	2704	2710	2716	2723	2729	2735	2742	2748	1	1	2	3	3	4	4	5	6
·44	2754	2761	2767	2773	2780	2786	2793	2799	2805	2812	1	1	2	3	3	4	4	5	6
·45	2818	2825	2831	2838	2844	2851	2858	2864	2871	2877	1	1	2	3	3	4	5	5	6
·46	2884	2891	2897	2904	2911	2917	2924	2931	2938	2944	1	1	2	3	3	4	5	5	6
·47	2951	2958	2965	2972	2979	2985	2992	2999	3006	3013	1	1	2	3	3	4	5	5	6
·48	3020	3027	3034	3041	3048	3055	3062	3069	3076	3083	1	1	2	3	4	4	5	6	6
·49	3090	3097	3105	3112	3119	3126	3133	3141	3148	3155	1	1	2	3	4	4	5	6	6

	0	1	2	3	4	5	6	7	8	9	1	2	3	4	5	6	7	8	9
·50	3162	3170	3177	3184	3192	3199	3206	3214	3221	3228	1	1	2	3	4	4	5	6	7
·51	3236	3243	3251	3258	3266	3273	3281	3289	3296	3304	1	2	2	3	4	5	5	6	7
·52	3311	3319	3327	3334	3342	3350	3357	3365	3373	3381	1	2	2	3	4	5	5	6	7
·53	3388	3396	3404	3412	3420	3428	3436	3443	3451	3459	1	2	2	3	4	5	6	6	7
·54	3467	3475	3483	3491	3499	3508	3516	3524	3532	3540	1	2	2	3	4	5	6	6	7
·55	3548	3556	3565	3573	3581	3589	3597	3606	3614	3622	1	2	2	3	4	5	6	7	7
·56	3631	3639	3648	3656	3664	3673	3681	3690	3698	3707	1	2	3	3	4	5	6	7	8
·57	3715	3724	3733	3741	3750	3758	3767	3776	3784	3793	1	2	3	3	4	5	6	7	8
·58	3802	3811	3819	3828	3837	3846	3855	3864	3873	3882	1	2	3	4	4	5	6	7	8
·59	3890	3899	3908	3917	3926	3936	3945	3954	3963	3972	1	2	3	4	5	5	6	7	8
·60	3981	3990	3999	4009	4018	4027	4036	4046	4055	4064	1	2	3	4	5	6	6	7	8
·61	4074	4083	4093	4102	4111	4121	4130	4140	4150	4159	1	2	3	4	5	6	7	8	9
·62	4169	4178	4188	4198	4207	4217	4227	4236	4246	4256	1	2	3	4	5	6	7	8	9
·63	4266	4276	4285	4295	4305	4315	4325	4335	4345	4355	1	2	3	4	5	6	7	8	9
·64	4365	4375	4385	4395	4406	4416	4426	4436	4446	4457	1	2	3	4	5	6	7	8	9
·65	4467	4477	4487	4498	4508	4519	4529	4539	4550	4560	1	2	3	4	5	6	7	8	9
·66	4571	4581	4592	4603	4613	4624	4634	4645	4656	4667	1	2	3	4	5	6	7	9	10
·67	4677	4688	4699	4710	4721	4732	4742	4753	4764	4775	1	2	3	4	5	7	8	9	10
·68	4786	4797	4808	4819	4831	4842	4853	4864	4875	4887	1	2	3	4	6	7	8	9	10
·69	4898	4909	4920	4932	4943	4955	4966	4977	4989	5000	1	2	3	5	6	7	8	9	10
·70	5012	5023	5035	5047	5058	5070	5082	5093	5105	5117	1	2	4	5	6	7	8	9	11
·71	5129	5140	5152	5164	5176	5188	5200	5212	5224	5236	1	2	4	5	6	7	8	10	11
·72	5248	5260	5272	5284	5297	5309	5321	5333	5346	5358	1	2	4	5	6	7	9	10	11
·73	5370	5383	5395	5408	5420	5433	5445	5458	5470	5483	1	3	4	5	6	8	9	10	11
·74	5495	5508	5521	5534	5546	5559	5572	5585	5598	5610	1	3	4	5	6	8	9	10	12
·75	5623	5636	5649	5662	5675	5689	5702	5715	5728	5741	1	3	4	5	7	8	9	10	12
·76	5754	5768	5781	5794	5808	5821	5834	5848	5861	5875	1	3	4	5	7	8	9	11	12
·77	5888	5902	5916	5929	5943	5957	5970	5984	5998	6012	1	3	4	5	7	8	10	11	12
·78	6026	6039	6053	6067	6081	6095	6109	6124	6138	6152	1	3	4	6	7	8	10	11	13
·79	6166	6180	6194	6209	6223	6237	6252	6266	6281	6295	1	3	4	6	7	9	10	11	13
·80	6310	6324	6339	6353	6368	6383	6397	6412	6427	6442	1	3	4	6	7	9	10	12	13
·81	6457	6471	6486	6501	6516	6531	6546	6561	6577	6592	2	3	5	6	8	9	11	12	14
·82	6607	6622	6637	6653	6668	6683	6699	6714	6730	6745	2	3	5	6	8	9	11	12	14
·83	6761	6776	6792	6808	6823	6839	6855	6871	6887	6902	2	3	5	6	8	9	11	13	14
·84	6918	6934	6950	6966	6982	6998	7015	7031	7047	7063	2	3	5	6	8	10	11	13	15
·85	7079	7096	7112	7129	7145	7161	7178	7194	7211	7228	2	3	5	7	8	10	12	13	15
·86	7244	7261	7278	7295	7311	7328	7345	7362	7379	7396	2	3	5	7	8	10	12	13	15
·87	7413	7430	7447	7464	7482	7499	7516	7534	7551	7568	2	3	5	7	9	10	12	14	16
·88	7586	7603	7621	7638	7656	7674	7691	7709	7727	7745	2	4	5	7	9	11	12	14	16
·89	7762	7780	7798	7816	7834	7852	7870	7889	7907	7925	2	4	5	7	9	11	13	14	16
·90	7943	7962	7980	7998	8017	8035	8054	8072	8091	8110	2	4	6	7	9	11	13	15	17
·91	8128	8147	8166	8185	8204	8222	8241	8260	8279	8299	2	4	6	8	9	11	13	15	17
·92	8318	8337	8356	8375	8395	8414	8433	8453	8472	8492	2	4	6	8	10	12	14	15	17
·93	8511	8531	8551	8570	8590	8610	8630	8650	8670	8690	2	4	6	8	10	12	14	16	18
·94	8710	8730	8750	8770	8790	8810	8831	8851	8872	8892	2	4	6	8	10	12	14	16	18
·95	8913	8933	8954	8974	8995	9016	9036	9057	9078	9099	2	4	6	8	10	12	15	17	19
·96	9120	9141	9162	9183	9204	9226	9247	9268	9290	9311	2	4	6	8	11	13	15	17	19
·97	9333	9354	9376	9397	9419	9441	9462	9484	9506	9528	2	4	7	9	11	13	15	17	20
·98	9550	9572	9594	9616	9638	9661	9683	9705	9727	9750	2	4	7	9	11	13	16	18	20
·99	9772	9795	9817	9840	9863	9886	9908	9931	9954	9977	2	5	7	9	11	14	16	18	20

TRIGONOMETRICAL TABLE.

Angle.	Radians.	Sine.	Tangent.	Cotangent.	Cosine.		
0°	0	0	0	∞	1	1·5708	90°
1	·0175	·0175	·0175	57·2900	·9998	1·5533	89
2	·0349	·0349	·0349	28·6363	·9994	1·5359	88
3	·0524	·0523	·0524	19·0811	·9986	1·5184	87
4	0698	·0698	·0699	14·3006	·9976	1·5010	86
5	·0873	·0872	·0875	11·4301	·9962	1·4835	85
6	·1047	·1045	·1051	9·5144	·9945	1·4661	84
7	·1222	·1219	·1228	8·1443	·9925	1·4486	83
8	·1396	·1392	·1405	7·1154	·9903	1·4312	82
9	·1571	·1564	·1584	6·3138	·9877	1·4137	81
10	·1745	·1736	·1763	5·6713	·9848	1·3963	80
11	·1920	·1908	·1944	5·1446	·9816	1·3788	79
12	·2094	·2079	·2126	4·7046	·9781	1·3614	78
13	·2269	·2250	·2309	4·3315	·9744	1·3439	77
14	·2443	·2419	·2493	4·0108	·9703	1·3265	76
15	·2618	·2588	·2679	3·7321	·9659	1·3090	75
16	·2793	·2756	·2867	3·4874	·9613	1·2915	74
17	·2967	·2924	·3057	3·2709	·9563	1·2741	73
18	·3142	·3090	·3249	3·0777	·9511	1·2566	72
19	·3316	·3256	·3443	2·9042	·9455	1·2392	71
20	·3491	·3420	·3640	2·7475	·9397	1·2217	70
21	·3665	·3584	·3839	2·6051	·9336	1·2043	69
22	·3840	·3746	·4040	2·4751	·9272	1·1868	68
23	·4014	·3907	·4245	2·3559	·9205	1·1694	67
24	·4189	·4067	·4452	2·2460	·9135	1·1519	66
25	·4363	·4226	·4663	2·1445	·9063	1·1345	65
26	·4538	·4384	·4877	2·0503	·8988	1·1170	64
27	·4712	·4540	·5095	1·9626	·8910	1·0996	63
28	·4887	·4695	·5317	1·8807	·8830	1·0821	62
29	·5061	·4848	·5543	1·8040	·8746	1·0647	61
30	·5236	·5000	·5774	1·7321	·8660	1·0472	60
31	·5411	·5150	·6009	1·6643	·8572	1·0297	59
32	·5585	·5299	·6249	1·6003	·8480	1·0123	58
33	·5760	·5446	·6494	1·5399	·8387	·9948	57
34	·5934	·5592	·6745	1·4826	·8290	·9774	56
35	·6109	·5736	·7002	1·4281	·8192	·9599	55
36	·6283	·5878	·7265	1·3764	·8090	·9425	54
37	·6458	·6018	·7536	1·3270	·7986	·9250	53
38	·6632	·6157	·7813	1·2799	·7880	·9076	52
39	·6807	·6293	·8098	1·2349	·7771	·8901	51
40	·6981	·6428	·8391	1·1918	·7660	·8727	50
41	·7156	·6561	·8693	1·1504	·7547	·8552	49
42	·7330	·6691	·9004	1·1106	·7431	·8378	48
43	·7505	·6820	·9325	1·0724	·7314	·8203	47
44	·7679	·6947	·9657	1·0355	·7193	·8029	46
45	·7854	·7071	1·0000	1·0000	·7071	·7854	45
		Cosine.	Cotangent.	Tangent.	Sine.	Radians.	Angle.

ANSWERS

CHAPTER I. p. 21.

1. 60 ft. sec.$^{-1}$; 82·7 ft. sec.$^{-1}$; 3·78 sec.   **2.** $32\frac{1}{4}$ m.p.h.

3. 95 ft.   **4.** 32 ft. sec.$^{-1}$.

5. 480 miles per hr. per hr. ; 1440 miles per hr. per hr. ; 60 miles per hr.

6. 240 ft.   **7.** 21·5 ft. sec.$^{-1}$; 35·5 ft. sec.$^{-1}$.

8. 57 ft. ; 9 ft. sec.$^{-2}$.   **10.** 498·7 ft.   **11.** 4·575 sec., 915 ft., 1250 ft.

12. $\frac{1}{2}gt^2$ ft. below balloon ; ut ft.

13. $u \cos \alpha$, $(u \sin \alpha - gt)$, $\dfrac{u^2 \sin^2\alpha}{2g}$, $\dfrac{u^2 \sin 2\alpha}{g}$, $45°$.

16. 2400 ft. sec.$^{-1}$.   **18.** 33·55 m.p.h., 26° 34' E. of South.

19. 7 knots.

CHAPTER II. p. 44.

1. 5° 21'.   **2.** 2·74 sec. ; 6 ft. and 10 ft.

3. V $\sin^2 \alpha \times 4·82 \times 10^{-4}$.   **5.** 605 poundals per sq. ft.

6. -6 and $+6$ ft. sec.$^{-1}$; 12 ft. poundals.   **8.** $e = 2/3$.

9. $2m\sqrt{gl}/(M+m)$; $2 \sin^{-1} m/(m+M)$; $2glmM/(m+M)$.

11. 80 lb.-ft. sec.$^{-1}$; 320 ft. poundals ; 3·2 ft. sec.$^{-1}$.

12. $-8/3$ ft. sec.$^{-1}$; $5/6$ ft. sec.$^{-1}$; 0·7.   **13.** 667 ft. sec.$^{-1}$.

CHAPTER III. p. 81.

1. 375 lb. wt.   **2.** $\sin^{-1} \dfrac{G}{a\text{W}}$, W.

3. If D is $\frac{1}{4}$AC from C, resultant acts at $\frac{1}{3}$DB from D.

4. $(4 \cos \theta - 2\sqrt{3} \sin \theta)$ lb. wt.

5. 2·5 lb. wt. bisecting angle BAC ;   9·68 lb. wt.

8. $\tan^{-1}\dfrac{(w_1-w_2)a}{2\mathrm{P}x+(w_1+w_2)x+\mathrm{W}(x+y)}$.

12. On the axis and $0\cdot403a$ from base.

15. (i) $\frac{2}{5}\mathrm{M}r^2$; (ii) $\frac{3}{10}\mathrm{M}a^2$.   16. $\frac{1}{8}\mathrm{M}a^2$; $3\cdot704$ inches.

17. $141\cdot4$ poundal-ft., 300 revolutions.

18. $3\cdot142$ sec.; $59\cdot36$ kg. wt. cm.   19. $2\cdot83$ ft. sec.$^{-1}$.

21. $18\cdot5$ lb. wt.   22. $119\cdot7$ ft. sec.$^{-1}$.

23. $\tan^{-1}1\cdot443=55°\,17'$ to the horizontal.

24. $80{,}000$ poundals; 30 stone wt.   25. 980 cm. sec.$^{-2}$.

CHAPTER IV. p. 105.

2. $428\cdot8$.   3. $324\cdot3$ ft.; $6\cdot37$ ft.   4. $2\cdot864$ ft.; $12\cdot99$ ft. sec.$^{-1}$.

5. $0\cdot7854$ sec.; $42\cdot67$ ft.-poundals.   6. $8\cdot46$ ft.; $0\cdot214$; $28°\,13'$.

9. $51\cdot5$ ft.; $1\cdot57$ sec.   10. 980 cm. sec.$^{-2}$.   12. $2\pi\sqrt{3a/2g}$.

13. $3\sqrt{2}\,l$.   14. $0\cdot04$ cm. approx.; $6'$.   15. $0\cdot229l$.

17. $2\pi\sqrt{2l(\sqrt{2}-1)/g}$.   18. $4\sqrt{2}a/3$.

19. $\mathrm{T}=2\pi\sqrt{(k^2+h^2)/gh}$, $m(a^2+b^2)/3$, $2\pi\sqrt{(4a^2+b^2)/3ag}$.

CHAPTER V. p. 124.

1. $6\cdot898\times10^{-8}$.   2. $988\cdot3$ cm. sec.$^{-2}$.   3. $3\cdot779$ sec.

4. $84\cdot4$ min.   8. $3\cdot40$ dynes.

CHAPTER VI. p. 150.

4. $7\cdot258\times10^6$ dynes.   5. $9\cdot913$ cm.

8. $mg+\sqrt{\dfrac{\mathrm{B}^2g}{mc}+m^2g^2}$ wt. units.

9. $fx^2/2l$, where f is the force to produce unit strain. $1\cdot99$ ft.

10. $m/\mathrm{M}=9/16$.   11. $\lambda x/l=w$.   12. $9/25$.

13. 5×10^{-4} joule.   14. $0\cdot429$.   15. $1\cdot31\times10^{11}$ dyne cm.$^{-2}$.

CHAPTER VII. p. 179.

1. $\pi h^3\tan^2\alpha$ gm. wt. Thrust $=\frac{2}{3}\pi h^3\tan^2\alpha$ gm. wt. Pressure $=\frac{2}{3}h$ gm. wt./cm.^{2}.

2. $4a/3$ from top edge; $8a/9$ from bottom edge.   3. $0\cdot0303$ ft.

4. 500 lb. wt.

5. $2a/3$ in. from the b in. side, $\left(\dfrac{h}{2}+\dfrac{a\cos\theta}{3}\right)\Big/\left(\dfrac{h}{a}+\dfrac{\cos\theta}{2}\right)$ from the b in. side.

6. $5r/4$, 245 lb. wt., 49 lb. wt.   7. $255\cdot5$ gm., $44\cdot5$ gm.

8. Angle with horizontal $=\sin^{-1}h/l\sqrt{s}$.

9. 1·571 gm. wt.-cm. ; 12·57 gm. wt.   10. 4·65 gm. wt.

12. 5 metres to level of water in tube.   13. 7·189 cu. m.

14. 69 ft.   15. 29·69 in.   16. 35 cm.

17. 53·34 metres.   18. 29·8 cm.   20. 77·16 cm.

21. Weight of tube and mercury column. Decreases owing to buoyancy of tube until tube is full. Then decreases to zero.

22. 14·6 inches of mercury.

CHAPTER VIII. p. 202.

1. $1/\sqrt{10}$ cwt.   2. 0·805.   3. 13 ft.

4. 1·706l.   6. (i) W tan $(\lambda + \alpha)$; (ii) W tan $(\lambda - \alpha)$; (iii) W sin $(\lambda - \alpha)$.

7. $a = \frac{1}{2}g(1 - \sin \alpha - \mu \cos \alpha)$.

8. $a(\frac{1}{2} - \mu - \frac{1}{2} \tan \alpha)$ from the upper edge on the plane ; $\dfrac{W}{2}(\cos \alpha - \sin \alpha)$.

CHAPTER IX. p. 214.

2. (a) 19·63 cm. (b) 7812 dynes. (c) No ; provided that all the water reaches the wall. Because the horizontal velocity and momentum are unchanged by gravity.

3. 0·888 cm. of mercury.   4. 73·2 cm. of mercury.

6. 3001 c.c. per sec.   7. 9·4 × 10⁵ c.c. per min.

CHAPTER X. p. 228.

2. 1·84 × 10⁵ cm. sec.⁻¹.   4. 4·93 × 10⁴ cm. sec.⁻¹.   5. 1·469 gm. cm.⁻³.

7. 2·3 × 10¹⁹.

CHAPTER XI. p. 248.

6. 0·691 standard atmos.   9. 57·8 cm. of mercury.

10. 10·1° C.

CHAPTER XII. p. 288.

4. 8·18 gm. wt.   5. 59·3 dyne cm.⁻¹.   7. 6·53 mm.

8. 1 : 6·52.   9. 0·0769 gm. wt.

10. (a) 1·51 cm. ; (b) 1·75 cm.   11. 0·799 gm. cm.⁻³.

12. 3·05 cm. The liquid will overflow until the tube is covered inside and out, and will then remain at rest.

13. 0·884 cm.   15. 1·027 × 10⁶ dyne cm.⁻².

16. 27·5 dyne cm.⁻¹.

CHAPTER XIII. p. 323.

8. 0·01 sin $2\pi(x/330 - 100t)$.

INDEX

Acceleration, 6.
  Angular, 48.
  in circle, 76.
  of gravity, 10.
Adam, 287.
Adiabatic elasticity, 391.
  flow, 210.
Adsorption, 285.
Air column, 305.
Amplitude, 88.
Aneroid barometer, 173.
Angle of contact, 252.
Angular acceleration, 48.
  impulse, 67.
  momentum, 66.
  velocity, 47.
Anti-elastic surface, 269.
Antinodes, 303.
Archimedes, Principle of, 162.
Atmolysis, 245.
Atomizer, 212.
Atwood's machine, 119.
Avogadro's law, 218.
Axle, Wheel and, 73.

Balance, Errors of the, 53.
  Gravity, 123.
  Sensitiveness of the, 53.
Balance, The, 52.
Ballistic pendulum, 31.
Band brake, 188.
Bar pendulum, 96.
Barometer, Aneroid, 173.
  Fortin's, 172.
Beam, Bending of, 143.
Beats, 315.
Bending moment, 145.
Bending of beam, 143.
Bernoulli's equation, 207.
Boiling point, 236, 239.
Boyle's law, 173, 218.
Boys, C. V., 116, 321.
Brahe, Tycho, 109.
Brake, Band, 188.
  Rope, 187.

Breaking point, 127.
Brown, Harkins and, 265.
Brownian movement, 245.
Bulk modulus, 128.
Buoyancy, 164.
  Centre of, 166.

c.g.s. system, 1.
Cantilever, 144.
Capillarity, 257.
Capillary tube, 257.
Cavendish, 115.
Centre of buoyancy, 166.
  gravity, 54.
  mass, 55.
  oscillation, 96.
  pressure, 159.
Centrifugal force, 77.
Centripetal force, 77.
Centroid, 54.
  of cone, 57.
  semicircular plate, 57.
  triangle, 56.
  uniform rod, 55.
Charles' law, 175.
Circular plate, Moment of inertia of, 66.
Clack, 232.
Clausius, 215, 220, 225.
Coefficient of friction, 183.
  restitution, 30.
  viscosity, 191.
Collision, 29.
Colloids, 230.
Combination of s.h.m., 103.
Comparison of velocities, 197.
Composition of forces, 37.
  velocities, 3.
Compound pendulum, 95.
Cone, Centroid of, 57.
Conical pendulum, 102.
Conservation of energy, 41.
  momentum, 29.
Constant of gravitation, 109, 115.
Contact, Angle of, 252.

Contracta, Vena, 208.
Contraction, Coefficient of, 208.
Couples, 60.
Critical velocity, 192.
Crystalloids, 230.
Cylinder, Moment of inertia of, 71.
Cylindrical film, 268.

Dalton's law, 219.
Densities, Comparison of, 157.
Density, Measurement of, 163.
Density of the earth, 117.
Dialysis, 233.
Diffusion, 221, 229.
  Coefficient of, 230.
  of gases, 242, 244.
  pump, 247.
Dimensions, 43.
Disc, Moment of inertia of, 71.
Dissociation, 241.
Dropping plate, 121.
Drop-weight method, 264.
Dyne, The, 27.

Earth, Density of the, 117.
Edser, 267.
Effusion, 219.
  of gases, 243.
Elastic limit, 127.
Elasticity, 127.
  Adiabatic, 391.
  Isothermal, 177.
  of gas, 176.
Energy, 34.
  Conservation of, 41.
  Kinetic, 35, 67, 206.
  of vibration, 91.
  Potential, 40, 206.
  Pressure, 205.
  Surface, 277.
Equilibrium, 58.
Erg, The, 34.
Errors of the balance, 53.
Ewing's extensometer, 133.
Extensometer, Ewing's, 133.
  Searle's, 133.

Ferguson, 261.
Fick's law, 230.
Field, Gravitational, 110.
Film, Cylindrical, 268.
Floating bodies, 165.
Flow, Lines of, 204.
  of gas, 210.
  Tubes of, 204.

Foot-poundal, The, 34.
Force, 27.
  and pressure, 154.
  Centrifugal, 77.
  Centripetal, 77.
Forces, Composition of, 37.
  Parallel, 51.
  Parallelogram of, 37.
  Polygon of, 38.
  Resolution of, 37.
  Triangle of, 38.
Fortin's barometer, 172.
Freezing point, 241.
Frequency, 88.
Friction, 183.

Galileo, 10, 109.
Gas, Perfect, 175.
  Permanent, 175.
Gases, Diffusion of, 242, 244.
  Effusion of, 243.
  Kinetic theory of, 215.
  Viscosity of, 199, 226.
Gauge, McLeod, 178.
Graham, 221, 229, 242, 244.
Gram, The, 27.
Gravitation, 109.
  Constant of, 109, 115.
Gravitational field, 110.
  potential, 110.
Gravity, Acceleration of, 10.
  balance, 123.
  Centre of, 54.
  Specific, 169.
Group velocity, 317.
Gyration, Radius of, 65.

Hare's apparatus, 157.
Harkins and Brown, 265.
Harmonic motion, Simple, 86.
Hodograph, The, 76.
Hooke's law, 126.
Horizontal range, 14.
Horse-power, 42.
Hydrometers, 168.

Impulse, 28.
  Angular, 67.
Inclined plane, 185.
Inertia, 27.
  Moment of, 64, 100.
Interference, 301.
Intrinsic pressure, 277.
Isothermal elasticity, 177.
  flow, 210.

Jaeger, 263.
Joule, The, 42.

Kater's pendulum, 97.
Kelvin, Lord, 232.
Kepler, 109.
Kilowatt, The, 43.
Kilowatt-hour, The, 43.
Kinetic energy, 35, 67, 206.
Kinetic theory of gases, 215.

Langmuir, 286.
Laplace, 277, 300.
Limit, Elastic, 127.
Longitudinal waves, 294, 297.

McLeod gauge, 178.
Mass, 26.
    Centre of, 55.
Maxwell, 215, 220.
Mean free path, 222, 226.
Metacentre, 166.
Meter, Venturi, 209.
Modulus, Bulk, 128.
    of elasticity, 127.
    of rigidity, 128.
    Young's, 131.
Molecular attractions, 282.
Moment, Bending, 145.
    of a force, 48.
    of circular plate, 66.
    of cylinder, 71.
    of disc, 71.
    of inertia, 64, 100.
    of plate, 69.
    of rod, 65.
Momentum, 25, 28.
    Angular, 66.
    Conservation of, 29.
Monomolecular layers, 286.
Motion, Newton's laws of, 25.
    in a circle, 75.
    Wave, 291.

Neumann, 253.
Neutral equilibrium, 58.
    surface, 145.
Newton, Sir Isaac, 13, 25, 31, 78, 109, 300.
Newton's laws of motion, 25.
Nicholson's hydrometer, 169.
Nodes, 302.

Oil on waves, 288.
Oscillation, Centre of, 96.

Osmosis, 232.
Osmotic pressure, 233.

Parallel axes, 68.
    forces, 51.
Parallelogram of forces, 37.
    velocities, 5.
Path, Mean free, 222, 226.
Pendulum, Ballistic, 31.
    Bar, 96.
    Compound, 95.
    Conical, 102.
    Kater's, 97.
    Simple, 93.
Perfect gas, 175.
Periodic time, 88.
Permanent gases, 175.
Perpendicular axes, 70.
Perrin, 246.
Pfeffer, 234.
Phase, 93.
Pitot tube, 209.
Plane, Inclined, 185.
Plate, Dropping, 121.
    Moment of inertia of, 69.
Plateau's spherule, 271.
Poiseuille, 192.
Poisson's ratio, 139.
Pollock, 124.
Polygon of forces, 38.
Potential, 110.
    due to shell, 111.
    due to sphere, 113.
    energy, 40, 206.
Power, 42.
Poynting, 116.
Pressure, 154.
    Centre of, 159.
    energy, 205.
    Intrinsic, 277.
    Osmotic, 233.
Projectiles, 11.
Pump, Diffusion, 247.
    Water, 210.

Radius of gyration, 65.
Range, Horizontal, 14.
    on inclined plane, 16.
Raoult's law, 237.
Rate of working, 42.
Ratio, Poisson's, 139.
Rayleigh, Lord, 286, 288, 313.
Relative velocity, 18.
Resolution of forces, 37.
Restitution, Coefficient of, 30.

Retardation, 6.
Rigidity, Simple, 128, 141.
Ripples, 313.
Rod, Moment of inertia of, 65.
    Uniform, Centroid of, 55.
    Vibrating, 305.
Rope brake, 187.
Rotating vector, 90.

Scalars, 2.
Searle, 132, 149.
Searle's extensometer, 133.
Semicircular plate, Centroid of, 57.
Semi-permeable membrane, 233.
Sensitiveness of the balance, 53.
Shearing strain, 128.
Simple harmonic motion, 86, 103.
    harmonic wave, 292.
    pendulum, 93.
Sine curve, 102.
Siphon, 171.
Sorption, 285.
Specific gravity, 169.
Speed, 2.
Sphere, Potential due to, 113.
Spherical shell, 111.
Spring, Spiral, 142.
Stable equilibrium, 58.
Stability, 189.
Stokes, Sir G., 198.
Strain, 126.
    Shearing, 128.
Stream-line, 204.
Stress, 126.
String, Vibrating, 304.
Surface energy, 277.
    Neutral, 145.
    tension, 249.
    tension, Vapour pressure and, 273.

Tension, Surface, 249.
Threlfall, 124.
Thrust, 158.
Torque, 60.
Torricelli, 171, 208.
Torsion, 139.
Torsional vibration, 99.
Transverse waves, 294.

Triangle, Centroid of, 56.
    of forces, 38.
Tube, Pitot, 209.

Uniform velocity, 2.
Units, 1.
Unstable equilibrium, 58.

van der Waals, 278.
van't Hoff, 235.
Vapour pressure, 235.
    pressure and surface tension, 273.
Variations in g, 122.
Vector, Rotating, 90.
Vectors, 2.
Velocities, Composition of, 3.
    Parallelogram of, 5.
Velocity, Angular, 47.
    Critical, 192.
    Relative, 18.
    Uniform, 2.
Vena contracta, 208.
Venturi meter, 209.
Vibrating rod, 305.
    string, 304.
Vibration, Energy of, 91.
    Torsional, 99.
Viscosities, Comparison of, 197.
Viscosity, 191.
    Measurement of, 194.
    of gases, 199, 226.

Water pump, 210.
    waves, 306.
Watt, The, 42.
Wave, Simple harmonic, 292.
Wave-length, 293.
Wave motion, 291.
Waves, Longitudinal, 294, 297.
    on water, 306.
    Transverse, 294.
Weight, 28.
Wheel and axle, 73.
Work, 34, 39.
    done in strain, 134.
    performed by couple, 63.
Working, Rate of, 42.

Yield point, 127.
Young's modulus, 127, 131.

PRINTED IN GREAT BRITAIN BY ROBERT MACLEHOSE AND CO. LTD.
THE UNIVERSITY PRESS, GLASGOW

BOOKS ON
PHYSICS

A Text-Book of Physics for the Use of Students of Science and Engineering.

By J. DUNCAN, Wh.Ex., M.I.Mech.E, and S. G. STARLING, B.Sc., A.R.C.Sc. 24s. Also in Parts: Dynamics, 8s. Heat, Light and Sound, 10s. 6d. Sound, 5s. Magnetism and Electricity, 7s. 6d.

Intermediate Practical Physics.

By T. M. YARWOOD, B.Sc. 9s. 6d.

A Text-Book of Practical Physics.

By Prof. H. S. ALLEN, M.A., D.Sc., and H. MOORE, A.R.C.Sc., B.Sc. *Third Edition.* 18s.

Mechanical Properties of Matter.

By S. G. STARLING, B.Sc. —

A Text-Book of Heat.

By Prof. H. S. ALLEN, M.A., D.Sc., F.R.S., and R. S. MAXWELL, M.A., B.Sc. Part I (Intermediate Degree standard). 12s. Part II (Degree standard). 10s. 6d.

MACMILLAN & CO., LTD., LONDON

BOOKS ON
PHYSICS

A Text-Book of Light.
By G. R. NOAKES, M.A. 8s. 6d.

A Text-Book of Heat.
By G. R. Noakes, M.A. 10s. 6d.

A Text-Book of Electricity and Magnetism.
By G. R. NOAKES, M.A. 12s.

A Text-Book of General Physics.
By G. R. NOAKES, M.A. 10s. 6d.

Magnetism and Electricity for Students.
By H. E. HADLEY, B.Sc. 10s.

MACMILLAN & CO., LTD., LONDON